intermediate algebra:
a college approach

By Milton D. Eulenberg and Theodore S. Sunko

ARITHMETIC: A COLLEGE APPROACH, 1966
INTRODUCTORY ALGEBRA: A COLLEGE APPROACH, 1968
INQUIRY INTO COLLEGE MATHEMATICS, 1969

intermediate algebra: a college approach

Milton D. Eulenberg
Theodore S. Sunko
Howard A. James

Wilbur Wright College
Chicago, Illinois

John Wiley & Sons, Inc.
New York • London • Sydney • Toronto

Library of Congress Catalogue Card Number: 74-180243

ISBN 0-471-24720-0

Printed in the United States of America

10   9   8   7   6   5   4   3   2

preface

IN THE LAST TWELVE YEARS, CONSIDERABLE EMPHASIS
has been placed on modern mathematics courses in our high schools. However,
many students who enter college still lack the mastery of algebraic techniques
necessary for success in college algebra or other courses of the same level of
difficulty.

Intermediate Algebra was written to correct this deficiency. We agree with the
recent report of the Committee on Undergraduate Programs in Mathematics
that remedial students should not be given more of the same type of mathematics instruction that baffled them in high school; however, we firmly believe
that the mastery of the content of elementary algebra is essential for success in
college mathematics. Therefore, although the topics included here are usually
dealt with in an intermediate algebra textbook, we approached them from a
different point of view. Our viewpoint recognizes the added maturity and sophis-
tication of the college-level student and affects the organization, scope, and
presentation of the entire book.

The book is organized so that sequences of related ideas appear as section
topics. Each section should be covered in one college lecture period, but flexibility
is possible and desirable. The characteristics of a particular group may indicate
that more than one class meeting should be devoted to a given section or that
more than one section should be considered in a single meeting. Each section,
however, is based on the principles that college students can be exposed to
longer sequences of ideas than high school students, that the main ideas introduced in the expository material must be reinforced through the exercises that
form an integral part of each section, and that these exercises develop relevant
concepts as well as necessary skills.

An important implication of these principles is that the purely manipulative
aspects of algegra are interwoven with the more logical aspects of the subject.
The development of factoring is immediately applied to the solution of quadratic

equations and, similarly, operations with fractional expressions are immediately followed by a discussion of fractional equations. After its introduction in Chapter 7, the function concept becomes the central theme of the book. Starting with an intuitive discussion, it is then carefully defined in the modern manner. Considerations of linear functions, quadratic functions, and linear programming further extend the concept so that the student gains a clear understanding of the use of functions in elementary applications and an appreciation of the role of functions in presenting a powerful interplay of mathematical ideas. Function notation is also employed in the subsequent discussions of sequences, series, variation, and logarithms.

The concept of set appears early in the book as a means of introducing the real numbers and their properties. Throughout the book, set concepts and notations are used wherever they promote understanding or lend clarity to the discussion. A consideration of a set of clock numbers serves as a natural vehicle for introducing the field axioms; they are then developed with respect to their role in successive subsets of the real numbers, and are subsequently applied to operations with algebraic expressions throughout the remainder of the course. Chapter 11 on variation is a thorough summary of some of the principles of algebra and functional relations; also it is readily applicable to other fields, particularly the sciences.

Finally, we have maintained a degree of rigor commensurate with the mathematical maturity of the student and used symbolism which should foster an understanding of material instead of obscuring it. The book is written for use by students in the way that students work in and outside of the classroom. We have tried to write with clarity, dignity, and accuracy for the growing audience of college students.

Milton D. Eulenberg
Theodore S. Sunko
Howard A. James

Chicago, Illinois, 1971

contents

5 FACTORING AND THE SOLUTION OF QUADRATIC EQUATIONS

6 FRACTIONS AND THE SOLUTION OF FRACTIONAL EQUATIONS

7 THE FUNCTION CONCEPT

8 SYSTEMS OF EQUATIONS AND INEQUALITIES

intermediate algebra:
a college approach

chapter 1

the number
system of algebra

ALGEBRA IS VIEWED TODAY AS A MATHEMATICAL
structure, whose ideas can be applied not only to numbers but to such diverse
elements as points, sets, or geometric configurations. Although algebra can
therefore be considered apart from its relation to arithmetic, its application
to numbers still represents an important view in much of the study of elementary algebra. Considered in this way, algebra uses symbols to represent numbers
and develops purposeful procedures for using these symbols in fundamental
operations, equations, inequalities, functions, and problem solving. In this book,
the principal approach to the study of algebra is through such applications to
numbers.

Appropriately, our first concern is with the number system of algebra. Since
these numbers form a mathematical entity known as a set, we begin with a
consideration of sets and set properties.

1.1 THE CONCEPT OF SET

The word "set" is probably the most important single term in modern mathematics. The study of sets links mathematics and logic, and provides a foundation
for all of mathematics. Additionally, it has clarified and extended many areas
of mathematics, including that of algebra. Although the concept of set is simple,
many of the ideas of the theory of sets involve profound and complex analysis;
therefore, we shall limit our discussion of sets to the elementary ideas that will
be useful to us in the remainder of this book.

Some students may feel that a term so important in mathematics should be carefully defined. A little reflection reveals that this is not possible since, as in every science, certain technical words are so basic that they cannot be defined in terms of simpler concepts. Such words are accepted as *primitive* or *undefined terms*, and they form the fundamental building blocks of the system. In geometry, for example, the notions of "point" and "line" are usually undefined, although the student does have an intuitive feeling for these concepts. Similarly, we shall accept the notion of "set" as undefined, but we shall describe the sense in which this term is to be used and develop some of its properties.

A set is usually described as a well-defined collection of objects, and these objects are called *elements*, or *members*, of the set. As examples of sets, one may speak of a set of bone china, a set of golf clubs, a set of points on a line, a set (or collection) of rare coins, or a set (or class) of college students. It is apparent that such words as "class" and "collection" can sometimes be used as substitutes for the term "set." They are considered to have equivalent meanings; behind each of these words is the concept of several things that are being considered as a coherent whole. Our preference is to use the word "set" in our discussions, although occasionally one of the other words may be used interchangeably.

Although in each of these examples the elements are closely related to each other in the sense that they have one or more properties in common, the need to treat a collection as a "coherent whole" requires no relation among the elements except that they belong to the same set. Thus, we could speak of a set consisting of the following elements: the Golden Gate bridge, the number π, the Heisman trophy winner for 1971, and the landing module of the Apollo 11 space vehicle. The only property shared by these elements is that they belong to the set under consideration.

One property required of every set, however, is that it be *well-defined*. This means that, given any object, it must be possible to decide whether it is or is not an element of the set under consideration. For example, the counting numbers 1, 2, 3, 4, and so on, constitute a well-defined set which is usually referred to as the set of *natural numbers*. (These numbers, and their properties, are discussed in Section 1.3.) We can easily judge that the number 387 is an element of the set, while the numbers $3\frac{1}{2}$ and 2.17 are not. A more sophisticated example is the set of prime numbers, that is, the numbers 2, 3, 5, 7, 11, 13, and so on. (Prime numbers are defined as natural numbers which cannot be expressed as a product of two natural numbers each greater than 1.) We can easily decide that the number 19 is a member of the set while the number 26 is not. Furthermore, although we cannot easily decide whether the number $2^{127} - 1$ is an element of the set, the answer is difficult rather than debatable. The set, therefore, is well-defined. On the other hand, if we speak of "a set of expensive automobiles," we would conclude that the set is not well-defined, since there is no way to determine whether a car that retails for, say, $3278 is or is not a member of the set. Similarly, the "set of good students," the "set of leading television personalities," or the "set of successful lawyers" is not considered to be well-defined.

We now introduce some conventional notation that not only will promote careful definition of the elements but will provide a convenient format for considering set properties and relations.

Set Notation

Two methods for designating a set are commonly used:

1. The *tabulation method* in which one simply lists, within braces, all the elements of a set. For example, the set consisting of the three primary colors is denoted as {red, blue, yellow}, and the set of all odd numbers can be denoted as {1, 3, 5, 7, ...}. (The three dots mean that the remaining elements are to be continued in regular succession.)

2. The *descriptive method* in which one chooses some symbol to represent any element of the set and then specifies the property or properties that the element must possess. In general, the notation takes the form

$$\{x \,|\, x \text{ has the property } P\}$$

which is read "the set of all x such that x has the property P." For example, the set of all natural numbers greater than 5 can be denoted by

$$\{x \,|\, x \text{ is a natural number greater than 5}\}$$

Used in this way, x is called a *variable*, and the set of elements that it represents is called the *domain* of the variable. More explicitly, a variable is a symbol that represents, during a given discussion, any element of a given set, and the set of permissible values from which x can be taken is the domain of the variable. As an important special case, a symbol used to denote the member of a set containing only one member is called a *constant*.

It is common practice to use capital letters to refer to sets and lower-case letters to represent elements. If x is an element of set A, we write

$$x \in A$$

which is read "x is an element of A," and if x is not an element of set A, we write

$$x \notin A$$

which is read "x is not an element of A."

It is possible that no element is a member of a given set: such a set is referred to as a *null* or *empty set*. For example, the set of all octogenarian winners of Major Leagues batting titles is a null set, as is the set of all even prime numbers greater than 2. The null set can be represented by the empty braces { }, or the symbol ϕ.

At the other extreme is a set with an unlimited number of elements, such as the set of all points on a line, or the set of all natural numbers. Such a set is called an *infinite set*. Sets may be very large and still not be infinite, such as the set of all stars, or the set of all marine life in all the waters on earth. Any set that is not infinite is called a *finite set*.

Set Relations

In mathematics, as in everyday usage, the term *relation* is used to describe the connectivity between two or more objects. There are three principal ways in which two sets may be related: equality, equivalence, and inclusion. The distinction between the first two of these terms is evident in the following definitions:

DEFINITION 1.1 Two sets A and B are said to be equal, written $A = B$, if and only if every element of A is an element of B and every element of B is an element of A.

DEFINITION 1.2 Two sets A and B are said to be equivalent, written $A \sim B$, if and only if they can be placed in *one-to-one correspondence*, that is, if each element of A corresponds to one and only one element of B, and each element of B corresponds to one and only one element of A.

One consequence of the first definition is that the order in which the elements of a set are listed is irrelevant. That is,

$$\{a, b, c, d\} = \{b, a, d, c\}$$

since the two sets have exactly the same elements. But the sets

$$\{a, b, c, d\} \quad \text{and} \quad \{1, 2, 3, 4\}$$

are not equal although, by the second definition, they are equivalent. This equivalence may be demonstrated by the pairing

$$
\begin{array}{cccc}
a & b & c & d \\
| & | & | & | \\
1 & 2 & 3 & 4
\end{array}
$$

which establishes a one-to-one correspondence between the elements. The principle of one-to-one correspondence is particularly useful in investigating the equivalence of infinite sets. For example, the set of all natural numbers is equivalent to the set of all even numbers since we can make the pairing

$$
\begin{array}{ccccc}
1 & 2 & 3 & 4 \cdots n \cdots \\
| & | & | & | & | \\
2 & 4 & 6 & 8 \cdots 2n \cdots
\end{array}
$$

It follows from the definitions that every pair of equal sets is also equivalent, but equivalent sets are not necessarily equal. At times the equality of two sets may be masked, as in the sets

$$A = \{x \mid x \text{ is a natural number less than 3}\}$$
$$B = \{x \mid x \text{ satisfies the relation } x^2 + 2 = 3x\}$$

Since the only elements that satisfy the conditions specified are the numbers 1 and 2, we have

$$A = B = \{1, 2\}$$

It should also be noted that, by Definition 1.1, all empty sets are equal. Thus if $R = \phi$ and $S = \{x \mid x \text{ is an odd number divisible by 2}\}$, then $R = S$.

If two sets fail to be equal we write $A \neq B$, which merely means that they do not have the same elements. Thus $A \neq B$ if $A = \{a, b, c, d\}$ and $B = \{a, b, c\}$, or if $A = (1, 3, 5, 9)$ and $B = \{2, 3, 6, 9\}$.

The third relation we wish to consider, that of set inclusion, is described as follows:

DEFINITION 1.3   A set A is said to be *included* in set B, written $A \subset B$, if and only if every element of A is an element of B. The set A is called a *subset* of the set B.

For example, the set $C = \{\text{red, blue, green}\}$ is a subset of $D = \{\text{red, blue, green, yellow}\}$. On reflection, we notice that the definition permits us to consider every set to be included in itself, and the null set to be a subset of every set. At times it is desirable to recognize that a particular subset differs from the set itself, that is, that $A \subset B$ and at least one element of B is not an element of A. The set A is then said to be a *proper subset* of set B. In the example above, C is a proper subset of D.

EXERCISE 1.1

The Concept of Set

List the elements of the following sets.

1. All single-digit odd numbers.
2. All block capitals of the English alphabet which can be written in one continuous stroke without retracing.
3. All natural numbers less than 100 that are multiples of 15.

4. All pairs of natural numbers whose sum is 7.
5. All months of the year that have less than 31 days.
6. All months of the year that have more than 31 days.
7. All natural numbers n such that $n^2 + 2n + 1$ is not a perfect square.
8. All classifications of triangles based on the relative lengths of the sides.
9. All schools you have attended.
10. All prime numbers of two digits.

State a property or condition that would place the following elements into a set.

11. The number pairs 6 and 4, 8 and 3, 12 and 2, 1 and 24.
12. The number pairs 6 and 4, 8 and 2, 5 and 5, 3 and 7, 1 and 9.
13. Infielder, outfielder, catcher, and pitcher.
14. King, queen, knight, pawn, and bishop.
15. Square, rectangle, trapezoid, and parallelogram.
16. January, March, May, July, August, October, and December.
17. 4, 14, 24, 34, 44.
18. 1, 4, 9, 16, 25.

If a and b are elements of the set of natural numbers N, indicate whether each of the following statements is or is not *always* true.

19. $a + b$ is an element of N.
20. $a - b$ is an element of N.
21. $2a - b$ is an element of N.
22. $2a$ is an element of N.
23. $\frac{1}{2}a$ is an element of N.
24. The product of a and b is an element of N.
25. a/b is an element of N.

If $S = \{1, 2, 3, 4, 5, 6, 7, 8, 9\}$, list the elements of the following sets.

26. $\{x \mid x \in S \text{ and } x \text{ is even}\}$ 27. $\{x \mid x \in S \text{ and } x \text{ is a multiple of 3}\}$
28. $\{x \mid x \in S \text{ and } x \text{ is prime}\}$ 29. $\{x \mid x \in S \text{ and } x \neq 7)$
30. $\{x \mid x \in S \text{ and } x = 2x\}$ 31. $\{x \mid x \notin S \text{ and } \frac{1}{2}x \in S\}$

Indicate whether each of the following is a finite or infinite set.

32. The set of all fractions less than 1.
33. The set of all people who have inhabited the earth up to the present moment.
34. The set of all grains of sand anywhere on earth.
35. The set of all multiples of 5.
36. The set of all points on a line $\frac{1}{2}$ inch in length.
37. The set of all chemical elements.
38. The set of all chemical compounds.

Which of the following pairs of sets have a one-to-one correspondence?

39. States of the United States and state capitals.
40. Trees and tree trunks.
41. Even numbers and odd numbers.
42. Natural numbers and odd numbers.
43. Nouns and verbs as they appear in sentences.
44. College students and college graduates.

For each of the following pairs of sets, indicate whether $A = B$ or $A \neq B$.

45. $A = \{4, 5, 6, 7\}$, $B = \{7,6,5,4\}$
46. $A = \{a, c, e, f, k\}$, $B = \{a, c, e, f, p\}$
47. $A = \{x \mid x$ is an even number$\}$, $B = \{x \mid x + 12 = 20\}$
48. $A = \{ \ \}$, $B = \{x \mid x$ is a perfect square and x is prime$\}$

State whether the following relations are or are not always true if A is the set of all squares, B is the set of all rectangles, $C = \{1, 2, 3, 4, 5, 6, 7, 8, 9\}$, $D = \{2, 4, 6, 8\}$, and $E = \{1, 3, 5, 7\}$.

49. $A \subset B$ 50. $A = B$ 51. $B \subset A$
52. $D \subset C$ 53. $D = E$ 54. $D \sim E$
55. $E \subset C$ 56. $E \subset E$ 57. $\{ \} \subset A$

1.2 SET OPERATIONS

In the preceding section we discussed set relations; we now consider certain set operations. The distinction between the concepts of *relation* and *operation* may be described informally as follows: the idea of relation involves a comparison of the elements of two sets to determine the connectivity between them, whereas the idea of a set operation involves a procedure for associating the elements of two sets to form another set.

The sets involved in operations are usually assumed to be subsets of some larger set U, called the universal set. For example, if we were discussing the sets {red, blue, green} and {white, yellow}, the universal set U might be the set of all colors, or if we were discussing the sets $\{x \mid x$ is a prime number$\}$, $\{1, 3, 5, 7, 9\}$, and $\{2, 4, 6, \ldots\}$, the universal set U might be the set of natural numbers. With this understanding we now define the following operations.

DEFINITION 1.4 The *union* of two sets A and B, written $A \cup B$, is the set of all elements which belong to A or to B or to both A and B.

DEFINITION 1.5 The *intersection* of two sets A and B, written $A \cap B$, is the set of all elements which belong to both A and B.

DEFINITION 1.6 The *complement* of a set A relative to a universal set U, written A', is the set of all elements of U that are not elements of A.

The union of two sets may be likened to the merger of two organizations resulting in a new board of directors composed of all individuals who were directors of either of the original organizations. Thus if $A = \{x \mid x$ is a director of the first organization$\}$ and $B = \{x \mid x$ is a director of the second organization$\}$, then $A \cup B = \{x \mid x$ is a director of either or both organizations$\}$. More explicitly, suppose that

$$A = \{\text{Adams, Brown, Johnson, Jones, Smith}\}$$

and $$B = \{\text{Brown, Clark, Johnson, Jones, Moore}\}$$

then $A \cup B = \{\text{Adams, Brown, Clark, Johnson, Jones, Moore, Smith}\}$

It is important to note that the elements that are in both sets are not repeated; Brown, Jones, and Johnson are in both sets A and B but are included only once in the set $A \cup B$.

The operation of intersection, as the name suggests, associates with a pair of sets that set consisting of all objects that the two sets have in common. It is helpful to observe that this operation is analogous to the idea of intersection in geometry, since when we speak of the intersection of two lines we are referring to the point common to the two lines. As an example of the operation of intersection, consider the sets

$$A = \{a, e, i, o, u\}$$
$$B = \{a, b, c, d, e\}$$
$$C = \{b, c, d\}$$

Then $A \cap B = \{a, e\}$, the set of elements common to A and B

$B \cap C = \{b, c, d\} = C$, since C is a proper subset of B

$A \cap C = \phi$, since there are no elements common to A and C

In the case where the intersection of two sets is the empty set, the given sets are said to be *disjoint sets*. The sets A and C, illustrated above, are disjoint sets.

The last of the defined operations, that of complementation, depends strongly on the universal set U. For example, if $A = \{1, 3, 5, 7, 9\}$ and the universal set is the set of one-digit natural numbers, then $A' = \{2, 4, 6, 8\}$, but if the universal set is the set of all natural numbers, then $A' = \{2, 4, 6, 8, 10, 11, 12, \ldots\}$. On the other hand, no matter what universal set is chosen,

$$\phi' = U \qquad \text{and} \qquad U' = \phi,$$

that is, the complement of the empty set is the universal set, and conversely.

Venn Diagrams

A convenient way of representing sets graphically is by the use of Venn diagrams, which picture the universal set as the set of all points in a rectangle, and subsets of the universal set as subregions inside the rectangle. Thus the

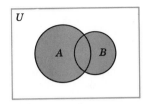

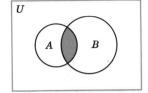

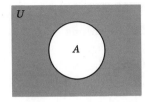

Figure 1.1 Union—A ∪ B is shaded area.

Figure 1.2 . Intersection—A ∩ B is shaded area.

Figure 1.3 Complementation—A′ is shaded area.

operations of union, intersection, and complementation may be illustrated as in Figures 1.1, 1.2, and 1.3, respectively.

Venn diagrams are very useful in verifying the relations among sets that result from various applications of set operations. Although such verification does not constitute mathematical proof, it is intuitively convincing and does serve as a useful test of the validity of a relation. The following examples illustrate these points.

EXAMPLE 1. Show that the complement of the complement of a set is the set itself, that is, that $(A')' = A$.

SOLUTION: Referring to Figure 1.3, we note that the shaded area represents the set A'. The complement of this set is the set of all points in the rectangle that are not in the shaded area, namely, the area within the circle. Therefore $(A')' = A$.

EXAMPLE 2. Show that $(A \cap B) \cap C = A \cap (B \cap C)$.

SOLUTION: In Figure 1.4, the shaded area represents $A \cap B$, and the double-shaded area represents the points common to this set and set C, that is, $(A \cap B) \cap C$. Similarly, in Figure 1.5 the shaded area represents $B \cap C$, and the double-shaded area represents $A \cap (B \cap C)$. Since the double-shaded areas in the two figures are the same, $(A \cap B) \cap C = A \cap (B \cap C)$.

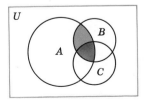

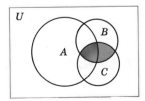

Figure 1.4 (A ∩ B) ∩ C.

Figure 1.5 A ∩ (B ∩ C).

EXERCISE 1.2

Set Relations

Given the sets $A = \{a, c, e\}$, $B = \{a, b, c, d\}$, and $C = \{a, e, i, o, u\}$, identify the set defined by each of the following operations (Problems 1–6).

1. $A \cup B$ 2. $A \cap B$ 3. $A \cap C$
4. $A \cup C$ 5. $B \cup C$ 6. $B \cap C$
7. Can the union of two nonempty sets ever be the null set? Explain.
8. Can the intersection of two nonempty sets ever be the null set? Explain.

Form the union and the intersection of each of the following pairs of sets (Problems 9–12).

9. $C = \{2, 4\}$ 10. $M = \phi$
     $D = \{0, 2, 4, 6\}$ $N = \{3, 6, 9\}$
11. $P = \{7\}$ 12. $R = \{2, 4, 6, 8\}$
     $Q = \{2, 3, 5\}$ $S = \{3, 6, 9, 12\}$
13. Consider the set $A = \{0, 1, 2, 3, 4, 5, 6\}$. Form any subset B, then tabulate $A \cap B$ and $A \cup B$. What conclusions are suggested by the results?
14. What is the complement of the universal set U?
15. What is the complement of the empty set ϕ?

If $U = \{a, b, c, d, e, f, g, h\}$, $A = \{a, b, c, d, f\}$, $B = \{b, c, d\}$, list the elements of each of the following sets.

16. B' 17. $A \cap B$ 18. $A \cap B'$
19. $A \cup B'$ 20. $A' \cap B$ 21. $A' \cup B'$
22. $(A \cap B)'$ 23. $(A \cup B)'$ 24. $A' \cap B'$

Use Venn diagrams to illustrate $A \cap B$ and $A \cup B$ if $A = \{a, b, c\}$ and:

25. $B = \{b\}$ 26. $B = \{b, c, e\}$ 27. $B = \{a, b, c, d, e\}$
28. $B = \phi$ 29. $B = \{b, c, a\}$ 30. $B = \{e, f, g\}$

Show, by means of Venn diagrams, that:

31. $A \cup (B \cap C) = (A \cup B) \cap (A \cup C)$
32. $A \cap (B \cup C) = (A \cap B) \cup (A \cap C)$

If A is any subset of U, find:

33. $A \cap A'$ 34. $A \cup A'$ 35. $A \cup (A')'$

1.3 THE SET OF NATURAL NUMBERS

The consideration of sets leads naturally to the concept of number. The following definition provides the bridge between these two ideas.

DEFINITION 1.7 Two sets that are equivalent are said to have the same *cardinal number*.

For example, all sets that can be placed in one-to-one correspondence with the set $\{a\}$ are said to have the *cardinal number one*, those that can be placed in one-to-one correspondence with the set $\{a, b\}$ are said to have the *cardinal number two*, those that can be placed in one-to-one correspondence with the set $\{a, b, c\}$ are said to have the *cardinal number three*, and so on. The numbers associated with the cardinality of nonempty sets form the set of natural numbers designated by the sequence 1, 2, 3, ... It is evident that the concept of cardinal number appears as a characteristic of a set rather than as a property of its particular elements.

There are various ways to describe this property; we can say, for example, that a given set has the cardinal number four, or that its cardinality is four, or that it contains four elements. We can, further, designate this number by such symbols as 4, IV, 3 + 1, or any other equivalent designation. The symbol for a number is properly called a *numeral*. The essential distinction is that number is an abstract concept—a property shared by equivalent sets—while a numeral is a symbol used to represent a number. We shall make this distinction whenever it is helpful in understanding the discussion.

The term "number," like "set," is undefined; however, certain properties of numbers are essential to the study of algebra. These properties can be demonstrated with striking clarity by considering one of several appropriate subsets of the natural numbers in which the elements are arranged in the format of a clock. We now consider one such subset.

Field Properties of Numbers in a Clock Arithmetic

Suppose we devise a five-hour clock (Figure 1.6) and designate the elements 1, 2, 3, 4, 5 as set S. We now define addition in a predictable way, 4 + 3 being interpreted as a movement of the clock hand from an initial position at 5 to the numeral 4, then an additional movement of 3 places. Thus 4 + 3 = 2. Multiplication, too, may be defined in a natural way. For example, the product of 3 × 2 may be interpreted as a two place movement of the clock hand performed three times. If we again assume the initial position of the clock hand at 5, then

Figure 1.6

$3 \times 2 = 1$. The complete listing of all possible addition and multiplication combinations is shown in Tables 1.1 and 1.2.

TABLE 1.1 Addition

+	1	2	3	4	5
1	2	3	4	5	1
2	3	4	5	1	2
3	4	5	1	2	3
4	5	1	2	3	4
5	1	2	3	4	5

TABLE 1.2 Multiplication

×	1	2	3	4	5
1	1	2	3	4	5
2	2	4	1	3	5
3	3	1	4	2	5
4	4	3	2	1	5
5	5	5	5	5	5

The following important properties of the elements of set S can now be verified by referring to the relations exhibited in Tables 1.1 and 1.2.

1. The set S is *closed with respect to addition*. This means that if a and b are in S, so is $a + b$. For example, $2 + 4 = 1$, where 1 is an element in S.
2. The set S is *closed with respect to multiplication*. This means that if a and b are in S, so is $a \times b$. For example, $2 \times 4 = 3$, where 3 is an element in S.
3. In set S, *addition is commutative*. This means that if a and b are in S, then $a + b = b + a$. For example, $4 + 3 = 2$ and $3 + 4 = 2$. Therefore, $4 + 3 = 3 + 4$.
4. In set S, *multiplication is commutative*, that is, if a and b are in S, then $a \times b = b \times a$. For example, $4 \times 5 = 5$ and $5 \times 4 = 5$. Therefore, $4 \times 5 = 5 \times 4$.
5. In set S, *addition is associative*. This means that if a, b, and c are in S, then $a + (b + c) = (a + b) + c$. For example, $2 + (3 + 4) = (2 + 3) + 4$ since $2 + (3 + 4) = 2 + 2 = 4$, and $(2 + 3) + 4 = 5 + 4 = 4$.
6. In set S, *multiplication is associative*, that is, if a, b, and c are in S, then $a \times (b \times c) = (a \times b) \times c$. The verification is left to the student.

7. In set S, *multiplication is distributive with respect to addition.* This means that if a, b, and c are in S, then $a \times (b + c) = (a \times b) + (a \times c)$. For example, $3 \times (5 + 2) = (3 \times 5) + (3 \times 2)$ since $3 \times (5 + 2) = 3 \times 2 = 1$, and $(3 \times 5) + (3 \times 2) = 5 + 1 = 1$.

8. There exists in set S an *identity element z for addition* such that for each element a in S, $a + z = a$. In set S the identity element z is 5. Thus $1 + 5 = 1$, $2 + 5 = 2$, and so on.

9. There exists in set S an *identity element u for multiplication* such that for each element a in S, $a \times u = a$. This identity element is obviously the number 1, since $1 \times 1 = 1$, $2 \times 1 = 2$, and so on.

10. For each a in S, there exists an *additive inverse a_1* such that $a + a_1 = z$, that is, the sum of any element and its additive inverse is the identity element for addition. For example, the additive inverse of 1 is 4 since $1 + 4 = 5$, and the additive inverse of 2 is 3 since $2 + 3 = 5$.

11. For each a in S, $a \neq z$, there exists a *multiplicative inverse a_2* such that $a \times a_2 = u$, that is, the product of any element and its multiplicative inverse is the identity element for multiplication. For example, the multiplicative inverse of 3 is 2 since $3 \times 2 = 1$, and the multiplicative inverse of 4 is 4 since $4 \times 4 = 1$.

These eleven properties of numbers are known as *field axioms* and any set of numbers that satisfies them is said to form a *field*. Thus the set S forms a field. These properties form the basis for all the fundamental operations involving algebraic expressions: collecting terms, factoring, simplifying expressions, and so on. We now examine the properties of natural numbers to determine whether they form a field.

Properties of Natural Numbers

Let us designate the set of natural numbers as N, where $N = \{1, 2, 3, \ldots\}$. We note that although there is a first natural number, 1, there is no last number since the set N is infinite. Therefore it is not possible to exhibit a complete table of addition or multiplication as was done previously for set S. However, since the reader is assumed to be familiar with the ordinary arithmetic of these numbers we shall test the properties listed in the field axioms against the background of this experience. The following properties appear to hold true for the set of natural numbers.

1. The set N is closed with respect to both addition and multiplication, that is, the sum and the product of two natural numbers is a natural number.

2. In set N, both addition and multiplication are commutative. For example, $5 + 8 = 8 + 5$, $7 \times 6 = 6 \times 7$, and so on.

3. In set N, both addition and multiplication are associative. As one example, $3 + (7 + 2) = (3 + 7) + 2 = 12$.

4. In set N, addition is distributive with respect to multiplication. For example, $3 \times (6 + 5) = (3 \times 6) + (3 \times 5) = 33$.

5. There exists an identity element, u, for multiplication. In set N, $u = 1$.

On the other hand, there are some field properties that do not hold true for the set. These are:

1. The set N does not contain an identity element for addition. Notice that in this set there is no element z such that, for example, $13 + z = 13$.

2. The set N does not contain an additive inverse for each element in the set.

3. The set N does not contain a multiplicative inverse for each element in the set. For example, there is no element m in N such that $7 \times m = 1$.

Thus the set of natural numbers does not form a field. The absence of some of the field properties places a severe restriction on the set of natural numbers in performing common algebraic operations. In the following sections we shall consider more extensive sets of numbers with the aim of developing and understanding a number system adequate for the study of algebra.

EXERCISE 1.3

The Set of Natural Numbers

What is the cardinal number of each of the following sets?

1. $\{x \mid x$ is a two-digit natural number$\}$
2. $\{y \mid y$ is a letter of the English alphabet$\}$
3. $\{d \mid d$ is a day in February of the year 2000$\}$
4. $\{n \mid n$ is a prime number of one digit$\}$

State which of the following subsets of natural numbers are closed under the given operation.

5. All even numbers; operation of multiplication by 3.
6. All odd numbers; operation of multiplication by 3.
7. All odd numbers; operation of multiplication by 2.
8. All even numbers; operation of division by 2.
9. All even numbers; operation of multiplication by any natural number.
10. All perfect squares; operation of multiplication by 2.
11. All perfect squares; operation of multiplication by 4.

Which of the following are commutative operations?

12. Rehearsing a play and presenting the play.
13. Combing your hair and brushing your teeth.

14.   Mixing paint and preparing the brush.

15.   Packing your luggage and leaving for a vacation.

16.   Subtracting 7 from 12.

17.   Dividing 24 by 6.

Which of the following operations are associative? (Problems 18–24.)

18.   Water plus egg plus heat.

19.   Paper plus carbon paper plus typing.

20.   Pipe plus tobacco plus lighted match.

21.   Water plus clothes plus soap.

22.   Water plus bleach plus clothes.

23.   24 divided by 6 divided by 2.

24.   24 minus 6 minus 2.

25.   In the set of natural numbers, multiplication is distributive with respect to addition, that is, $a \times (b + c) = (a \times b) + (a \times c)$. Show by an appropriate example that addition is not distributive with respect to multiplication, that is, $a + (b \times c) \neq (a + b) \times (a + c)$.

26.   Show, by use of Venn diagrams, that the operation of union of sets is distributive with respect to intersection, and that the operation of intersection is distributive with respect to union. Thus, if A, B, and C are any three sets, then

$$(a)\ A \cup (B \cap C) = (A \cup B) \cap (A \cup C)$$

and

$$(b)\ A \cap (B \cup C) = (A \cap B) \cup (A \cap C)$$

Problems 27–34 refer to a set of clock numbers $\{1, 2, 3, 4\}$ as illustrated in Figure 1.7, with addition defined as a forward movement of the indicator and multiplication defined as repeated addition. Formulate several examples to illustrate each of the following statements.

27.   The set is closed with respect to addition and multiplication.

28.   In this set, addition and multiplication are commutative.

29.   In this set, addition and multiplication are associative.

30.   In this set, addition is distributive with respect to multiplication.

31.   The set contains an identity element for addition and an identity element for multiplication.

Figure 1.7

32.   The set contains an additive inverse for each element in the set.

33.   The set *does not* contain a multiplicative inverse for each element a in the set, $a \neq 4$.

34.   (a) Does the set of clock numbers $\{1, 2, 3, 4, 5\}$ form a field? (b) Does the set of clock numbers $\{1,2,3,4\}$ form a field? (The student is invited to conjecture as to what other sets of clock numbers do or do not form fields, and whether any generalized principle can be formulated.)

1.4   THE SET OF INTEGERS

We have noted that in the set of natural numbers there is no element z such that $a + z = a$ for each a in N. The lack of an identity element for addition presents a serious handicap in the application of natural numbers to common arithmetic and algebraic operations. For this and other reasons the introduction of a new element, representing the identity element for addition, to our number system has been described as one of the most important advances in mathematical history. We introduce it in the following definition.

DEFINITION 1.8 The symbol "0" (read zero) represents a unique number such that if n is any natural number or zero, then

$$(1)\ 0 + n = n + 0 = n$$
$$(2)\ 0 \cdot n = n \cdot 0 = 0$$

The set composed of the natural numbers and zero is called W, the set of whole numbers. Thus $W = \{0, 1, 2, 3, \ldots\}$.

Inverse Operations with Zero

Definition 1.8 characterizes the behavior of zero under addition and multiplication. The role of zero in the operations of subtraction and division requires a brief discussion of the relations between these operations.

Subtraction is the *inverse* of addition and division is the inverse of multiplication. In this sense, the inverse of digging a hole would be filling the hole, and the inverse of entering a room would be leaving the room. If we begin with a number n and add to it a number k, then subtract k from the sum, we return to the number n. Thus the operation of subtraction counteracts the operation of addition and, similarly, the operation of division counteracts the operation of multiplication. Any two operations so related are said to be inverse operations.

For example, using a five-hour clock as discussed in Section 1.3, we noted that $3 + 4 = 2$. Therefore the inverse of this relation is $2 - 4 = 3$. Similarly, since in this system $2 \cdot 3 = 1$, then $1 \div 3 = 2$. In general:

$$(a)\ \text{If } a + b = c \quad \text{then} \quad c - b = a \text{ or } c - a = b$$
$$(b)\ \text{If } a \cdot b = c \quad \text{then} \quad c \div b = a \text{ or } c \div a = b$$

As a consequence of these considerations the role of zero in subtraction is defined as follows.

$$(1)\ n - n = 0$$
$$(2)\ n - 0 = n$$

If zero is divided by any natural number n the result is zero, that is,

$$0 \div n = 0 \quad \text{where} \quad n \in N$$

This relation is easily verified since it is consistent with the related multiplication $n \cdot 0 = 0$ by virtue of part 2 of Definition 1.8. However, if we attempt to use zero as a divisor in a division operation some important complications develop. Division of any number by zero is said to have no meaning and is not defined for the following reasons.

1. Assume that $n \div 0 = k$, where n is a natural number. Then the relation of inverse operations requires that $k \cdot 0 = n$. But, by the definition of zero, $k \cdot 0 = 0$. Therefore we have a contradiction.

2. Assume that $0 \div 0 = k$. Then it is required that the corresponding multiplication relation is $k \cdot 0 = 0$. But this is true for *every* value of k. While a result may be said to exist, it is not unique and therefore is excluded.

The inadmissibility of division by zero has direct implication when solving certain types of algebraic equations; therefore reference will be made to it later, at an appropriate point in our study of equations.

Additive Inverses

Subtraction has been introduced as an operation such that if b and c are any two natural numbers, then $c - b$ is that natural number a (if it exists) for which $c = a + b$. We know, from our past experience, that such a natural number does not exist for certain selections of b and c, such as $b = 7$ and $c = 2$. This means that in the set of natural numbers we cannot, in general, solve the equation $x = c - b$, nor can we solve such problems as the following.

(a) What is the expected low temperature on a day when the temperature is expected to drop 30° from a reading of 16°?

(b) What is the new balance in a checking account if \$52 is drawn against a balance of \$47.75?

These restrictions on the operation of subtraction are overcome by introducing new numbers that are the additive inverses of the natural numbers. For each natural number n we let $-n$ be that number for which $n + (-n) = 0$. Thus the inverse of the natural number 1 is the number -1, the inverse of 2 is -2, and so on. This generates the set of numbers $\{-1, -2, -3, -4, \ldots\}$, and the union of this set with the set of whole numbers is called I, the *set of integers*. Thus $I = \{\ldots -3, -2, -1, 0, 1, 2, 3, 4, \ldots\}$.

The subset $\{1, 2, 3, 4,...\}$ is called the set of *positive integers* (or the set of natural numbers), the subset $\{-1, -2, -3, -4,...\}$ is called the set of *negative integers*, and the subset $\{0, 1, 2, 3,...\}$ is called the set of *nonnegative integers* (or the set of whole numbers). The positive integers can also be written as $+1, +2, +3,...$, although in general the positive integer $+n$ is simply written as n.

Addition and Subtraction of Integers

Although it is expected that the student is familiar with the mechanics of performing the fundamental operations with integers, it is important to recognize that these procedures are not formulated arbitrarily but follow as a logical consequence of previous mathematical commitments. A number of different approaches to such discussion is possible; we shall use a geometric interpretation because it is simple and intuitively plausible, but we shall also introduce more sophisticated alternatives in the exercises because of their general mathematical significance.

In order to establish a geometric correspondence for the set of integers we need three things: a convenient straight line, an arbitrary zero point on the line, and an arbitrary distance to represent one unit (Figure 1.8). The distance OA corresponds to the number 1, the distance OB corresponds to the number 2, the distance OF corresponds to the number -1, and so on. These distances are called *directed distances*, since there is a d rection as well as a magnitude associated with each. We note that a one-to-one correspondence can be established between these distances and their corresponding end points; we can also say that a one-to-one correspondence exists between the points themselves and the elements of the set. This geometric representation is called a *line graph* or a *number line*. The number corresponding to a point on the line is called the *coordinate* of the point, and the point is called the *graph* of the number.

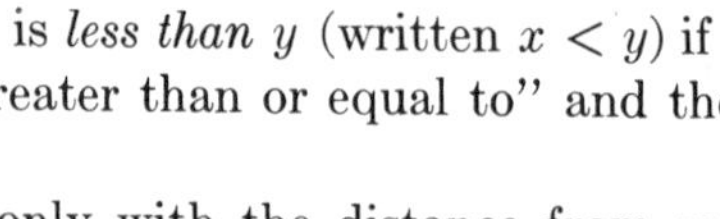

Figure 1.8

We may now describe a number x to be *greater than* a number y (written $x > y$) if x is to the right of y on the number line. For example, $5 > 3$, and $-2 > -4$. Similarly, x is *less than* y (written $x < y$) if x is to the left of y. The symbol $\geq$ is read "is greater than or equal to" and the symbol $\leq$ is read "is less than or equal to."

If we are concerned only with the distance from zero to the point corresponding to a given number without regard to its direction, we call this distance the *absolute value* of the number and indicate it by writing the number between vertical bars. Thus

$$|-3| = 3, \qquad |+2| = 2, \qquad |0| = 0$$

Notice that the absolute value of a whole number is the number itself, and the absolute value of a negative integer is its additive inverse. These relations may be summarized formally by the following statement.

$$|x| = \begin{cases} x \text{ if } x \geq 0 \\ -x \text{ if } x < 0 \end{cases}$$

When a distance *and* a direction are associated with a given number, that number is called a *vector*. Therefore, integers may be represented as vectors on the number line, with the agreement that the vectors associated with positive integers will be directed from zero to the right, and those associated with negative integers will be directed from zero to the left.

Let us now consider the sum of 4 and 3. To find this sum on the number line we represent the vectors as in Figure 1.9. We note that in adding the two vectors we have transposed the position of the vector 3 (without changing its direction) so that its initial point coincides with the terminal point of the vector 4. Since the combined lengths of these two vectors terminates at the integer 7 on the number line, we define the sum of 4 and 3 as 7. This is, of course, consistent with the sum of 4 and 3 as natural numbers.

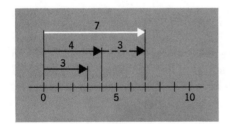

Figure 1.9

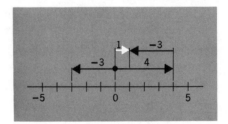

Figure 1.10

Suppose now that we wish to find the sum of 4 and −3 (Figure 1.10). If we follow the same procedure as in the previous example, we transpose the vector −3 so that its initial point coincides with the terminal point of the vector 4 (for clarity we have shown the vector −3 directly above this position); then the resulting length of the two vectors terminates at 1 on the number line. Therefore we define the sum of 4 and −3 to be 1.

Let us continue our discussion with the sum of 2 and −5. Figure 1.11 shows this addition, performed in the same manner as in the previous examples. Since the combined lengths of these two vectors terminates at −3 on the number line, the sum of 2 and −5 is defined to be −3.

As a final example, consider the sum of −4 and −2 (Figure 1.12). Since the combined lengths of these two vectors terminates at −6 on the number line, their sum is equivalent to the single vector −6, and we define the sum of −4

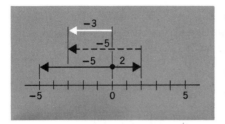

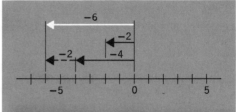

Figure 1.11   **Figure 1.12**

and -2 to be -6. We now summarize these results by writing the four additions in column form:

$$
\begin{array}{rrrr}
4 & -3 & -5 & -4 \\
3 & 4 & 2 & -2 \\
\hline
7 & 1 & -3 & -6
\end{array}
$$

A generalization based on these kinds of examples leads to the following procedures for the addition of two integers x and y:

1. If x and y have like signs, find the sum of their absolute values and prefix the common sign.

2. If x and y have unlike signs, find the difference of their absolute values and prefix the sign of the number having the larger absolute value.

The matter of subtraction of two integers follows directly, since we have already established a relation between addition and subtraction, that is, if $c - b = a$, then $a + b = c$. Using this relation for the subtraction of integers, note the following examples.

(a) $9 - 4 = 5$ because $5 + 4 = 9$
(b) $(-7) - (-5) = -2$ because $(-2) + (-5) = -7$
(c) $(-12) - 3 = -15$ because $(-15) + 3 = -12$
(d) $8 - (-2) = 10$ because $10 + (-2) = 8$

The difference in each case can be determined as the value necessary to satisfy the corresponding inverse operation of addition. This property, of course, is the basis for our usual method of checking problems in subtraction. Let us again consider these four problems with the sign of the number to be subtracted changed. If we now *add* each pair of numbers, we have the same results as before. Thus

(a) $9 + (-4) = 5$
(b) $(-7) + (5) = -2$
(c) $(-12) + (-3) = -15$
(d) $8 + (2) = 10$

It is apparent that subtracting a number is the same as adding its additive inverse. We may, indeed, define the subtraction of two integers x and y in this manner:

$$x - (-y) = x + y$$
$$x - (y) = x + (-y)$$

In other words, to subtract one integer from another, we change the sign of the number to be subtracted and follow the procedure for addition. With practice, the sign changes are made mentally.

Multiplication and Division of Integers

Since multiplication represents repeated addition, we can use this relation to determine a necessary definition for the product of a positive and a negative integer. Consider, for example, the product $(5) \cdot (-6)$ which can be written as

$$(-6) + (-6) + (-6) + (-6) + (-6) = -30$$

Generally, we define the product $(a)(-b)$ to be $-ab$. Since the commutative law of multiplication is to hold for integers, we state the definition in the form

$$(a)(-b) = (-b)(a) = -ab \tag{1}$$

What value shall we assign to $(-a)(-b)$, that is, the product of two negative numbers? Consider the product $(-5)(-6)$. We conceivably could define this product to be 30 or -30; the postulates of closure, commutativity, and associativity could be satisfied by either definition. However, the distributive axiom demands that we define the product to be 30. To verify this, consider the expression $(-5) \cdot [(6) + (-6)] = (-5)[0]$, which has the value zero. Applying the distributive axiom, we have

$$(-5)(6) + (-5)(-6) = 0$$

or

$$-30 + (-5)(-6) = 0 \text{ by virtue of statement 1}$$

Now, to avoid contradiction of our definition of additive inverses we find it necessary to choose that $(-5)(-6) = 30$. In a similar manner, if we apply the distributive axiom to the product $(-a) \cdot [(b) + (-b)]$ we are led to the necessary definition:

$$(-a)(-b) = ab \tag{2}$$

From previous experience with natural numbers we also have

$$(+a)(+b) = +ab \tag{3}$$

Statements 1, 2, and 3 are equivalent to the following definition for the multiplication of two integers: The product of two integers having opposite signs is negative and the product of two integers having like signs is positive. Illustrating this definition, we have

$$(-7)(8) = -56$$
$$(4)(-9) = -36$$
$$(-6)(-8) = 48$$
$$(3)(13) = 39$$

Since division is the inverse of multiplication, the procedure for determining the sign of the quotient of two integers is the same as that for the product:

The quotient of two integers having unlike signs is negative and the quotient of two integers having like signs is positive. Thus

$$14 \div 2 = 7 \text{ since } 7 \cdot 2 = 14$$
$$(-14) \div (-2) = 7 \text{ since } 7 \cdot (-2) = -14$$
$$(-14) \div 2 = -7 \text{ since } (-7) \cdot 2 = -14$$
$$14 \div (-2) = -7 \text{ since } (-7) \cdot (-2) = 14$$

EXERCISE 1.4

The Set of Integers

Place the proper sign, $>$ or $<$, between each of the following pairs of numbers:

1. 7 13	2. 7 -13	3. -7 -13	4. -7 13
5. 0 -4	6. 8 0	7. -3 $+3$	8. -9 -5

Which of the following operations with zero have meaning? Where the operation is possible, indicate the result.

9. $0 \div 7$	10. $0 + 2$	11. $-6 \cdot 0$	12. $0 - 8$
13. $0 \div 0$	14. $0 + 0$	15. $13 \div 0$	16. $0 \div (-5)$

Using the definition of zero, prove each of the following relations for the set of whole numbers.

17. $(a + 0) + b = a + (0 + b)$ 18. $(a \cdot 0) \cdot b = a \cdot (0 \cdot b)$
19. $a \cdot (0 + b) = a \cdot 0 + a \cdot b$ 20. $0 \cdot (a + b) = 0 \cdot a + 0 \cdot b$

Replace the symbol $\square$ with an element of the set of integers in such a way as to make each of the following statements true.

21. $2 + \square = 17$	22. $5 \cdot \square = -35$	23. $\square + 7 = 3$
24. $16 \div \square = -8$	25. $-2 \cdot \square = 18$	26. $11 - \square = -5$
27. $\square \cdot 6 = -60$	28. $\square - (-4) = 23$	29. $\square \div 6 = -7$
30. $-15 + \square = 0$	31. $-2 - \square = -3$	32. $\square \cdot (-6) = -54$

Determine the value of $a + b$, $a - b$, $a \cdot b$, and $a \div b$ for the following values of a and b, respectively.

33. 16 and 2	34. 12 and 4	35. 4 and -1	36. 6 and -2
37. -20 and 5	38. -9 and 3	39. -5 and -1	40. -16 and -8
41. 7 and -7	42. -6 and 6	43. 9 and 9	44. -3 and -3
45. 0 and -4	46. 0 and 5	47. -22 and 11	48. -6 and -3

Draw a number line and sketch in appropriate vectors to illustrate each of the following relations.

49. $-5 + 2 = 2 + (-5)$, that is, addition is commutative in the set of integers.
50. $(-4 + 2) + 1 = (-4) + (2 + 1)$, that is, addition is associative in the set of integers.

The following problems, 51 to 70, indicate an alternative approach to developing procedures for operations with integers. We define the number pair (a,b) where a and b are whole numbers to represent the integer $a - b$. Thus $(2,9)$ represents the integer -7, and $(7,1)$ represents the integer $+6$. Write the integer represented by each of the following number pairs.

51. $(7,2)$	52. $(10,5)$	53. $(2,8)$	54. $(0,4)$
55. $(5,1)$	56. $(3,10)$	57. $(6,0)$	58. $(1,7)$

We now define the sum of two numbers pairs (a,b) and (c,d) as the number pair $(a + c, b + d)$. For example, the sum of $(7,3)$ and $(2,11)$ is $(9,14)$, which is equivalent to the representation $4 + (-9) = -5$. Write the sum of each of the following as a number pair, and then express each sum in terms of integers.

59. $(4,3) + (4,6)$	60. $(3,5) + (3,7)$	61. $(7,8) + (3,3)$
62. $(1,3) + (3,1)$	63. $(2,7) + (12,3)$	64. $(3,8) + (2,12)$

We further define the product of two number pairs (a,b) and (c,d) as the number pair $(ac + bd, bc + ad)$. Thus $(1,3) \cdot (2,7) = (23,13)$, or $(-2) \cdot (-5) = 10$.

Write the product of each of the following as a number pair, and express each product in terms of integers.

65. $(4,1) \cdot (6,2)$	66. $(3,6) \cdot (1,5)$	67. $(7,3) \cdot (2,7)$
68. $(1,4) \cdot (9,2)$	69. $(5,7) \cdot (3,0)$	70. $(0,6) \cdot (5,0)$

Another approach to determining the necessary definitions for operating with integers is based on pure mathematical deduction, similar to that used to prove theorems in geometry. For example, to prove that the sum of two negative integers (say -7 and -2) is negative, we contrive the expression $[(-2) + (-7)] + (2 + 7)$ and show that (a) it must equal zero, and (b) the sum of -2 and -7 must therefore be -9. Supply the reason for each step in this proof (Problems $71 - 79$):

71. $[(-2) + (-7)] + (2 + 7) = [(-2) + (-7)] + (7 + 2)$
72. $\qquad\qquad\qquad\quad = [[(-2) + (-7)] + 7] + 2$

73. $= [(-2) + \overline{(-7) + 7}] + 2$
74. $= [(-2) + 0] + 2$
75. $= (-2) + (0 + 2)$
76. $= (-2) + 2$
77. $= 0$
78. $(-2) + (-7) + 9 = 0$
79. Therefore, $(-2) + (-7) = -9$

1.5 THE SET OF REAL NUMBERS

The enlargement of the set N of natural numbers to the set I of integers was motivated by a necessity to remove the algebraic deficiency that not every equation of the form $a + x = b$ had a solution in N.

The set I, however, also has algebraic deficiencies in that not every nonzero element in I has a multiplicative inverse with the consequence that not every equation of the form $ax = b$, $a \neq 0$, has a solution in I. For example, there is no element x in I such that $6x = 1$. To include numbers such as $1/6$ and other fractions familiar to us in a set of numbers adaptable for use in algebra, we find it desirable to enlarge set I in such a way as to include multiplicative inverses for nonzero elements.

Our purpose is to construct a set R that preserves the operations already defined for set I and in which I is a subset. In effect, we desire that R preserves the properties of addition and multiplication as established for the set I, and R removes the deficiency of a lack of multiplicative inverses for nonzero elements. The enlarged set R is called the set of *rational numbers*. These numbers appear in algebra in a sufficient variety of forms to warrant careful definition.

Rational Numbers

DEFINITION 1.9 The set of rational numbers is the set R consisting of the numbers that can be expressed as the quotient of two integers, that is,

$$R = \left\{ \frac{a}{b} \,\middle|\, a, b, \in I \text{ and } b \neq 0 \right\}$$

Therefore, any common fraction such as $13/5$, $-2/17$, or $-4/-9$ is rational since it is expressed as a quotient of two integers. So also is any mixed number, such as $3\frac{1}{2}$, since it can be written as $7/2$. Any integer n is rational since it can be written as $n/1$. Finally, any *terminating* or *repeating* decimal is rational. For example, the terminating decimal 2.09 can be written as $\dfrac{209}{100}$, and the familiar

repeating decimal 0.6666... can be written as 2/3. (The conversion of other repeating decimals, such as 2.017017017... to a quotient of two integers involves
the solution of certain equations and therefore will be considered in Chapter 3).

Even as a quotient of two integers, however, a given rational number may be
expressed in many different ways. For example,

$$\frac{3}{8}, \quad \frac{-6}{-16}, \quad \frac{9}{24}, \quad \frac{21}{56}$$

are really different numerals for the same rational number. Given two such
representations for a rational number, we can determine whether they represent
the same number by applying this important definition:

DEFINITION 1.10 Two rational numbers $\frac{a}{b}$ and $\frac{c}{d}$ are equal if and only if
$ad = bc$.

For example, $\frac{6}{21} = \frac{10}{35}$ because $6 \cdot 35 = 21 \cdot 10$, and $\frac{11}{16} \neq \frac{12}{17}$ because $187 \neq 192$.

The definition of equality of two rational numbers gives rise to a very useful
relation,

$$\frac{a}{b} = \frac{ka}{kb} \text{ for any integer } k,\ k \neq 0$$

since $a(kb) = b(ka)$. This property, called the *fundamental property of fractions*,
justifies the common procedures of reduction and expansion of fractions. For
example,

$$\frac{34}{51} = \frac{17 \cdot 2}{17 \cdot 3} = \frac{2}{3}$$

and

$$\frac{4}{7} = \frac{4 \cdot 5}{7 \cdot 5} = \frac{20}{35}$$

The *negative* or additive inverse of a rational number $\frac{a}{b}$ is usually written as
$-\frac{a}{b}$, although the forms $\frac{-a}{b}$ or $\frac{a}{-b}$ are equivalent. Thus the negative of $\frac{3}{5}$ may
be written as $\frac{-3}{5}, \frac{3}{-5}$, or $-\frac{3}{5}$. In contrast, the multiplicative *inverse* of a rational number is defined as follows:

DEFINITION 1.11 The multiplicative inverse of an element a/b, where a/b
is a rational number, is a number x such that $\frac{a}{b} \cdot x = 1$.

Thus, the multiplicative inverse of 5/9 is 9/5, the multiplicative inverse of 7 is 1/7, and in general the multiplicative inverse of a/b is b/a. The numbers a/b and b/a are also referred to as *reciprocal numbers*.

Irrational Numbers

It might appear that the system of rational numbers is a final and complete system in that no further extension is required. From the standpoint of operations of addition, multiplication, and their inverses, this is true. However, other considerations, such as the solution of quadratic and higher degree equations, show a need for numbers that are not rational.

A number that cannot be expressed as a quotient of two integers is called an *irrational number*. The possibility of the existence of such numbers is not obvious. Since any rational number can be expressed as a decimal that either terminates or generates a repeating cycle, it follows that an irrational number, when expressed in decimal notation, will never end and never develop a repeating cycle of digits. We introduce this concept by examining a common example of an irrational number—the square root of 2.

The square root of a number is one of its two equal factors, that is, if $b^2 = a$ then b is the square root of a. Although tables of square roots are available, a generalized procedure for evaluating square roots is useful because of the necessary limitations of a given table. The procedure that follows is based on a repetitious process which is easily adaptable to programming on a computer. It is called an *iterative* process (from the word "iterate" which means "to repeat").

The square root of 2, represented by the symbol $\sqrt{2}$, is a number x such that $x \cdot x = 2$ or $2 \div x = x$. Therefore we can determine its decimal representation by setting up a division process that approximates the value x in the relation $2 \div x = x$.

Iterative Process for Approximating $\sqrt{2}$

Step 1. Estimate $\sqrt{2} = 1.3$

Step 2. Divide $2 \div 1.3 = 1.54$

Step 3. Average $\dfrac{1.3 + 1.54}{2} = 1.41$

Repeat steps 2 and 3:

$$2 \div 1.41 = 1.418$$

$$\frac{1.41 + 1.418}{2} = 1.414$$

$$2 \div 1.414 = 1.414428$$

$$\frac{1.414 + 1.414428}{2} = 1.414214$$

$$2 \div 1.414214 = 1.414213$$

It is not difficult to see why the process works. We are seeking a value of x such that $2 \div x = x$. If we choose a value $x_1 < x$ as a first estimate, then $2 \div x_1 = x_2$ where $x_2 > x$. Hence x is between x_1 and x_2, and taking their average is, therefore, a plausible way of selecting a value of x between x_1 and x_2.

Our computations indicate that the decimal representation of $\sqrt{2}$, correct to five decimal places, is 1.41421. Obviously, the process has not terminated, but this does not *prove* that it never will. To prove this, we have to show that $\sqrt{2}$ is irrational.

The proof of the irrationality of $\sqrt{2}$ is based on an understanding of a simple property of integers that are perfect squares, such as 25, 36, or 144. If we write each number in terms of its prime factors, then

$$25 = 5 \cdot 5$$
$$36 = 6 \cdot 6 = 2 \cdot 3 \cdot 2 \cdot 3$$
$$144 = 12 \cdot 12 = 2 \cdot 2 \cdot 3 \cdot 2 \cdot 2 \cdot 3$$

We observe that an integer is a perfect square if and only if each of its prime factors occurs an even number of times.

The central idea in the proof is to *assume* that $\sqrt{2}$ is a rational number and then show that this leads to an impossibility. Therefore we assume

$$\sqrt{2} = \frac{a}{b}$$

where a and b are integers that have no common factor. Then

$$\frac{a}{b} \cdot \frac{a}{b} = 2 \qquad \text{by definition of square root}$$

$$\frac{a^2}{b^2} = 2 \qquad \text{by multiplication}$$

$$a^2 = 2b^2 \qquad \text{by definition of inverse operations}$$

Let us examine this last statement very carefully. The number a^2 is a perfect square; therefore, 2 is a factor of a^2 either an even number of times or not at all. Similarly, 2 is a factor of b^2 either an even number of times or not at all. In either case, the expression $2b^2$ must have a factor 2 an odd number of times. But this is impossible because the numbers a^2 and $2b^2$ are equal. Since we have reached an impossible conclusion, our assumption that $\sqrt{2}$ is rational cannot be sustained. Therefore, $\sqrt{2}$ is an irrational number.

An extension of this procedure can be used to show that the square roots of many other numbers are irrational. Actually, it can be shown that the only integers that have rational square roots are those that are perfect squares of integers. Therefore, each of the following is irrational:

$$\sqrt{2}, \sqrt{3}, \sqrt{5}, \sqrt{6}, \sqrt{7}, \sqrt{8}, \sqrt{10}, \sqrt{11}, \sqrt{12}, \sqrt{13}, \ldots$$

Other important irrationals, such as π, cube roots, and logarithms, will be encountered in subsequent sections of this book.

Real Numbers

If we designate the set of rationals as R, and the set of irrationals as R', then the union of these two sets constitutes Z, the set of real numbers. Thus

$$Z = R \cup R'$$

The relation of the set of real numbers to the other sets we have considered is shown in Figure 1.13.

The number line, which has been used to present a graphic representation of the set of integers, can now be used to further depict graphically the elements of each subset of real numbers. The ultimate result is that a one-to-one correspondence can be shown to exist between the set of all points on the number line and the elements of the set of real numbers.

We have noted throughout these discussions the important properties of number sets—properties relating to closure, commutativity, associativity, and distributivity. Of course, the extension of the number set from natural numbers through real numbers does not routinely preserve all the properties introduced in successive enlargements of the set but, fortunately, this proves to be true. A demonstration of this in detail, however, is beyond the scope of this book; our interest is limited to suggesting the motivation for extending a number set and introducing some of the mathematical ideas involved in such extensions.

Although one further extension of our number set will be considered later, the set of real numbers is the number system that has major relevance to the study of algebra. Hereafter, in this book (unless otherwise specified) the word number will mean real number.

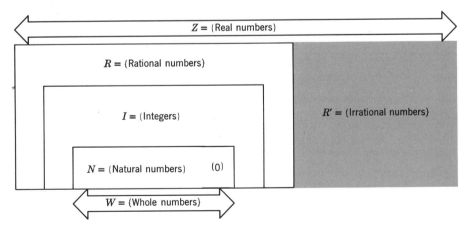

Figure 1.13 Subsets of the real numbers.

EXERCISE 1.5

The Set of Real Numbers

Write (a) the additive inverse, and (b) the multiplicative inverse of each of the following rational numbers.

1. $\dfrac{2}{3}$ 2. $\dfrac{-2}{7}$ 3. 8 4. -5

5. $\dfrac{3}{8}$ 6. $\dfrac{5}{4}$ 7. $-\left(\dfrac{5}{2}\right)$ 8. $-\dfrac{1}{2}$

Write three indicated quotients representing each of the following numbers.

9. $\dfrac{3}{4}$ 10. $\dfrac{8}{12}$ 11. $-\dfrac{2}{5}$ 12. $-\dfrac{11}{33}$

Determine whether the following pairs of rational numbers are equal or unequal.

13. $\dfrac{-3}{7}, \dfrac{3}{-7}$ 14. $\dfrac{-5}{-12}, \dfrac{65}{156}$ 15. $\dfrac{3}{8}, \dfrac{51}{137}$ 16. $\dfrac{-8}{13}, \dfrac{-11}{17}$

If Z is the set of real numbers, R the set of rationals, R' the set of irrationals, I the set of integers, W the set of whole numbers, and N the set of natural numbers, list *all* sets to which each of the following elements belong.

17. 6 18. -2 19. $\dfrac{3}{7}$ 20. $\dfrac{-5}{9}$

21. $\sqrt{8}$ 22. 0.37 23. 0 24. $0.333\ldots$

Perform the indicated division until the process terminates or develops a repeating cycle of digits.

25. $\dfrac{5}{16}$ 26. $\dfrac{5}{12}$ 27. $\dfrac{7}{9}$ 28. $\dfrac{4}{13}$

Using the iterative process, approximate the decimal representation of each of the following numbers to three digits.

29. $\sqrt{5.11}$ 30. $\sqrt{51.1}$ 31. $\sqrt{511}$
32. $\sqrt{0.511}$ 33. $\sqrt{7.13}$ 34. $\sqrt{830}$

Given the two rational numbers $m = 3.71$ and $n = 3.72$,

35. Write three other rational numbers that lie between m and n on the number line.

36. (a) Does the number $p = 3.71727374\ldots$ lie between m and n? (b) Is it a rational or irrational number?

37. Show that, as a result of considerations implicit in the two preceding problems, an unlimited number of rational and irrational numbers lie between any two given real numbers.

chapter 2
algebraic expressions

IN ALGEBRA IT IS FREQUENTLY DESIRABLE TO REFER TO some element of a set of numbers without specifying its value. At times this may be a matter of convenience, but when we are dealing with a quantity whose value is either unknown or changing it becomes a necessity. In such cases various letter symbols are used to represent numerical quantities. Thus s may represent the distance above ground of a falling object, n may represent the number of bacteria in a culture at a given time, or x may represent some measurable quantity in a problem situation. As noted in Section 1.1, such a symbol is called a *variable* and the *domain* of the variable is the set of elements that may be substituted for it. The domain is often referred to as the *replacement set* or the *set of permissible values*.

The introduction of literal symbols into a mathematical discussion makes possible immense savings of mental effort. It enables us to build other expressions by making use of the properties of the given variable and to perform mathematical operations on the expressions. This leads to two very important applications of algebra: the formulation of generalized statements and the determination of specific values that satisfy prescribed conditions in problem situations. Since the concept of an algebraic expression is fundamental to these applications, we now consider it in some detail.

2.1 TYPES OF ALGEBRAIC EXPRESSIONS

The fundamental operations, together with the process of taking roots, are known as *algebraic operations*. In this sense, the use of an exponent to indicate a product of like factors is included as an algebraic operation since it represents repeated multiplication. Thus $x \cdot x \cdot x \cdot x$ may be written as x^4, and $5 \cdot 5 \cdot 5$ may be written as 5^3. In the relation $5^3 = 125$, 5 is called the *base*, and 125 is said to be a *power* of the base. In general, a positive, integral exponent is defined as follows.

DEFINITION 2.1 $b^n = b \cdot b \cdot b \ldots b$ (n factors), where b is a real number, and n is a positive integer.

When a finite number of algebraic operations are applied to a collection of variables and real numbers, the result is called an *algebraic expression*. Examples of algebraic expressions are:

$$\text{(a) } 3x^2 - 2x + 5 \qquad \text{(b) } x + \sqrt{3x - y} \qquad \text{(c) } \frac{x + 3y}{x - 2z}$$

If an algebraic expression is regarded as a succession of partial expressions separated by plus and minus signs, each partial expression together with its preceding sign is called a *term*. In the given examples, expression (a) consists of the three terms $3x^2$, $-2x$, and $+5$; expression (b) consists of the two terms x and $\sqrt{3x - y}$; and expression (c) consists of a single term.

Terms that have identical literal parts are of special significance since they can be combined. Such terms are called *like terms* or *similar terms*. Thus $4x^2y$ and $-3x^2y$ are like terms, but $4x^2y$ and $-3xy^2$ are not like terms.

Certain types of algebraic expressions occur with such frequency in the study of algebra that they warrant identification. A *monomial* in given variables is an algebraic expression that can be written as the product of a real number and *nonnegative integral* powers of the variables. Thus a monomial in x is an algebraic expression that can be written in the form ax^n where a is a real number and n is a nonnegative integer. Similarly, $ax^m y^n$ is a monomial in x and y, such as $-3xy$, $\frac{1}{2}x^2y^3$, or $5xy^2$. In the monomial $-3xy$, any factor is called the *coefficient* of the remaining part. Thus -3 is the coefficient of xy, and $-3y$ is the coefficient of x. The real number a is called the numerical coefficient of the monomial $ax^m y^n$; in practice it is often referred to simply as the coefficient of the term.

The *degree of a monomial* is the sum of all the exponents of the variables that appear in the monomial, while the degree of a monomial *in one of its variables* is simply the exponent of that variable. Thus the degree of the monomial $-7x^2y^3z$ is 6; it is also of degree 2 in x, 3 in y, and 1 in z.

An indicated sum of two monomials is called a *binomial*, and an indicated sum of three monomials is called a *trinomial*. We have noted that a difference $x - y$ can be treated as a sum $x + (-y)$; similarly any difference can be viewed as a sum. Consequently, the following group (a) consists of examples of binomials, and group (b) consists of examples of trinomials.

$$\text{(a) } x + 2y; \, 3x - 2y; \, -2x - 3$$
$$\text{(b) } x^2 - 3x - 5; \, 2x + 3y - z; \, -x^2 - 2xy - 4y^2$$

A *polynomial* is any sum of monomials, including a single monomial as a limiting case. Thus

$$x^2; \tfrac{1}{2}x^2 - 2xy; 3x^3 - 7x^2 + 8x - 7$$

are examples of polynomials, but expressions such as $\sqrt{x}$, $\dfrac{1}{x}$, and $\dfrac{x-1}{y+2}$ are not polynomials since they cannot be expressed in terms of monomials.

The degree of a polynomial is simply the degree of the term of highest degree. Thus the degree of the polynomial

$$x^2 - 3x^3y - 2xy^2 + 7y$$

is 4 since that is the degree of the monomial $-3x^3y$, the term of highest degree. The degree of a polynomial in a given variable is the exponent of the highest power of that variable which occurs in any term of the polynomial. In the preceding example, the polynomial is of degree 3 in x and 2 in y.

It is customary to arrange the terms of a polynomial in descending order of degree in the variable involved. For example, the terms of the polynomial $2x^3 - 3x^2 + 7x - 6$ are arranged in descending order. The degree of the term -6 is regarded as zero since, as will be shown in Section 4.2, it can be written in the form $-6x^0$.

EXERCISE 2.1

Types of Algebraic Expressions

Express each of the following monomials in the form ax^n or ax^my^n.

1. xxx
2. $-3xx$
3. $-2 \cdot 4 \cdot x \cdot x \cdot x$
4. $7xyyy$
5. $-xxxyy$
6. $(-3)(-7)xxxxy$

The following is a list of common formulas. Identify as many as you can by indicating what each variable represents, as illustrated in Problem 7.

7. $A = bh$ Solution: A represents the area of a rectangle or parallelogram, b represents the length of its base, and h represents its height.

8. $A = \tfrac{1}{2}bh$
9. $C = 2\pi r$
10. $A = \tfrac{1}{2}h(b + b')$
11. $A = \pi r^2$
12. $V = \tfrac{4}{3}\pi r^3$
13. $i = prt$
14. $d = rt$
15. $V = lwh$
16. $S = 4\pi r^2$
17. $V = \pi r^2h$
18. $V = \tfrac{1}{3} Bh$
19. $c^2 = a^2 + b^2$
20. $p = 2l + 2w$
21. $E = I \cdot R$
22. $s = 16t^2$

For each of the following relations, write and verify two statements that result from replacing the variable by an element from the set of real numbers.

23. $x^2 \cdot x^3 = x^5$ 24. $(x^2)^3 = x^6$ 25. $a + a + a = 3a$

26. $3y + y = 4y$ 27. $\sqrt{a^2b^2} = |ab|$ 28. $p^2q^2 = (pq)^2$

Identify each of the following polynomials as a monomial, binomial, or trinomial, and indicate the degree of the polynomial.

29. $\frac{1}{2}\pi d^2$ 30. $x^3 - 3x$ 31. $2p - 5q + 2$

32. w 33. $b + b'$ 34. $4x^2 - 12xy + 9y^2$

35. $(-3)(4)u - v$ 36. -12 37. $7rs^2t + 1$

38. $3x^2 - x + 5$ 39. $2\pi r^2 + 2\pi rh$ 40. $2 - y$

What is the degree of each of the following polynomials in (a) x, (b) y, and (c) x and y?

41. $2x^2y - 3y + 2x - 5$ 42. $4x^3 - x^2y + 5xy^2 - y^3$

43. $y - y^2 + 3xy^3$ 44. xy

Arrange each of the following polynomials in descending powers of the variable and indicate its degree.

45. $7v - 3v^2 + 5 - v^3$ 46. $w - 1 + \frac{1}{2}w^3 - \frac{1}{4}w^2$

47. $x^n + x^{n-3} - 2 - 4x^{n-2}$ 48. $2y^{n-1} + 5y^{n+1} - y$

Indicate the terms that are similar to the first term listed in each problem.

49. $2xy$: $3xy^2$, $-x^2y$, $-xy$, $3xy$, $-7x^2y^2$, $2x$, $2xyz$, $-3yx$, $\sqrt{4xy}$, $\dfrac{1}{xy}$

50. $5a^2b$: ab, $-2ab^2$, $5ab^2$, $3ab$, $-a^2b^2$, $7a^2b$, $\sqrt{2}a^2b$, $\sqrt{2a^2b}$, $-b^2a$

Which of the following algebraic expressions are not polynomials in x?

51. $7 + \dfrac{7}{x}$ 52. $2 - 2x$ 53. $x^2 - 6x + \sqrt{2x}$

54. $\dfrac{1}{2} - 3x^2$ 55. $\dfrac{x}{x+1} - \dfrac{x}{x-1}$ 56. $\dfrac{x^2}{3} + \dfrac{x}{4}$

2.2 EVALUATION OF ALGEBRAIC EXPRESSIONS

When numerical values of variables are known or assigned, the value of an algebraic expression can be determined. The procedure is one of replacing the variable by its value and performing the indicated operations. For example, the value of the binomial $2x - 3$ when x equals 8 is $16 - 3$ or 13. The process of substitution and evaluation, although very simple in this case, has extensive application in mathematics. It is used to evaluate formulas, check applied problems and equations, find corresponding values of related variables, make estimates, and determine roots of certain equations. It is therefore important to develop the ability to evaluate algebraic expressions with assurance and accuracy.

Symbols of Grouping

In discussing properties of addition and multiplication, we noted that parentheses were used to group certain quantities. For example, the associative property of addition

$$a + (b + c) = (a + b) + c$$

indicated that the numbers b and c were to be treated as one group or quantity, and the numbers a and b were to be treated as another group or single quantity. The parentheses in this case represented a symbol of grouping.

Other symbols commonly used to indicate groupings are brackets, [ ], braces, { }, and the vinculum (a bar placed above the grouped quantities). Thus, $a - (b - c)$, $a - [b - c]$, $a - \{b - c\}$, $a - \overline{b - c}$ are equivalent expressions; each indicates that the difference of b and c is to be subtracted from a. The division bar and the radical sign may also serve to indicate groupings, as in the expression $\sqrt{a + b}$ and $\dfrac{a + b}{2}$.

Symbols of grouping may be used to indicate explicitly the order of operations in certain expressions. Thus the expression $3 + (5 \cdot 9)$ means that the quantity $5 \cdot 9$ is to be added to 3. The result, of course, is 48. On the other hand, the expression $(3 + 5) \cdot 9$ means that the sum of 3 and 5 is to be multiplied by 9; the result then is 72.

It is not uncommon to encounter several signs of grouping in a single expression. Thus $3[x - 2(x + 6)]$ means that the entire quantity $x - 2(x + 6)$ is to be multiplied by 3, and that within it, the binomial $x + 6$ is to be considered as a single quantity to be multiplied by -2. When two or more signs of grouping are nested, one within the other, it is best to simplify them one at a time beginning with the innermost. For example, if $x = 7$, the expression

$$3[x - 2(x + 6)]$$

becomes

$$3[7 - 2(7 + 6)]$$

which simplifies in successive steps to

$$3[7 - 2(13)]$$
$$3[7 - 26]$$
$$3[-19] = -57$$

EXERCISE 2.2

Evaluation of Algebraic Expressions

Evaluate each expression for $x = -3$:

1. $4(x - 5)$ 2. $3(2x + 4)$ 3. $x(5 - x)$
4. $5x(3x - 2)$ 5. $-3x(7 + 2x)$ 6. $4 + 7(x + 1)$
7. $x + 3 - (2x + 8)$ 8. $x + 5(x - 3)$ 9. $(x + 4)(x - 8)$

What is the value of each of the following expressions for $x = 4$, $y = -3$?

10. $3[x - (4y + 5)]$ 11. $2x^2 - [7 - (3x + 2)]$
12. $x - [2x - (x^2 - y)]$ 13. $x^2 - [3x - (2x - \overline{y + 2})]$
14. $(x^2 - 3)(x + 1)$ 15. $5 - [x + 6(x - y)]$
16. $(x^2 + 2x + 1)(2x - 3)$ 17. $(y^2 - 2y)(3y + 1)$
18. $(x - 2y)^3$ 19. $\sqrt{x^2 + y^2}$

Determine whether the following expressions are equal for the given value of the variable.

20. $2(y - 5)$ and $8y + 2$ for $y = -2$
21. $2x^2 + 3x - 14$ and $x^2 + 4$ for $x = 3$
22. $2x^2 + 3x - 14$ and $x^2 + 4$ for $x = -6$
23. $b^3 + 3b^2$ and $-2b + 4$ for $b = -1$
24. $r - 2(2 - 3r)$ and $3(1 + r)$ for $r = \frac{1}{2}$
25. $4x^2 - 6$ and $10x$ for $x = -\frac{1}{2}$
26. $4v^2 + 2(7 - v)$ and $(2v - 3)^2$ for $v = -\frac{1}{2}$
27. $y^2(y^2 + 2)$ and $y^3 - 4(y + 2)$ for $y = -1$

The following expressions are true for all permissible values of the variable. Verify the equality by substituting a specific number for the variable.

28. $9y^2 + 1 = (3y + 1)^2 - 6y$ 29. $\dfrac{x^2 + x - 6}{x - 2} = x + 3$

30. $\dfrac{b^3 - 1}{b - 1} = b^2 + b + 1$ 31. $4(c - 1) + 1 = c - 3(1 - c)$

By substituting $x = -3, -1, 0, 1, 3$, determine whether each of the following expressions is increasing in value, decreasing in value, or both in the interval $-3 \le x \le 3$.

32. $2x - 7$ 33. $-3x + 1$ 34. $2x + 5$
35. $-x + 13$ 36. $x^2 - x - 2$ 37. $-3x^2 + 2x - 2$
38. $x^2 + 1$ 39. $-x^2 + x$ 40. $-x^3$

Evaluate each of the following formulas for the given values of the variables.

41. $A = p + prt$ for $p = 100$, $r = 0.05$, $t = 6$
42. $s = \frac{1}{2}at^2$ for $a = 32$, $t = 3$

43. $v = v_0 + gt$ for $v_0 = 30$, $g = 32$, $t = 4$
44. $s = -16t^2 + v_0 t + h$ for $t = 5$, $v_0 = 1600$, $h = 150$
45. $V = \frac{4}{3}\pi r^3$ for $\pi = 3.14$, $r = 2$

By using signs of grouping show that:

46. $2p + 3$ is to be subtracted from $7q$.
47. The sum of $2a$ and $3b$ is to be multiplied by c.
48. Twice the difference of 7 and y is to be added to $5x$.
49. The difference of $5m$ and $4n$ is to be multiplied by the sum of m and n.
50. The square of the sum of u and v is to be divided by the sum of the squares of u and v.

2.3 OPERATIONS WITH MONOMIALS

Combining Monomials

Two monomials may be combined by addition or subtraction if they are similar or like terms. For example, the terms $6y$ and $9y$ may be combined as follows:

$$
\begin{aligned}
6y + 9y &= y \cdot 6 + y \cdot 9 && \text{Commutative property of multiplication} \\
&= y(9 + 6) && \text{Consequence of the distributive property} \\
&= y \cdot 15 && \text{Closure property of addition} \\
&= 15y && \text{Commutative property of multiplication}
\end{aligned}
$$

Once the basis for the procedure is understood, of course, it is not necessary to perform all of the steps. Notice that to add two like monomials, we add the numerical coefficients and assign the common literal factors.

This procedure is readily extended to the operation of subtraction or to the combining of more than two monomials, as illustrated in the following examples.

EXAMPLE 1. $5x - 8x = [5 + (-8)]x = -3x$

EXAMPLE 2. $7y^2z + y^2z + 4y^2z = (7 + 1 + 4)y^2z = 12\,y^2z$

The addition of monomials that are not similar can only be indicated; thus the sum of $3x$ and $-5y$ is simply written as $3x - 5y$. If a series of similar monomials, both positive and negative are to be combined, it is often expedient to add the positive and negative terms separately and then combine the two partial sums. Thus

EXAMPLE 3. $3k + 7k - 5k + 4k - 6k = 14k - 11k = 3k$

Multiplication and Division of Monomials

Consider the product $(-4xy^2)(9xy)$. Since multiplication is commutative we can rearrange the factors as follows.

$$(-4xy^2)(9xy) = -4 \cdot 9 \cdot x \cdot x \cdot y^2 \cdot y = -36x^2y^3$$

Notice that the numerical coefficient of the product is obtained by multiplying the numerical coefficients of the given monomials, and the exponents of the variables are determined by applying the definition of an exponent, stated in Definition 2.1. (In Chapter 4, general laws for operating with exponential quantities will be reviewed; however, at this point it is useful to keep in mind the meaning of an exponent as repeated multiplication). As further examples of the multiplication of monomials we have

$$
\begin{array}{cccc}
-3ab^2 & -4m^2 & 6ax^2 & 7x^2yz^3 \\
\underline{5ac} & \underline{-\,n} & \underline{-3} & \underline{3xy^3} \\
-15a^2b^2c & 4m^2n & -18ax^2 & 21x^3y^4z^3
\end{array}
$$

A power of a monomial is treated simply as a special case of multiplication. Thus $(-2ax^2)^3 = (-2ax^2)(-2ax^2)(-2ax^2) = -8a^3x^6$.

Since division is the inverse of multiplication, the procedure for dividing monomials follows as a consequence of the multiplicative process. For example, to determine the quotient $\dfrac{14u^2v^3}{-2uv^3}$ we need to satisfy the corresponding multiplication relation that the product of the quotient Q and the divisor $-2uv^3$ is $14u^2v^3$. Therefore

$$\frac{14u^2v^3}{-2uv^3} = -7u$$

The same result can be obtained, of course, by treating the indicated division as a rational number and dividing both numerator and denominator by like factors. Thus, in division,

$$
\frac{18ab^2}{-3ab^2} = -6 \qquad \frac{-24u^2v^2w}{-8uw} = 3uv^2 \qquad \frac{7ax^2}{a} = 7x^2 \qquad \frac{9x^2y}{-9x^2y} = -1
$$

Roots of Monomials

If we ask ourselves what number squared is 49, then we are asking for one of its two equal factors, that is, its square root. But there are two such numbers; 7 and -7. Similarly, there are two real numbers which are fourth roots of 81, namely 3 and -3, but there appears to be only one real cube root of -8 (which is -2), and there appears to be no real square root of -25. These, and other similar examples, readily illustrate that none, one, or two real roots may exist for a given real number.

For purposes of mathematical discussion it is useful to use a symbol for a root to represent a number that exists and is unique. Such a symbol is called the *principal root* of the number, and is commonly designated by $\sqrt[n]{b}$ where $\sqrt{}$ is called the *radical*, b is the *radicand*, and n is the *index*. (The index is usually not written when $n = 2$). For the set of real numbers, the principal root is defined as follows.

DEFINITION 2.2 The principal nth root of b, denoted by $\sqrt[n]{b}$, is that unique real number y such that $y^n = b$. In particular,

$$\sqrt[n]{y^n} = |y| \quad (n \text{ even})$$
$$\sqrt[n]{y^n} = y \quad (n \text{ odd})$$

EXAMPLE 4. $\sqrt{9} = |\pm 3| = 3; -\sqrt{9} = -|\pm 3| = -3; \sqrt{-9}$ is not defined in the set of real numbers.

EXAMPLE 5. $\sqrt[3]{-125} = \sqrt[3]{(-5)^3} = -5; \sqrt[3]{125} = \sqrt[3]{5^3} = 5$

EXAMPLE 6. $-\sqrt[3]{8} = -2; -\sqrt[3]{-8} = -(-2) = 2$

EXAMPLE 7. $\sqrt[5]{-32} = -2; \sqrt[4]{-32}$ is not defined; $\sqrt[3]{-32} = -3.1748$, an irrational number.

These procedures can be readily extended to the case when the radicand is an algebraic expression. Thus, for positive values of the variables, we have:

EXAMPLE 8. $\sqrt{64x^6} = 8x^3; -\sqrt{64x^6} = -8x^3; \sqrt[3]{64x^6} = 4x^2; \sqrt[3]{-64x^6} = -4x^2$

Each of these results can be verified by using the relation that finding a given power is the inverse of extracting the given root of an expression. For example,

$$\sqrt{64x^6} = 8x^3 \text{ because } (8x^3)^2 = 64x^6$$

and

$$\sqrt[3]{-64x^6} = -4x^2 \text{ because } (-4x^2)^3 = -64x^6$$

EXERCISE 2.3

Operations with Monomials

Add the following monomials.

1. $-7a$	2. $-9y$	3. $8k$	4. $-6v$
$-4a$	$5y$	$-13k$	$2v$

5. $7ab^2c$
 $6ab^2c$

6. $-4m^2n$
 $-4m^2n$

7. $-b$
 b

8. $-3uv$
 $8uv$

9. $2(x + y)$
 $5(x + y)$

10. $-6(p - 2q)$
 $-5(p - 2q)$

11. $4(a^2 - b^2)$
 $-9(a^2 - b^2)$

12. $-11(x^2 + 2y)$
 $4(x^2 + 2y)$

13. $2k, -k, -3k, 7k, k, -5k$

14. $-p^2, 7p^2, -4p^2, -9p^2, p^2$

15. $3mn, -4mn, -2mn, mn, -8mn$

16. $y, 2y, -3y, 13y, -4y, 6y, 5y$

Subtract and check:

17. $2pq$
 $6pq$

18. $3y^2$
 $-8y^2$

19. $9ab$
 $-2ab$

20. $-15x^3$
 $19x^3$

21. $9(a^2 + a)$
 $-6(a^2 + a)$

22. $-3(p + q)$
 $-(p + q)$

23. $8(x + 2y)$
 $-8(x + 2y)$

24. $-2(s - t^2)$
 $7(s - t^2)$

Find the following products.

25. $3x^2$
 $-2x$

26. $-5a$
 $-2a$

27. $-6p^2q$
 $5pq$

28. $8abx$
 $-7a^2xy$

29. $(-x)(-y)$

30. $(-1)(-a^2cx)$

31. $3(-2st)$

32. $(7mn)(-3mn^2)$

33. $b \cdot b^4$

34. $12x \cdot 3x$

35. $-4t \cdot 3t^2$

36. $3 \cdot 3^2$

37. $7^2 \cdot 7^3$

38. $(-6u)(-8u^3)$

39. $(-x)(-x)(-x)$

40. $(-3ac)(-bd)(2abc)$

41. $(-3b^3)^2$

42. $(2p^2q)^3$

43. $(-2uv^2)^4$

Find the following quotients.

44. $(-x^7) \div (-x)$

45. $-b^4 \div b^4$

46. $-20a^3 \div 4a^2$

47. $-27k^2 \div 9k^2$

48. $-42c^5 \div 7c^3$

49. $8a^2by^2 \div (-4aby^2)$

50. $(-11ax^2) \div (-11ax^2)$

51. $12p^2q \div 6pq$

52. $3x^2y \div (-x)$

Determine the principal root of each monomial for positive values of the variables.

53. $\sqrt{36p^4q^2}$

54. $\sqrt{y^2}$

55. $\sqrt{121a^2x^4y^2}$

56. $\sqrt{49x^6}$

57. $\sqrt[3]{b^6}$

58. $\sqrt[3]{8a^3c^6}$

59. $\sqrt[3]{-64m^6}$

60. $\sqrt[3]{-27u^9}$

61. $\sqrt[4]{a^4c^{12}}$

62. $\sqrt[5]{32k^{10}}$

63. $\sqrt[5]{-x^5y^5}$

64. $\sqrt[3]{-125m^6n^3}$

2.4 OPERATIONS WITH POLYNOMIALS

Addition and Subtraction of Polynomials

The procedures for adding and subtracting polynomials are based on those previously developed for combining monomials. The commutative and associative properties of real numbers are used to group like terms. Consider, for example, the addition of the binomials $2x + 3y$ and $5x - 9y$:

EXAMPLE 1. $(2x + 3y) + (5x - 9y)$

$= (2x + 3y) + (-9y + 5x)$	Commutative property of addition
$= 2x + (3y - 9y) + 5x$	Associative property of addition
$= 2x - 6y + 5x$	Addition of monomials
$= 2x + 5x - 6y$	Commutative property of addition
$= (2x + 5x) - 6y$	Associative property of addition
$= 7x - 6y$	Addition of monomials

Once the basis for the procedure is understood, of course, it is not necessary to perform all the steps. The following examples illustrate commonly accepted methods for combining polynomials.

EXAMPLE 2. Combine the expressions $2a - 5b - c$ and $8a + 4b - 3c$.

SOLUTION: $(2a - 5b - c) + (8a + 4b - 3c) = (2a + 8a) + (-5b + 4b)$
$$+ (-c - 3c) = 10a - b - 4c$$

This solution can also be written directly, as

$$(2a - 5b - c) + (8a + 4b - 3c) = 10a - b - 4c,$$

or it can be arranged so that like terms appear in columns, as

$$2a - 5b - c$$
$$8a + 4b - 3c$$
$$\overline{10a - b - 4c}$$

EXAMPLE 3. Subtract $4y^2 - 5y + 2$ from $7y^2 - 6$

SOLUTION: $(7y^2 - 6) - (4y^2 - 5y + 2) = 7y^2 - 6 - 4y^2 + 5y - 2$
$$= 3y^2 + 5y - 8$$

Notice that the sign of *each* term in the polynomial to be subtracted is changed when the problem is converted to addition. As with addition, like terms may be arranged in columns for convenience.

Multiplication of Polynomials

The multiplication of a polynomial by a monomial is a direct application of the distributive property which, it will be recalled, takes the form $a(b + c) = ab + ac$. Therefore, the product $3x(2x - 7y)$ becomes $3x(2x) + 3x(-7y)$ which simplifies to $6x^2 - 21xy$. This procedure may be extended to yield the product of a monomial and a polynomial of any number of terms. In each case the product will be equal to the sum of all the partial products obtained by multiplying each term of the polynomial by the monomial.

EXAMPLE 4. $3a(a^2 - 4ab + 8b^2) = 3a^3 - 12a^2b + 24\,ab^2$

EXAMPLE 5. $-2uv^2(u^3 - 2u^2 + u - 6) = -2u^4v^2 + 4u^3v^2 - 2u^2v^2 + 12uv^2$

Although it is not readily apparent, the same principles are the basis for multiplication when both factors are polynomials. Thus to find the product of $4x^2 - 7x - 5$ and $2x + 3$ the distributive property is used twice, as follows.

EXAMPLE 6. $(4x^2 - 7x - 5)(2x + 3)$

$$= (4x^2 - 7x - 5)(2x) + (4x^2 - 7x - 5)(3) \quad \text{Distributive property}$$

$$= 2x(4x^2 - 7x - 5) + 3(4x^2 - 7x - 5) \quad \text{Commutative property}$$

$$= 8x^3 - 14x^2 - 10x + 12x^2 - 21x - 15 \quad \text{Distributive property}$$

$$= 8x^3 - 2x^2 - 31x - 15 \quad \text{Combining like terms}$$

It is evident that the product of two polynomials is the sum of all the partial products obtained by multiplying each term of one polynomial by each term of the other. Therefore, the work can be arranged so that the similar cross products appear conveniently in columns, as follows:

$$
\begin{array}{l}
4x^2 - 7x - 5 \\
\underline{\,2x + 3} \\
8x^3 - 14x^2 - 10x \qquad\qquad \text{(Multiplication of the trinomial by } 2x) \\
\underline{12x^2 - 21x - 15} \quad \text{(Multiplication of the trinomial by } 3) \\
8x^3 - 2x^2 - 31x - 15
\end{array}
$$

A final refinement is to write the product of the two polynomials directly in horizontal form by mentally adding the similar cross products. Thus

$$(4x^2 - 7x - 5)(2x + 3) = 8x^3 - 2x^2 - 31x - 15$$

1. $4x^2 \cdot 2x$
2. $4x^2 \cdot 3 + (-7x) \cdot 2x$
3. $(-7x) \cdot 3 + (-5) \cdot 2x$
4. $(-5) \cdot 3$

Applications of this procedure are many and varied. The following are some typical examples.

EXAMPLE 7. $(5b^2 + 3)(2b - 4) = 10b^3 - 20b^2 + 6b - 12$

EXAMPLE 8. $(2\sqrt{3} + 5)(4\sqrt{3} - 7) = 24 + 6\sqrt{3} - 35 = -11 + 6\sqrt{3}$

EXAMPLE 9. $(m + 2n)(4m - 3n) = 4m^2 + 5mn - 6n^2$

EXAMPLE 10. $(x^2 + 3y)(x^2 - 3y) = x^4 - 9y^2$

Division of Polynomials

The division of polynomials falls naturally into two categories: the division of a polynomial by a monomial, and the division of a polynomial by another polynomial. The procedure for the first is again related to the distributive property. Since division is related to multiplication, the distributive property $a(b + c) = ab + ac$ leads to the relationship

$$(ab + ac) \div a = b + c$$

Generalizing this relationship we observe that to divide any polynomial by a monomial we divide *each* term of the polynomial by the monomial and form the algebraic sum of the resulting partial quotients. Thus:

EXAMPLE 11. $(8b^3 - 14b^2 + 12b) \div 2b = 4b^2 - 7b + 6$

EXAMPLE 12. $(x^3 - 3x^2 + x) \div (-x) = -x^2 + 3x - 1$

The division of one polynomial by another is analogous to the "long division" algorithm used in arithmetic. The algorithm for the division of two polynomials is based on the following principle.

For any two polynomials A and B with B $\neq$ 0, there exists two expressions Q and R such that A = B·Q + R.

Q is called the quotient, and R is the remainder. If $R = 0$, then Q and B are said to be exact divisors of A. The procedure for determining the quotient Q and the remainder R for a specific case is illustrated in the following example.

EXAMPLE 13. Divide $(37 + 8x^3 - 4x)$ by $(2x + 3)$

SOLUTION: Arrange both polynomials in descending powers of the variable, making provision for missing powers in the dividend. Then follow the steps as indicated:

$$
\begin{array}{r}
8x^3 \div 2x = 4x^2 \\
-12x^2 \div 2x = -6x \\
4x^2 - 6x + 7 \qquad 14x \div 2x = 7 \\
2x + 3\,\overline{)8x^3 + 0x^2 - 4x + 37} \\
8x^3 + 12x^2 \qquad 4x^2(2x + 3) \\
-12x^2 - 4x \\
-12x^2 - 18x \qquad -6x(2x + 3) \\
14x + 37 \\
14x + 21 \qquad 7(2x + 3) \\
16 \qquad \text{Remainder}
\end{array}
$$

Therefore, the quotient is $4x^2 - 6x + 7$ and the remainder is 16. This result may be verified by showing that

$$(4x^2 - 6x + 7)(2x + 3) + 16 = 8x^3 - 4x + 37$$

EXERCISE 2.4

Operations with Polynomials

Find the sum of each of the following:

1. $3x - 9$
   $4x + 2$

2. $6a - 3b + c$
   $2a - 3b - c$

3. $2x^2 - 6xy + y^2$
   $-x^2 + xy + y^2$

4. $(m^2 - 6mn + 8n^2) + (3m^2 - 2mn - 5n^2)$
5. $(4x^2 - 2y^2) + (x^2 - y^2) + (3x^2 + 5y^2)$
6. $(2p - q + 7r) + (p + 2q + 3r) + (6p - 5r)$
7. $7b^3 + b^2 + 6 - b - 2b^2 + 4b + 7 - 5b^2 - 4b + 11b^3$
8. $2p - 3q + 4r - 6q + 11 + 12p - 8 - r - q + 3r + 5p$

Subtract as indicated:

9. $(2x^2 + 5x - 1) - (x^2 - 2x + 4)$

10. $(3a^2 - 2ab + 5b^2) - (a^2 - 2ab - b^2)$

11. $(mn - m^3 + 3n^2) - (m^3 + 5mn + 6n^2)$

12. From $b^2 - 3b + 2$ subtract $4b^2 - 4b - 1$

13. Subtract $y^2 - 1$ from $2y^2 + 5y + 9$

14. What must be added to $6a - 2$ to produce $2a + 6$?

15. What must be added to $2u$ to produce $-3v$?

16. From the sum of $3x$ and $4y$, subtract their difference.

Find the following products and check by substituting specific numbers for the variables.

17. $(3a - b)(2a + c)$

18. $(x^2 - x)(x - 1)$

19. $(y + 7)(2y - 3)$

20. $(7m - 2n)(7m - 2n)$

21. $(3u - 8v)(3u + 8v)$

22. $(b - 4)(4b - 5)$

23. $(2a - 3b + c)(2a - c)$

24. $(x - 2y + 7)(x + 6)$

25. $(2p - q + r)^2$

26. $(u - 3v + 2)(u - 3v - 2)$

Divide and check by multiplication:

27. $(k^3 - 3k^2) \div k$

28. $(6b^3 - 9b^2 - 12b) \div (-3b)$

29. $(x - y - z) \div (-1)$

30. $(m^2n^2 - 7m^4n^3) \div mn^2$

31. $(2\pi r^2 + 2\pi rh) \div 2\pi r$

32. $(a^2bc + ab^2c + abc^2) \div ac$

33. $(4a^2x^3 - 6a^2x^2 + 2ax^2 + 14ax^3 - 8a^3x^2) \div (-2ax^2)$

Using division, determine whether:

34. $(a - 2)$ is an exact divisor of $a^3 - a^2 - 14a + 24$

35. $(x - 1)$ is an exact divisor of $x^3 + 2x^2 - x + 2$

36. $(y - 2)$ or $(2y - 1)$ is an exact divisor of $4y^3 + 4y^2 - 7y + 2$

37. $(3n + 2)$ or $(3n + 1)$ is an exact divisor of $9n^3 + 9n^2 - 4n - 4$

Perform the following indicated operations and simplify the result:

38. $\dfrac{(2x + h)^2 - 4x^2}{h}$

39. $\dfrac{5(x + h)^2 + 8 - (5x^2 + 8)}{h}$

40. $\dfrac{(x + h)^2 - (x + h) - x^2 + x}{h}$

41. $\dfrac{(x + h)^2 + 2(x + h) - 5 - (x^2 + 2x - 5)}{h}$

42. $\dfrac{2(x + h)^2 + 3(x + h) + 2 - (2x^2 + 3x + 2)}{h}$

chapter 3
linear equations and linear inequalities

3.1 EQUALITY AS A RELATION

IN SECTION 1.1 SEVERAL SET RELATIONS WERE STUDIED: the equality of sets, the equivalence of sets, and the concept of subset. A relation was defined to be a statement that describes the connectivity between two or more objects.

An example of a relation is the following sentence: Alaska is larger in area than Texas. Here we are comparing the areas of two states. The phrase "is larger than" is frequently used in the statement of relations in general usage as well as in mathematical usage. Other phrases that are often used to indicate relations between objects are:

is parallel to	is heavier than
is not equal to	is a classmate of
is similar to	is a brother of
is greater than	is a neighbor of

We shall now investigate three properties that relations sometimes possess: the reflexive property, the symmetric property, and the transitive property.

If we let a, b, and c represent three objects and R represent a general relation, then we can write "a has the relation R to b" as aRb. Using this notation we can write the three properties of relations as:

Reflexive Property: aRa
Symmetric Property: If aRb, then bRa.
Transitive Property: If aRb and bRc, then aRc.

Stated verbally the reflective property is "a has the relation R to a." For the relation "is equal to" then, the reflexive property would be $a = a$. We would accept this as true. Although it may seem that the reflexive property is trivial and always true, this is not the case. Consider the relation "is perpendicular to" using lines as elements. No line is ever perpendicular to itself so for the relation "is perpendicular to" the reflexive property would not be valid.

A relation R is said to be symmetric when for two elements a and b, if a has the relation R to b, then b has the relation R to a. The relation "is parallel to" is symmetric when we consider a and b to represent lines; whereas, the relation "is larger than" is not symmetric. This can be seen from the relation given earlier in this section, namely, "Alaska is larger than Texas." This statement is true but the statement "Texas is larger than Alaska" is false, so the relation is not symmetric.

A relation R is said to be transitive if when a has the relation R to b and b has the relation R to c, then a has the relation R to c. Let us consider three triangles, a, b, and c, and "is congruent to" as the relation. Then the transitive property would be

$$\text{If } \triangle a \cong \triangle b \text{ and } \triangle b \cong \triangle c, \text{ then } \triangle a \cong \triangle c.$$

We recall from geometry that the relation "is congruent to" is a transitive relation.

In the preceding paragraphs we have defined relation, the reflexive property, the symmetric property, and the transitive property. We are now ready to state the following axioms for equality.

Axiom 3.1   Equality is a reflexive relation, symbolically: $a = a$.
Axiom 3.2   Equality is a symmetric relation, symbolically: If $a = b$, then $b = a$.
Axiom 3.3   Equality is a transitive relation, symbolically: If $a = b$ and $b = c$, then $a = c$.

A relation that is reflexive, symmetric, and transitive is called an equivalence relation. Equality therefore is an equivalence relation.

Additional Axioms of Equality

Two additional axioms of equality that are needed before we can solve algebraic equations are:

Axiom 3.4   If $a = b$, then $a + c = b + c$.
Axiom 3.5   If $a = b$, then $ac = bc$.

Stated verbally, Axiom 3.4 is "if the same quantity is added to equals, the sums are equal." Axiom 3.5 would be stated as "if equals are multiplied by the same quantity, the products are equal." Some examples of the use of Axioms 3.4 and 3.5 are:

EXAMPLE 1. If $x - 3 = 5$,

$$\text{then } x - 3 + 3 = 5 + 3 \qquad\qquad\qquad\qquad \text{(Axiom 3.4)}$$

EXAMPLE 2. If $\dfrac{1}{6} x = \dfrac{7}{2}$,

$$\text{then } 6\left(\frac{1}{6} x\right) = 6\left(\frac{7}{2}\right) \qquad\qquad\qquad\qquad \text{(Axiom 3.5)}$$

EXAMPLE 3. If $x + 7 = 9$,

$$\text{then } x + 7 + (-7) = 9 + (-7) \qquad\qquad\qquad \text{(Axiom 3.4)}$$

EXAMPLE 4. If $4x = 36$,

$$\text{then } \frac{1}{4}(4x) = \frac{1}{4}(36) \qquad\qquad\qquad\qquad \text{(Axiom 3.5)}$$

Notice that Axiom 3.4 permits the addition of either a positive or a negative quantity to both members. Therefore, it permits the addition of equals to both members of an equation and the subtraction of equals from both members of an equation. Axiom 3.5 permits multiplication by a quantity or the reciprocal of a non-zero quantity; therefore, both members of an equation may be divided by the same nonzero quantity.

EXERCISE 3.1

Equality as a Relation

In Problems 1–10 determine which of the properties—reflexive, symmetric, transitive—are satisfied by each relation for the specified set.

1. The relation $<$ for real numbers.
2. The relation $\not<$ for real numbers.
3. The relation "has the same number of sides" for polygons.

4. The relation "is north of" for cities in the United States.
5. The relation "is exactly divisible by" for the set of natural numbers.
6. The relation "is a cousin of" for persons.
7. The relation "has the same residence as" for persons.
8. The relation "is a subset of" as applied to sets.
9. The relation "is heavier than" for persons.
10. The relation "is in the same mathematics class as" for students.

In Problems 11–20 determine which of the five axioms of equality justifies the equation or statement.

11. If $x - 5 = 7$, then $x = 12$.
12. If $x = y$ and $y = 5$, then $x = 5$.
13. If $x = 3w$, then $3w = x$.
14. $7x + 3 = 7x + 3$.
15. If $3x = 39$, then $x = 13$.
16. If $5x - 3 = x$, then $x = 5x - 3$.
17. If $s = \frac{n}{2}(a + 1)$, then $2s = n(a + 1)$.
18. If $2A = h(b + B)$, then $A = \frac{h}{2}(b + B)$.
19. If $5x = 15 + 2x$, then $3x = 15$.
20. If $F - 32 = \frac{9}{5}C$, then $F = \frac{9}{5}C + 32$.

3.2 SOLVING LINEAR EQUATIONS

Equations may be classified in various ways. One method is to identify an equation as an identity equation or a conditional equation.

DEFINITION 3.1: An *identity* is an equation that is satisfied by all values in the domain of the variable.

EXAMPLE 1. $2x - 8 = 2(x - 4)$ is an identity.

EXAMPLE 2. $x^2 - x = (x + 2)(x - 3) + 6$ is an identity.

EXAMPLE 3. $\dfrac{x^2 - 4}{x + 2} = x - 2$ is an identity for all x except $x = -2$.

Any numerical value of x will satisfy Examples 1 and 2. In Example 3 all $x \neq -2$ satisfy the equation. The value $x = -2$ must be excluded because it will make the denominator zero; therefore, the left member of the identity is not defined for $x = -2$.

DEFINITION 3.2: A *conditional equation* is one that is not satisfied by all values in the domain of the variable.

DEFINITION 3.3: A *solution* or *root* of an equation is a value of the variable which when substituted for the variable will reduce the equation to an identity.

EXAMPLE 4. $3x - 4 = 8$ is a conditional equation. The only solution is $x = 4$.

EXAMPLE 5. $x^2 + 2x = 3$ is a conditional equation. There are two roots, $x = 1$ and $x = -3$.

EXAMPLE 6. $x^3 - 6x^2 + 11x - 6 = 0$ is a conditional equation. The solutions are $x = 1$, $x = 2$, and $x = 3$.

DEFINITION 3.4: *Equivalent linear equations* are *linear* equations which have exactly the same roots.

EXAMPLE 7. $x - 5 = 0$ and $2x = 10$ are equivalent equations. They both have $x = 5$ as a root.

EXAMPLE 8. $x + 3 = 0$ and $x^2 + 3x = 0$ are not equivalent equations. While $x = -3$ is a root of both equations, the second equation also has a root of zero which is not a root of the first equation.

Before using the axioms of equality to solve linear equations, we will define a linear equation.

DEFINITION 3.5: A *linear equation* is a polynomial equation of first degree. That is, the highest degree term in the variable is of the first degree.

An alternate definition might be given in the following form. A linear equation in one variable (x) is any equation of the form $ax + b = 0$ where a and b are real numbers and a is not zero or any equation which can be put into that form by operations which lead to equivalent equations.

Let us now solve some simple examples by using the axioms of equality.

EXAMPLE 9. Solve $3x - 5 = 4$ for x.

SOLUTION:

$$3x - 5 = 4$$
$$3x - 5 + 5 = 4 + 5 \qquad \text{by Axiom 3.4}$$
$$3x = 9 \qquad \text{combining terms}$$
$$\frac{1}{3}(3x) = \frac{1}{3}(9) \qquad \text{by Axiom 3.5}$$
$$x = 3$$

Check: By substituting $x = 3$ into the original equation we have

$$3(3) - 5 \stackrel{?}{=} 4$$
$$9 - 5 \stackrel{?}{=} 4$$
$$4 = 4.$$

Note that, upon substitution of the solution into the original equation, the equation is reduced to the identity $4 = 4$.

EXAMPLE 10. Solve $2(y - 4) + 12 = 3(y + 3)$ for y.

$$2(y - 4) + 12 = 3(y + 3)$$
$$2y - 8 + 12 = 3y + 9 \qquad \text{by the Distributive Property}$$
$$2y - 8 + 12 + 8 - 12 - 3y = 3y + 9 + 8 - 12 - 3y \qquad \text{by Axiom 3.4}$$
$$-y = 5 \qquad \text{combining terms}$$
$$y = -5 \qquad \text{by Axiom 3.5}$$

Check:

$$2(-5 - 4) + 12 \stackrel{?}{=} 3(-5 + 3)$$
$$2(-9) + 12 \stackrel{?}{=} 3(-2)$$
$$-18 + 12 \stackrel{?}{=} -6$$
$$-6 = -6$$

We are now ready to consider the order in which the various operations, used to solve linear equations, are performed. In general, the procedure may be summarized as follows.

1. Eliminate parentheses by performing the indicated operations.
2. Add to both members of the equation the additive inverses of (a) the constant terms in the left member of the equation and (b) the terms containing the variable in the right member of the equation (Axiom 3.4).

3. Combine like terms.

4. Multiply both members by the multiplicative inverse of the coefficient of the variable (Axiom 3.5).

5. Check the solution in the original equation.

In Example 9 it was not necessary to perform step 1, since the equation did not contain parentheses. In Example 10 the five steps were performed in order. Now let us consider an example where it would be advantageous to deviate slightly from the steps as outlined above.

EXAMPLE 11. Solve $\frac{1}{3}(x - 4) + 2 = \frac{1}{2}(x + 3)$ for x.

$$\frac{1}{3}(x - 4) + 2 = \frac{1}{2}(x + 3)$$

$$6\left(\frac{1}{3}\right)(x - 4) + 6(2) = 6\left(\frac{1}{2}\right)(x + 3) \qquad \text{by Axiom 3.5}$$

$$2(x - 4) + 12 = 3(x + 3).$$

The original equation of Example 11 is now transformed to the original equation of Example 10 except for the change in notation for the variable.

Changing the Subject of a Formula

The formula $A = \frac{h}{2}(b + B)$ is used to determine areas of trapezoids; A is said to be the subject of this formula. When we are given values of h, b, and B, we would use this formula to determine the corresponding value of A. However, if we were given sets of values for A, b, and B, the formula in the given form would not afford the most convenient means of determining the corresponding values of h. It would be much more efficient to determine the set of values of h by using a form of this formula in which the subject was h; that is, we would change the subject of the formula.

To change the subject of the formula we would consider all of the literal symbols, except the one we want as the new subject of the formula, to be constants. Then the procedure for solving linear equations is used to solve for the new subject. Using the above formula as an illustration we would proceed as follows:

EXAMPLE 12. Solve $A = \frac{h}{2}(b + B)$ for h.

SOLUTION: $A = \frac{h}{2}(b + B)$

$$2A = h\,(b + B) \qquad \text{Multiply by 2}$$

$$h(b + B) = 2A \qquad \text{Symmetric property of equality}$$

$$h = \frac{2A}{b + B} \qquad \text{Divide by the coefficient of } h$$

This is the form of the formula to use to determine values of h for a set of trapezoids if the area and lengths of the bases are known.

EXAMPLE 13. Solve $\dfrac{1}{R} = \dfrac{1}{a} + \dfrac{1}{b}$ for a.

SOLUTION:

$$\frac{1}{R} = \frac{1}{a} + \frac{1}{b}$$

$ab = Rb + Ra$ Multiply by Rab

$ab - Ra = Rb$ Subtract Ra

$(b - R)a = Rb$ Distributive Law

$$a = \frac{Rb}{b - R}$$ Divide by coefficient of a

EXERCISE 3.2

Solution of Linear Equations

Solve the following linear equations and check your answers:

1. $x + 7 = 3$

2. $y + 5 = 4$

3. $x - 6 = 4$

4. $y - 3 = 2$

5. $3x = 15$

6. $4y = 12$

7. $\dfrac{2}{3}x = 8$

8. $\dfrac{5}{4}y = 20$

9. $3x + 8 = -1$

10. $4y - 6 = 14$

11. $6x - 11 = 13$

12. $2y + 5 = 11$

13. $3(x - 4) = 15$

14. $3(y + 5) = 21$

15. $4(x + 3) = 20$

16. $5(y - 7) = 15$

17. $3(x + 3) = x + 17$

18. $7(y - 3) = y + 9$

19. $2(x + 7) = 19 + 3x$

20. $3(y + 8) = 12 + y$

21. $\dfrac{2}{3}(x - 5) = \dfrac{3}{2}(x + 5)$

22. $\dfrac{3}{2}(y + 3) = \dfrac{2}{3}(y - 2)$

23. $\dfrac{1}{2}(x + 6) + \dfrac{1}{4}(x - 5) = 7$

24. $\dfrac{1}{2}(y - 3) + \dfrac{1}{4}(y + 2) = 8$

25. $\dfrac{1}{2}(x - 3) - \dfrac{1}{3}(x - 2) = 4$

26. $\dfrac{1}{2}(y - 5) - \dfrac{1}{3}(y - 4) = 5$

27. $\dfrac{x}{2} + \dfrac{2x}{3} - \dfrac{5x}{6} = 4$

28. $\dfrac{y}{2} - \dfrac{2y}{3} + \dfrac{5y}{6} = 4$

29. $3\left(x - \dfrac{1}{2}\right) - 5\left(x - \dfrac{1}{3}\right) = \dfrac{25}{6}$

30. $5\left(y - \dfrac{1}{2}\right) - 6\left(y - \dfrac{1}{3}\right) = \dfrac{7}{2}$

Change the subjects of the following formulas to the letter indicated.

31. $F = ma$, solve for m.
32. $p = a + b + c$, solve for a.
33. $p = a + b + c$, solve for c.
34. $A = lw$, solve for w.
35. $E = IR$, solve for I.
36. $p = 4s$, solve for s.
37. $C = 2\pi r$, solve for r.
38. $V = s^2h$, solve for h.
39. $V = \dfrac{1}{3}Bh$, solve for B.
40. $V = \dfrac{1}{3}Bh$, solve for h.
41. $V = lwh$, solve for h.
42. $I = prt$, solve for p.
43. $V = \pi r^2h$, solve for h.
44. $p = 2l + 2w$, solve for w.
45. $A = p + prt$, solve for r.
46. $A = p + prt$, solve for p.
47. $S = 2\pi rh + 2\pi r^2$, solve for h.
48. $l = a + (n - 1)d$, solve for n.
49. $l = a + (n - 1)d$, solve for d.
50. $F = \dfrac{9}{5}C + 32$, solve for C.

3.3 INEQUALITY THEOREMS

DEFINITION 3.6: An open sentence that contains the symbol for "greater than" or "less than" or either of these symbols combined with equality ("greater than or equal to" or "less than or equal to") is called an *inequality*.

Inequalities may be categorized as *absolute inequalities* or *conditional inequalities*. An absolute inequality is similar to an identity equation in that all permissible real values of the variable satisfy the inequality. That is, any real number is a solution of the inequality or the solution set for an absolute inequality is the set of real numbers. A conditional inequality is similar to a conditional equation in that some values of the variable, or perhaps none, but not all values of the variable, constitute the set of solutions.

Examples of absolute inequalities are:

EXAMPLE 1. $x^2 + 1 > 0$

EXAMPLE 2. $x^2 - 4x + 6 > 0$

To prove that Example 1 is an absolute inequality, consider the term x^2. It is always positive or zero for any real value of x; thus, the left member of the first example will always be one or larger and therefore greater than zero.

Example 2 can best be shown to be an absolute inequality by rewriting it in another form. It can be shown by multiplication that $(x - 2)^2 + 2$ is equivalent to $x^2 - 4x + 6$. Therefore, the inequality can be written as:

$$(x - 2)^2 + 2 > 0$$

For any real number x, the quantity $x - 2$ is a real number and its square will be positive or zero. The left member of the inequality will therefore be two or more for all real values of x.

To facilitate the proofs of the theorems necessary for solving conditional inequalities we shall define "greater than" in a more precise manner than we did earlier in Section 1.4.

DEFINITION 3.7: $a > b$ if $a = b + P$ where $P > 0$.

The above definition can be modified slightly to define "less than."

DEFINITION 3.8: $a < b$ if $a + P = b$ where $P > 0$.

A phrase we shall find useful in discussing inequalities is "sense of inequalities." To illustrate this concept consider $a > b$ and $c > d$; these two inequalities are said to have the *same order* or *same sense*. That is, both inequalities would be read by using the words greater than. The inequalities $c > d$ and $e < f$ are said to be of *opposite order* or *opposite sense*.

THEOREM 3.1.   If $a > b$, then $a + c > b + c$ for any real number c.

PROOF:

$a > b$	Given
$a = b + P$	Definition 3.7
$a + c = b + P + c$	Addition Axiom of Equality
$a + c = b + c + P$	Commutative Property of Addition
$a + c = (b + c) + P$	Associative Property of Addition
$a + c > b + c$	Definition 3.7

Theorem 3.1, called the *addition theorem* for *inequalities*, can be expressed as follows: If equal quantities (either positive or negative) are added to both members of an inequality, the sense of the inequality is preserved.

Examples 3 and 4 illustrate the use of Theorem 3.1.

EXAMPLE 3. Solve: $x - 5 > 3$

$$x - 5 + 5 > 3 + 5 \qquad \text{by Theorem 3.1}$$

$$x > 8$$

EXAMPLE 4. Solve: $y + 7 < 3$

$$y + 7 - 7 < 3 - 7 \qquad \text{by Theorem 3.1}$$
$$y < -4$$

THEOREM 3.2. If $a > b$ and $m > 0$, then $am > bm$.

PROOF:

$a > b$	Given
$a = b + P$	Definition 3.7
$am = (b + P)m$	Multiplication Axiom of Equality
$am = bm + Pm$	Distributive Property
let $P^1 = Pm$	
$P^1 > 0$	Product of the two positive factors P and m
$am = bm + P^1$	Substitution
$am > bm$	Definition 3.7

Example 5 illustrates the use of Theorem 3.2.

EXAMPLE 5. Solve: $\dfrac{1}{3}x > 4$

$$\frac{1}{3}(3)x > 3(4) \qquad \text{by Theorem 3.2}$$
$$x > 12$$

THEOREM 3.3. If $a > b$ and $n < 0$, then $an < bn$.

PROOF.

$a > b$	Given
$a = b + P$	Definition 3.7
$an = (b + P)n$	Multiplication Axiom of Equality
$an = bn + Pn$	Distributive Property
$an + (-Pn) = bn$	Adding $- Pn$ to both members
let $P' = -Pn$	
$P' > 0$	Law of signs for Multiplication
$an + P' = bn$	Substitution
$an < bn$	Definition 3.7

EXAMPLE 6. Solve: $6 - x > 3$

$$-6 + x < -3 \qquad \text{Theorem 3.3}$$
$$x < -3 + 6 \qquad \text{Theorem 3.1}$$
$$x < 3$$

Note. Multiplying both members of an inequality by a positive number preserves the sense of the inequality, but *if both members of an inequality are multiplied by a negative number the sense of the inequality is reversed.*

Although Theorems 3.2 and 3.3 are usually referred to as the multiplication theorems for inequalities, they do permit multiplication by multiplicative inverses. Therefore, they pertain to division as well as to multiplication.

EXERCISE 3.3

Theorems of Inequalities

In Problems 1–14, indicate the theorem that should be used to change the first inequality to the second.

1. If $5x - 3 > 1$, then $5x > 4$.
2. If $3x > 21$, then $x > 7$.
3. If $-2x > 12$, then $x < -6$.
4. If $-5y < -25$, then $y > 5$.
5. If $6y - 4 < 3$, then $6y < 7$.
6. If $x - 2a < 3b$, then $x < 2a + 3b$.
7. If $\frac{1}{2}y < -2$, then $y < -4$.
8. If $5 - 4x > 9$, then $-5 + 4x < -9$.
9. If $y - 5m < -2n$, then $y < 5m - 2n$.
10. If $2x + 3 > 4$, then $2x > 1$.
11. If $-3y - 7 < 14$, then $3y + 7 > -14$.
12. If $9x < -27$, then $x < -3$.
13. If $7y + d < c$, then $7y < c - d$.
14. If $4y > 8$, then $y > 2$.

In Problems 15–24, replace R (the general symbol for a relation) with the appropriate specific inequality symbol.

15. If $2x - 5 > 6$, then $2x \; R \; 11$.
16. If $3y - 2 < 8$, then $3y \; R \; 10$.
17. If $x + 7 < 9$, then $x \; R \; 2$.
18. If $y - 4 > 4$, then $y \; R \; 8$.
19. If $4 - \frac{1}{2}x < 2$, then $8 - x \; R \; 4$.
20. If $16 - 4y > 20$, then $4 - y \; R \; 5$.
21. If $16 - 4x > 20$, then $-4 + x \; R \; -5$.
22. If $6 - 3y < -9$, then $-2 + y \; R \; 3$.
23. If $8k - \frac{1}{3}x > -2$, then $-24k + x \; R \; 6$.
24. If $\frac{1}{2}x + 4 < 8$, then $x + 8 \; R \; 16$.

3.4 SOLUTIONS OF INEQUALITIES

The theorems of Section 3.3 afford us the rules by which elementary inequalities can be solved. Several examples will illustrate how to proceed.

EXAMPLE 1. Solve the inequality $2x - 5 > 3$.

SOLUTION:

$2x - 5 > 3$	Given
$2x - 5 + 5 > 3 + 5$	5 is added to both members. The sense of the inequality is preserved.
$2x > 8$	Combining terms
$x > 4$	Both members are divided by 2. The sense of the inequality is preserved.

The solution set is all real numbers greater than 4.

EXAMPLE 2. Solve the inequality $\frac{1}{3}x + 6 < 2$.

SOLUTION:

$\frac{1}{3}x + 6 < 2$	
$\frac{1}{3}x + 6 - 6 < 2 - 6$	-6 is added to both members. The sense is preserved.
$\frac{1}{3}x < -4$	Combining terms
$x < -12$	Both members are multiplied by 3. The sense of the inequality is preserved.

The solution set is all real numbers less than -12.

EXAMPLE 3. Solve $4 - 5x < -3$.

SOLUTION:

$4 - 5x < -3$	
$-5x < -7$	Adding -4 to both members
$-5\left(-\frac{1}{5}\right)x > (-7)\left(-\frac{1}{5}\right)$	Multiplying both members by a negative number reverses the sense of the inequality.
$x > \frac{7}{5}$	

The solution set is all real numbers greater than $\frac{7}{5}$.

EXAMPLE 4. Solve $7\left(\dfrac{2}{3}x - 1\right) > 2(x - 6)$

SOLUTION:

$$7\left(\frac{2}{3}x - 1\right) > 2(x - 6)$$

$$\frac{14}{3}x - 7 > 2x - 12 \qquad \text{Distributive Property}$$

$$\frac{14}{3}x - 2x > -12 + 7 \qquad \text{Adding } -2x \text{ and } 7 \text{ to both members}$$

$$\frac{8}{3}x > -5 \qquad \text{Combining terms}$$

$$x > \frac{-15}{8} \qquad \text{Multiplying both members by } \frac{3}{8}$$

The solution set is all real numbers greater than $\dfrac{-15}{8}$.

To solve inequalities involving absolute values it is necessary to utilize a property of absolute values before applying the theorems of inequalities. The property that is used is that $|x| > a$ means $-x > a$ or $x > a$. Also $|x| < a$ means $-x < a$ and $x < a$.

EXAMPLE 5. Solve the inequality $|5 - 2x| > 3$.

SOLUTION: Application of the property of absolute values results in two inequalities:

$$
\begin{array}{ll}
-(5 - 2x) > 3 \quad \text{or} & 5 - 2x > 3 \\
2x - 5 > 3 & -2x > -2 \\
2x > 8 & x < 1 \\
x > 4 &
\end{array}
$$

In Example 5 the solution set consists of two disjoint sets: x greater than 4 and x less than 1.

To check a solution set for an inequality essentially involves two or more checks. This will be illustrated by checking Examples 2 and 5.

Check for Example 2. We determined the solution set of the inequality $\dfrac{1}{3}x + 6 < 2$ to be $x < -12$.

PART I. The value $x = -12$ should satisfy the equation

$$\frac{1}{3}x + 6 = 2$$

$$\frac{1}{3}(-12) + 6 \stackrel{?}{=} 2$$

$$-4 + 6 \stackrel{?}{=} 2. \qquad \text{It does satisfy the equation.}$$

$$2 = 2$$

PART II. Any value of x less than -12, say -15 should satisfy the inequality

$$\frac{1}{3}x + 6 < 2.$$

$$\frac{1}{3}(-15) + 6 \stackrel{?}{<} 2$$

$$-5 + 6 \stackrel{?}{<} 2$$

$$1 < 2. \qquad x = -15 \text{ does satisfy the inequality.}$$

Although this does not assure us that we have the complete solution, it is a useful check of the work.

Check for Example 5: $|5 - 2x| > 3$ the solution set was determined to be: x greater than 4 and x less than 1.

PART I. Both $x = 4$ and $x = 1$ should satisfy the equation:

$$|5 - 2x| = 3.$$

$$|5 - 2(4)| \stackrel{?}{=} 3 \qquad\qquad |5 - 2(1)| \stackrel{?}{=} 3$$

$$|5 - 8| \stackrel{?}{=} 3 \qquad\qquad\quad |5 - 2| \stackrel{?}{=} 3$$

$$|-3| \stackrel{?}{=} 3 \qquad\qquad\qquad 3 = 3 \qquad \text{Both check}$$

$$3 = 3$$

PART II. Use a value greater than 4 and a value less than 1. These values should satisfy the inequality.

$x > 4$ use $x = 5$ $\qquad\qquad\qquad$ $x < 1$ use $x = -1$

$$|5 - 2(5)| \stackrel{?}{>} 3 \qquad\qquad |5 - 2(-1)| \stackrel{?}{>} 3$$

$$|5 - 10| \stackrel{?}{>} 3 \qquad\qquad\quad |5 + 2| \stackrel{?}{>} 3$$

$$|-5| \stackrel{?}{>} 3 \qquad\qquad\qquad |7| \stackrel{?}{>} 3$$

$$5 > 3 \qquad\qquad\qquad\quad 7 > 3 \text{ Both check.}$$

The two sets comprising the solution set both satisfy the two parts of the check; therefore, the solution set is probably correct.

EXERCISE 3.4

Solution of Linear Inequalities

Solve the following inequalities and check your solutions.

1. $x + 7 < 4$

2. $x - 11 > 2$

3. $x - 5 > 3$

4. $x + 1 < -2$

5. $3x < -6$

6. $4x > -52$

7. $4x > 8$

8. $7x < -21$

9. $-\frac{1}{3}x > 2$

10. $-\frac{1}{4}x < 3$

11. $6x > -\frac{1}{2}$

12. $3x < -\frac{1}{4}$

13. $2x - 1 > 7$

14. $5x - 3 > 7$

15. $3 - \frac{1}{2}x < 4$

16. $7 - \frac{1}{3}x > 5$

17. $4(2 - x) > 5$

18. $3(3 - x) < 7$

19. $2(3 - 2x) < -3$

20. $4(1 - 3x) > -2$

21. $\left| x - 2 \right| > 1$

22. $\left| x - 3 \right| > 2$

23. $\left| 2x - 1 \right| < 2$

24. $\left| 3 - 2x \right| > 4$

25. $\left| 2x - 3 \right| > 4$

26. $\left| 4 - 3x \right| < 1$

27. $\left| 3x + 1 \right| < 2$

28. $\left| \frac{1}{2}x - 3 \right| < 1$

29. $\left| 3 - \frac{1}{4}x \right| > 3$

30. $\left| 5 - 2x \right| > 1$

31. Without solving the inequalities, can you determine how the solution sets of the two inequalities $\left| 3x - 4 \right| < 1$ and $\left| 4 - 3x \right| < 1$ are related?

3.5 APPLICATIONS OF LINEAR EQUATIONS AND LINEAR INEQUALITIES

Many types of word problems can be expressed in the form of linear equations and therefore can be solved by the use of the axioms of this chapter. However, because of the variety of types of stated problems, no specific procedure can be prescribed for the solution of all of them.

The following steps indicate a broad outline of a method to solve stated problems which should prove helpful.

1. Read the statement of the problem carefully at least twice.

2. Represent the quantity you want to determine, or a quantity related to it, by an algebraic symbol. Write down what the symbol is to represent.

3. Determine the relationships between the variable and the other quantities in the problem.   This can frequently be done more effectively by using a figure or a table.

4. Write the algebraic equation from the statement of the problem. This may be done from a statement of equality or by the use of the appropriate formula.

5. Solve the algebraic equation.

6. Check your solution by substituting your result in the statement of the original problem.

Since significant problems that are met in practice are likely to be complicated and technical, the problems that we consider will represent simplified situations. The following types of problems are important because they indicate approaches which can be adapted to more specialized situations.

Motion Problems

The formula $d = rt$ is used to solve problems dealing with objects moving at constant speed. The speed is represented by r, the time the object is in motion at that speed is denoted by t, and d represents the distance the object travels. The units of length in d and r must be the same and the time units in r and t must be the same.

EXAMPLE 1. Two cars traveled the same distance. One car traveled at 50 mph and the other car traveled at 60 mph. It took the slower car 50 minutes longer to make the trip. How long did it take the faster car to make the trip?

Step 1. Read problem again.

SOLUTION: *Step* 2. If we let t represent the number of hours the faster car travels, we can construct the following table from the given statements.

Note: The 50 minutes must be converted to $\frac{5}{6}$ hr.

Step 3

	Distance	Rate	Time
Faster car	D	60 mph	t
Slower car	D	50 mph	$t + \dfrac{5}{6}$

Step 4

$$\text{Formula } D = rt$$
$$D = 60t$$
$$D = 50\left(t + \frac{5}{6}\right)$$

Since the distances are the same, we can set the two expressions for D equal as in Step 5.

$$Step\ 5 \qquad 60t = 50\left(t + \frac{5}{6}\right)$$

$$60t = 50t + \frac{250}{6}$$

$$60t - 50t = \frac{250}{6}$$

$$10t = \frac{250}{6}$$

$$t = \frac{25}{6} = 4\frac{1}{6} \text{ hr or 4 hr 10 min}$$

It took the faster car $4\frac{1}{6}$ hr traveling at a rate of 60 mph.

Step 6. The faster car would have traveled 250 miles. The slower car took 4 hr 10 min + 50 min or 5 hr and traveled at a rate of 50 mph. The second car would also have traveled 250 miles.

Investment Problems

If an amount is invested at simple interest, the interest can be determined by using the formula $I = Prt$. I represents the amount of interest, P represents the principal invested, r represents the annual interest rate, and t represents the number of years the money is invested.

EXAMPLE 2. $10,000 is to be invested for one year. A part of the $10,000 is invested at 6% and the remainder at 7%. The income from the $10,000 is $640 per year. Find the amount invested at each rate.

SOLUTION: Let x represent the amount invested at 6%, then the remaining amount $10,000 - x$ would be invested at 7%. The money is invested for one year, therefore $t = 1$.

	P	r	t	$I = Prt$
Investment No. 1	x	.06	1	.06x
Investment No. 2	10,000 − x	.07	1	.07(10,000 − x)

The income $640 from the $10,000 invested is the sum of the amount of interest from the two investments. If I_1 represents the income from the first investment and I_2 represents the income from the second investment, then

$$I_1 + I_2 = \$640$$
$$.06x + .07(\$10,000 - x) = \$640$$
$$.06x + \$700 - .07x = \$640$$
$$-.01x = \$640 - \$700$$
$$-.01x = -\$60$$
$$x = \$6000 \text{ invested at } 6\%$$
$$\$10,000 - x = \$4000 \text{ invested at } 7\%$$

Check: The interest on the $6000 invested at 6% is .06(6000) = $360. The interest on the $4000 invested at 7% is .07(4000) = $280. The total income from investments = $640.

Mixture Problems

Many mixture problems are expressed in terms of the percent of concentration. For a liquid in solution the percent of concentration is given by the expression

$$\frac{\text{volume of substance in solution}}{\text{total volume}} \times 100.$$

For example, if 2 quarts of pure antifreeze are added to 3 quarts of water the percent concentration $= \dfrac{2}{2 + 3} \times 100 = 40\%$. We also have occasion to use this principle to determine the amount of substance in a solution. The formula to find the volume of substance in solution can be obtained from the formula for percent concentration; it is

$$\text{Volume of substance} = \left(\frac{\text{Percent of concentration}}{100}\right)(\text{total volume})$$

EXAMPLE 3. How much water must be added to 5 gallons of 90% ammonia solution to reduce the solution to a 60% solution?

SOLUTION: The volume of the original solution is 5 gallons. If we let x represent the number of gallons of water added to the original solution, then the final solution will have a volume of $(5 + x)$ gallons. No ammonia is added so the only ammonia in the final solution is the ammonia in the original solution. We can now record our given information in tabular form:

	Total Volume (Gallons)	Percent Concentration	Gallons of 100% Ammonia
Original solution	5	90	4.5
Final solution	5 + x	60	4.5

Using the formula for amount of substance in solution for the final solution we have:

$$.60(5 + x) = 4.5$$
$$3 + .60x = 4.5$$
$$.6x = 4.5 - 3$$
$$.6x = 1.5$$
$$x = \frac{1.5}{.6} = 2.5 \text{ gallons}$$

Therefore 2.5 gallons of water must be added to reduce the concentration to 60%.

Check: If 2.5 gallons of water are added to the original solution, we will have 7.5 gallons of solution. The amount of 100% ammonia remains the same 4.5 gallons. The concentration equals

$$\frac{4.5}{7.5} \times 100 = \frac{450}{7.5} = 60\%$$

Age Problems

EXAMPLE 4. John is 4 times as old as Harry. In six years John will be twice as old as Harry. What are their ages now?

SOLUTION: Let x represent Harry's age now. John's age now is then represented by $4x$. In six years their respective ages will be $(x + 6)$ and $(4x + 6)$. In tabular form our data is:

	Now	Six Years Hence
John's Age	4x	4x + 6
Harry's Age	x	x + 6

From the statement six years from now John will be twice as old as Harry, we can write the equation necessary to solve the problem.

$$4x + 6 = 2(x + 6)$$
$$4x + 6 = 2x + 12$$
$$2x = 6$$
$$x = 3 \text{ years} \qquad \text{Harry's age now.}$$
$$4x = 12 \text{ years} \qquad \text{John's age now.}$$

Check: In six years Harry will be 9 years old and John will be 18 years old. John will then be twice as old as Harry.

Number Problems

There are many different types of problems involving number relationships; we shall illustrate only three types.

EXAMPLE 5. The sum of four consecutive even numbers is 140. What are the numbers?

SOLUTION: An even number can be represented by $2n$, where n is an integer. Consecutive even integers (or odd integers) differ by 2. Therefore, four consecutive even integers can be represented by $2n$, $2n + 2$, $2n + 4$, and $2n + 6$. Then

$$2n + (2n + 2) + (2n + 4) + (2n + 6) = 140$$
$$8n + 12 = 140$$
$$8n = 128$$
$$n = 16$$

The four consecutive even integers are 32, 34, 36, and 38. Their sum is 140.

EXAMPLE 6. Find the common fraction form of the repeating decimal $0.4242\ldots$.

SOLUTION: Although this type of problem is not usually included in a section on stated problems, it is included here because it is readily solved by the methods of this chapter.

Let x represent the repeating decimal.

$$x = 0.4242\ldots$$
$$100x = 42.42\ldots \qquad \text{by multiplying by 100}$$
$$\underline{x = 0.42\ldots}$$
$$99x = 42 \qquad \text{by subtracting } x \text{ from } 100x$$
$$x = \frac{42}{99}$$
$$x = \frac{14}{33}$$

The repeating decimal of this example had a set of two digits that repeated. The first step in the solution was to multiply both members of the original equation by 10^2 or 100. If the set of repeating digits is a set of three digits, the first step would be to multiply both members of the equation by 10^3 or 1000.

EXAMPLE 7. The units digit of a two digit number is two larger than the tens digit. When the digits are reversed, the new two digit number is equal to seven times the sum of the digits. What is the original number?

SOLUTION: When dealing with number problems that are concerned with the digits of a number, we must utilize position values and write a two digit number as $10a + b$, a three digit number as $100x + 10y + z$, and so on.

Let x represent the digit in the tens position, then the digit in the units position must be $x + 2$. The original number is then

$$10x + (x + 2) \text{ or } 11x + 2.$$

When the digits are reversed, the new number can be expressed as

$$10 (x + 2) + x \text{ or } 11x + 20.$$

The sum of the digits is $x + (x + 2) = 2x + 2$. Setting the new number equal to seven times the sum of the digits, we have:

$$11x + 20 = 7(2x + 2)$$
$$11x + 20 = 14x + 14$$
$$20 - 14 = 14x - 11x$$
$$6 = 3x$$
$$x = 2, x + 2 = 4$$

The original number $10x + (x + 2) = 10(2) + 4$
$$= 24.$$

If the digits are reversed, we get 42, and this is the product of seven and the sum of the digits (six).

EXERCISE 3.5

Applications of Linear Equations and Linear Inequalities

Write an algebraic expression for each of the following:

1. A man's age now if he is three times as old as his son. Let x be the son's age.
2. The cost of ten books if each book costs d dollars.
3. The cost of two shirts and a pair of slacks if the shirts cost x dollars each and the slacks cost y dollars.

4. The length of a rectangle if it is 5 units longer than the width w.
5. The amount invested at 7% if a total of $20,000 is invested, x dollars is invested at 6% and the rest is invested at 7%.
6. The number of liters of 100% acid in y liters of 70% acid solution.
7. The value in cents of d dimes and n nickels.
8. The total cost in dollars of x adult tickets and y children tickets if the adult's tickets are $2 each and the children's tickets are 75¢ each.
9. The amount of simple interest for n years from $9000 invested at 6% per year.
10. A man's age three years from now if he is now twice as old as his son. Let x be the son's present age.

Find the common fractions that are equivalent to the repeating decimals.

11. 0.5454 . . .
12. 0.162162 . . .
13. 0.417417 . . .
14. 0.7272 . . .

The line above the 47 in Problem 15 and above the 36 in Problem 16 indicates that those digits are repeated. Change these repeating decimals to fractions.

15. 1.3$\overline{47}$
16. 2.1$\overline{36}$

Solve the following problems and check your solutions.

17. A car traveling 45 mph takes 1 hour longer to make a trip than another car traveling at 50 mph. How many hours did it take the slower car to make the trip?
18. A man is 25 years older than his son. Ten years from now the father will be twice as old as the son. How old is the son now?
19. One-half of a number increased by one-third of the number is equal to 56 less than twice the number. Find the number.
20. An investment at 6% and a second investment at 8% produce an annual income of $900. The total amount invested is $12,000. Find the amount invested at 6%.
21. How many gallons of water must be added to 8 gallons of 60% solution to obtain a 48% solution?
22. On a 3-hour trip of 139 miles a car is driven at a uniform rate of speed for 1 hour and then the speed is increased by 5 mph for the rest of the trip. What was the speed of the car at the beginning of the trip?
23. One side of a triangle is 5 inches shorter and the second side is 10 inches shorter than the longest side. If the perimeter of the triangle is 84 inches, what is the length of the shortest side?
24. The sum of the digits of a two-digit number is 8. If the order of the digits is reversed, the new number is 54 larger than the original number. What is the original number?
25. Part of $10,000 is invested at $5\frac{3}{4}$% and the remainder is invested at $6\frac{1}{4}$%. The total annual income is $605. How much was invested at $6\frac{1}{4}$%?

26. Four members of a family were born in consecutive even-numbered years. The sum of their ages is 100 years. What is the age of the youngest of the four?

27. The length of a rectangle is 9 inches more than 4 times its width. The perimeter is 228 inches. What are the dimensions of the rectangle?

28. Two different kinds of candy that sell for $1.50 and $2.20 a pound are to be used in a mixture that will sell for $1.80 a pound. How many pounds of the candy selling for $1.50 a pound must be used to make 70 pounds of the mixed candy?

29. At 3 P.M. a plane flying east and a plane flying west cross over St. Paul. An hour and a half later they are 1770 miles apart. Find their speeds if the east-bound plane is traveling 40 mph faster than the west-bound plane.

30. One hundred cards were purchased for $16.40. Some of the cards were 15¢ each and the rest were 20¢ each. How many 20¢ cards were purchased?

31. The oldest of three brothers is three years older than one brother and twice as old as the other. The sum of their ages is 82 years. What are their ages?

32. Two canoes leave the same pier going in opposite directions. The canoe going downstream travels three miles an hour faster than the one going upstream. At the end of two hours the canoes are 24 miles apart. How fast is the canoe going downstream traveling?

33. The sum of an angle and one-third of its complement is 62°. What is the angle?

34. One hundred and forty coins are either nickels or dimes. If they have a total value of $12.40, how many are nickels?

35. The cost of road construction in a city is shared: 65% by the state, 10% by the county and 25% by the city. If the state paid $20,000,000 more than the city, what was the cost of the road construction?

36. Part of $70,000 is invested at 6% and the remainder is invested at 8%. At the end of the year the amounts of interest from the two investments were the same. How much was invested at 6%?

37. If the units digit of a two-digit number is 6 more than the tens digit and the number is three more than three times the sum of the digits, what is the number?

38. Joe's uncle is twice as old as Joe is now. In two years his uncle will be three times as old as Joe was four years ago. How old is Joe's uncle?

chapter 4

extending the concept of exponents

IN CHAPTER 2 WE CONSIDERED THE EXPRESSION b^n where the domain of n was restricted to the set of natural numbers. We now wish to extend the domain of n with the intent of examining such expressions as b^0, $b^{1/3}$, $b^{3/4}$, and b^{-4}. It is clear that the definition of b^n as the product of n factors each equal to b cannot apply to exponents other than natural numbers. What meaning, for example, could be given to $4^{2/3}$? From a purely mathematical point of view our interest in extending the domain of n beyond the set of natural numbers is simply to make the expression b^n as general as possible, that is, to remove the restriction of n to natural numbers. From a practical point of view, where we are concerned with applications of mathematics, we cannot ignore the many formulas in which exponents other than the natural numbers occur. Some examples of these formulas are Kepler's third law of planetary motion

$$T = a^{3/2}$$

the formula for the present value of an investment

$$P = A(1 + r)^{-n}$$

and a formula used to determine an index of safety for pedestrian crossings

$$P = e^{-Rt}$$

We see, from the above considerations, the necessity for extending the domain of n in the expression b^n beyond the set of natural numbers.

4.1 THE LAWS OF EXPONENTS

We now introduce certain theorems, known as the *laws of exponents*, concerning expressions with exponents which are positive integers. These laws are developed not only to facilitate operations involving exponents but to form a basis for removing the restriction of exponents to positive integers.

THEOREM 4.1.   If m and n are positive integers, then $b^m \cdot b^n = b^{m+n}$

PROOF.
$$b^m = b \cdot b \cdot b \cdots b \ (m \text{ factors of } b)$$
$$b^n = b \cdot b \cdot b \cdots b \ (n \text{ factors of } b)$$
$$b^m \cdot b^n = \underbrace{(b \cdot b \cdot b \cdots b)}_{m \text{ factors}} \underbrace{(b \cdot b \cdot b \cdots b)}_{n \text{ factors}}$$
$$= (m + n) \text{ factors of } b$$
$$= b^{m+n}$$

THEOREM 4.2.   If m and n are positive integers and $b \neq 0$, then

$$\frac{b^m}{b^n} = b^{m-n} \ (m > n) \text{ or } \frac{b^m}{b^n} = \frac{1}{b^{n-m}} \ (m < n)$$

PROOF.   For $m > n$,

$$\frac{b^m}{b^n} = \frac{b \cdot b \cdot b \cdots b}{b \cdot b \cdots b} \quad \begin{array}{l} (m \text{ factors of } b) \\ (n \text{ factors of } b) \end{array}$$

After dividing numerator and denominator by the factor b, n times, we are left with $(m - n)$ factors in the numerator. Hence,

$$\frac{b^m}{b^n} = \frac{b^{m-n}}{1} = b^{m-n}$$

For $m < n$, the proof follows a similar form.

THEOREM 4.3. If m and n are positive rational numbers, then

$$(b^m)^n = b^{mn}$$

PROOF. $(b^m)^n = b^m \cdot b^m \cdot b^m \cdots b^m$ (n factors of b^m)
$$= b^{m+m+m+\cdots+m} \quad (n \text{ terms in the exponent, each equal to } m)$$
$$= b^{mn}$$

The proof here applies only to the case where m and n are positive integers.

THEOREM 4.4.   If n is a positive integer, then

$$(ab)^n = a^n b^n \text{ and } \left(\frac{a}{b}\right)^m = \frac{a^m}{b^m}, \ b \neq 0$$

PROOF. $(ab)^n = (ab)(ab)(ab)\cdots(ab)$ (*n* factors of *ab*)

$\qquad\qquad = (a\cdot a\cdot a\cdots a)(b\cdot b\cdot b\cdots b)$ (*n* factors of *a* and *n* factors of *b*)

$\qquad\qquad = a^n b^n$

For $\left(\dfrac{a}{b}\right)^m$, the proof follows a similar form.

EXAMPLE 1. $y^3 \cdot y^4 = y^7$ by Theorem 4.1

EXAMPLE 2. $(5^3)^4 = 5^{12}$ by Theorem 4.3

EXAMPLE 3. $\dfrac{x^5}{x^2} = x^3.$ by Theorem 4.2

EXAMPLE 4. $(3c^2)^3 = 27(c^2)^3$ by Theorem 4.4

$\qquad\qquad\quad = 27c^6$ by Theorem 4.3

EXAMPLE 5. $\left(\dfrac{2}{3}\right)^3 = \dfrac{2^3}{3^3} = \dfrac{8}{27}$ by Theorem 4.4

EXERCISE 4.1

The Laws of Positive Integral Exponents

Simplify each of the following expressions.

1. $x^3 \cdot x^2$ 2. $a^2 \cdot a$ 3. $x^2 \cdot x^2$

4. $\dfrac{x^3}{x^2}$ 5. $\dfrac{x^2}{x^3}$ 6. $(y^2)^3$

7. $(ab^2c^3)^2$ 8. $(-x^2)^3$ 9. $-(x^2)^3$

10. $(3c^3)^2$ 11. $3(c^3)^2$ 12. $(-3c)^3$

13. $x^2 \cdot x^3 \cdot x^4$ 14. $\left(\dfrac{x^6}{x^3}\right)^2$ 15. $\dfrac{x^6}{(x^3)^2}$

16. $\dfrac{3x^2}{(5x^3)^2}$ 17. $\dfrac{-3x}{(-2x)^2}$ 18. $\dfrac{-3x}{(-2x)^3}$

19. $(-3)^2(-3^2)$ 20. $(-3)^2\,(-3)^2$ 21. $(-3)^2\,(-3)^3$

22. $(-3)^2\,(-3)^4$ 23. $\dfrac{9x^2}{(-3x)^2}$ 24. $\dfrac{x^2 \cdot x^3}{x^6}$

In problems 25 to 33, first simplify the expression. Then check your results by substituting $n = 5$ and $m = 2$, as in Problem 25.

25. $x^m \cdot x^n = x^{m+n}$

$\quad\; x^2 \cdot x^5 = x^{2+5}$

$\qquad\quad x^7 = x^7$

26. $\dfrac{3^m}{3^n}, \; m < n$

27. $(x^m)^n$

28. $x^m \cdot x^{n-m}$

29. $(x^{n+m})\,(x^{n-m})$

30. $\dfrac{x^{2m}}{x^m}$

31. $\dfrac{(x^{n+m})\,(x^{n-m})}{x^{2n}}$

32. $\dfrac{(x^{n+m})\,(x^{n-m})}{x^2}$

33. $\dfrac{(x^{n+m})\,(x^{n+m})}{x^2}$

4.2 ZERO, FRACTIONAL, AND NEGATIVE EXPONENTS

In determining a meaning for exponents other than positive integers, we can assign a meaning to them and then develop laws similar to those of Section 4.1 to govern their use, or we can define them in such a way that they obey the laws already developed for positive integral exponents.   Clearly the latter approach is preferable because in this way we shall have just one set of laws applying to all exponents.   It would not be unreasonable, for example, to define b^0 as zero, since the product of zero factors of any number might be taken as zero.   But we shall see that this definition (that is, $b^0 = 0$) would not be consistent with Theorem 4.1 for positive integral exponents. Certainly it would be better to frame our definition of b^0 so that the laws of exponents of Section 4.1 would apply, and this is what we shall do with the larger set of exponents in what follows.

Zero Exponents

Let us consider the expression b^0. If it is to satisfy Theorem 4.1, then we must have

$$b^0 \cdot b^n = b^{0+n} = b^n \tag{1}$$

It follows that

$$b^0 = \frac{b^n}{b^n} = 1 \quad (b \neq 0) \tag{2}$$

We are therefore led to the following definition:

DEFINITION 4.1 $b^0 = 1 \; (b \neq 0)$

It should be noted that we have not shown that Definition 4.1 satisfies the other laws of exponents, but in Exercise 4.2 the student will be asked to verify that it does.

EXAMPLE 1. $2^0 = 1$

EXAMPLE 2. $(-2ab)^0 = 1$ $(a \neq 0, b \neq 0)$

EXAMPLE 3. $(a + b)^0 = 1$ $(a \neq -b)$

EXAMPLE 4. $a^0 + b^0 = 1 + 1 = 2$ $(a \neq 0, b \neq 0)$

EXAMPLE 5. $(4 - 2)^0 = 2^0 = 1$

The student should note that while $(-3)^0 = 1$, $-3^0 = -1$.

Fractional Exponents

We now consider the exponent $b^{1/3}$. If it is to satisfy Theorem 4.3, we must have

$$(b^{1/3})^3 = b^{3/3} = b \tag{3}$$

It follows from Equation 3 that $b^{1/3}$ is the cube root of b, and we may write

$$b^{1/3} = \sqrt[3]{b} \tag{4}$$

More generally, since

$$(b^{1/n})^n = b^{n/n} = b \tag{5}$$

we are led to the definition:

DEFINITION 4.2. $b^{1/n} = \sqrt[n]{b}$

Definition 4.2 does not apply to the case where n is even and $b < 0$, since an even root of a negative number has not yet been defined.

EXAMPLE 6. $8^{1/3} = \sqrt[3]{8} = 2$.

EXAMPLE 7. $(-32)^{1/5} = \sqrt[5]{-32} = -2$.

EXAMPLE 8. $(-16)^{1/2}$ is undefined.

Again it should be noted that we have not shown that Definition 4.2 satisfies the other laws of exponents, but it can be verified that it does.

We now consider the expression $b^{2/3}$. If we again require that Theorem 4.3 is to be satisfied, we must have

$$(b^{2/3})^3 = b^{6/3} = b^2 \tag{6}$$

It follows from Equation 6 that $b^{2/3}$ is the cube root of b^2, that is,

$$b^{2/3} = \sqrt[3]{b^2} \tag{7}$$

Using Definition 4.2 and Theorem 4.3, we may find another expression for $b^{2/3}$, since

$$b^{2/3} = (b^{1/3})^2 = (\sqrt[3]{b})^2 \tag{8}$$

Equations 7 and 8 lead us to the definition:

DEFINITION 4.3. $b^{m/n} = \sqrt[n]{b^m}$ or $(\sqrt[n]{b})^m$

As in Definition 4.2, Definition 4.3 does not apply to the case where n is even and $b < 0$.

It can be verified that all four laws of exponents are satisfied by Definition 4.3.

EXAMPLE 9. $27^{2/3} = \sqrt[3]{27^2} = \sqrt[3]{729} = 9.$
$\qquad\qquad 27^{2/3} = (\sqrt[3]{27})^2 = 3^2 = 9.$

Example 9 shows that it is usually advantageous to find the root first (the second form of Definition 4.3) since $\sqrt[3]{27}$ is more readily found than $\sqrt[3]{729}$.

Negative Exponents

To find a meaning for negative exponents we consider the expression b^{-3}. If Theorem 4.1 is to be satisfied

$$b^{-3} \cdot b^3 = b^0 = 1 \tag{9}$$

It follows from Equation 9 that

$$b^{-3} = \frac{1}{b^3} \tag{10}$$

By generalizing Equation 10, we are led to the definition:

DEFINITION 4.4. $b^{-n} = \dfrac{1}{b^n}.$

It may be verified that Definition 4.4 satisfies all of the four laws of exponents.

EXAMPLE 10. $2^{-1} = \dfrac{1}{2}$

EXAMPLE 11. $27^{-2/3} = \dfrac{1}{27^{2/3}} = \dfrac{1}{9}$

EXAMPLE 12. $\left(\dfrac{2}{3}\right)^{-2} = \dfrac{2^{-2}}{3^{-2}} = \dfrac{3^2}{2^2} = \dfrac{9}{4}$

EXAMPLE 13. $\dfrac{1}{2^{-3}} = \dfrac{1}{\dfrac{1}{2^3}} = 2^3 = 8$

It can be seen that Example 12 may be generalized to obtain the relation

$$\left(\frac{a}{b}\right)^{-n} = \left(\frac{b}{a}\right)^{n}$$

Examples 10 and 13 show that any factor of an expression may be changed from numerator to denominator, or vice versa, by changing the sign of its exponent.

EXAMPLE 14. $\dfrac{a^{-2}b^3}{c^{-3}} = \dfrac{b^3c^3}{a^2}$

EXAMPLE 15. $\dfrac{2 \cdot 10^{-3}}{3 \cdot 10^{-4}} = \dfrac{2 \cdot 10^4}{3 \cdot 10^3} = \dfrac{2}{3} \cdot \dfrac{10^4}{10^3} = \dfrac{2}{3} \cdot 10 = \dfrac{20}{3}$

It should be noted, however, that Example 15 may be solved by a direct application of Theorem 4.2

$$\frac{2 \cdot 10^{-3}}{3 \cdot 10^{-4}} = \frac{2}{3} \cdot 10^{-3-(-4)} = \frac{2}{3} \cdot 10^1 = \frac{20}{3}$$

EXERCISE 4.2

Zero, Fractional, and Negative Exponents

Simplify each of the following expressions.

1. 3^0
2. $(-3)^0$
3. $(4x)^0$
4. $4x^0$
5. $2a + (3b)^0$
6. $2a + 3b^0$

7. $(2a + 3b)^0$ 8. $(a^2 + b^2)^0$ 9. $2^0 - 3^0$

10. $(2^3 + 3^3)^0$ 11. $(2^3)^0 + (3^3)^0$ 12. $\left(\dfrac{x^2 y}{z}\right)^0$

13. $(x - y - 1)^0$ (What condition must be imposed on x and y?)

Write each of the following expressions with radicals and simplify when possible.

14. $9^{1/2}$ 15. $27^{1/3}$ 16. $(-27)^{1/3}$

17. $49^{1/2}$ 18. $(-125)^{1/3}$ 19. $(-125)^{2/3}$

20. $(-64)^{1/2}$ 21. $(4a^2)^{1/2}$ 22. $(-27)^{4/3}$

23. $81^{1/4}$ 24. $32^{2/5}$ 25. $-32^{2/5}$

26. $-(32)^{2/5}$ 27. $(-32)^{2/5}$ 28. $(9x^2)^{3/2}$

29. $81^{1/3} \cdot 9^{1/2}$ 30. $(8^{1/3})^0$ 31. $2 \cdot (8^{1/3})^0$

32. $(2 \cdot 8^{1/3})^0$ 33. $8^{1/3} + 9^{1/2}$ 34. $\left(\dfrac{64^{1/3}}{16^{1/2}}\right)^{1/2}$

35. $(64^{1/3} + 16^{1/2})^{1/3}$ 36. $\left(\dfrac{64^{2/3}}{4^{1/2}}\right)^{2/3}$ 37. $\left(\dfrac{64^{2/3}}{4^0}\right)^{1/3}$

Write each of the following expressions with positive exponents and simplify when possible.

38. 3^{-1} 39. 3^{-2} 40. 2^{-3}

41. $\dfrac{1}{3^{-2}}$ 42. $\left(\dfrac{2}{3}\right)^{-2}$ 43. $4^{-1/2}$

44. $\left(\dfrac{4^{-1/2}}{8^{-2}}\right)^{1/5}$ 45. $(-3)^{-2}$ 46. $(-3)^{-3}$

47. $\left(\dfrac{4}{9}\right)^{-3/2}$ 48. $(4^{1/2})^{-3}$ 49. $(x^3)^{-1/3}$

50. $(x^2 y^{-2})^{-1/2}$ 51. $\dfrac{3^{-1} x^{-2}}{27^{-1/3}}$ 52. $\dfrac{1}{2(2a)^{-2}}$

Rewrite each of the following expressions without fractions, as in Example 53.

53. $\dfrac{5x}{3y^2} = 3^{-1} \cdot 5xy^{-2}$ 54. $\dfrac{4}{x^2}$ 55. $\dfrac{2}{5x}$

56. $\dfrac{4(x + 2y)}{(x - y)}$ 57. $\dfrac{3x}{4y} + \dfrac{1}{2y}$ 58. $\dfrac{8x^2 y^3}{2x^3 y^2 z}$

59. $\left(\dfrac{a^n}{a^{n+2}}\right)^{1/2}$ 60. $\left(\dfrac{a^n}{a^{n+2}}\right)^{-1/2}$ 61. $\left(\dfrac{b^{n+2}}{b^{n-2}}\right)^{1/2}$

62. $\left(\dfrac{b^{n+2}}{b^{n-2}}\right)^{-1/2}$ 63. $\left(\dfrac{x^{2n}}{y^3 x^{-4n}}\right)^{1/3}$

Solve each of the following inequalities:

64. $|x - 2| < 2^{-2}$ 65. $3x < \left(\dfrac{1}{4}\right)^{-2}$ 66. $\left(\dfrac{3}{x}\right)^{-1} + 5 \geq 7$

67. $2x + 5 > 4x - \left(\dfrac{1}{3}\right)^{-2}$ 68. $\left(\dfrac{3}{2p}\right)^{-1} - p^0 > p - 3$ 69. $x + 2 > (x + 2)^0$

70. $\left(\dfrac{2}{x}\right)^{-1} < -5x + \dfrac{2}{3}$ 71. $2^{-1}x + x^0 > x - 14$

72. $2x - 4^{-1/2} > 3x + \left(\dfrac{3}{2}\right)^{-1}$

73. Verify that the definition $b^0 = 1$ satisfies Theorems 4.2, 4.3, and 4.4 by letting $m = 1$ and $n = 0$.

4.3 SCIENTIFIC NOTATION

A very useful application of exponents which are elements of the set of integers is in writing very large and very small numbers which frequently occur in scientific work. For example, the mass of the sun is approximately

$$2,200,000,000,000,000,000,000,000,000 \text{ tons,}$$

while the mass of an electron is approximately

$$0.000\ 000\ 000\ 000\ 000\ 000\ 000\ 000\ 000\ 911 \text{ gram.}$$

How would you read these numbers?

To simplify the writing and reading of such numbers, they are usually written in *scientific notation*. A number is written in scientific notation (sometimes called standard form) when it is expressed according to the following definition:

DEFINITION 4.5.   The number N is written in scientific notation when it is expressed as

$$N = n \times 10^c$$

where $1 \leq n < 10$, and c is an integer.

The mass of the sun, written in scientific notation, is 2.2×10^{27} tons, and the mass of an electron is 9.11×10^{-28} gram. Each of these numbers, when written in scientific notation, is much easier to read and much easier to write than when written in ordinary notation as above. As we shall see later in this section, scientific notation is very helpful in computation, particularly with a slide rule.

Changing from Ordinary to Scientific Notation

To write a number in scientific notation, we count the number of places the decimal point must be moved from its original position to standard position. This number is the power of 10 to be used; it is positive if the decimal point is moved to the left and negative if moved to the right. This rule may be easily remembered if we keep in mind that a positive power of 10 represents a number greater than 1, and a negative power of 10 represents a number less than 1. The reason for this procedure is clear; if we move the decimal point to the left, say three places, we divide the number by 10^3, so that to retain the original number we must multiply by 10^3. If we move the decimal point three places to the right, we multiply the number by 10^3, and must therefore multiply by 10^{-3} to retain the original value.

EXAMPLE 1. $4\,01,000,000. = 4.01 \times 10^8$

EXAMPLE 2. $0.000003\,12 = 3.12 \times 10^{-6}$

Changing from Scientific to Ordinary Notation

When a number is written in scientific notation, it is clear from the preceding discussion that the power of 10 indicates the number of places the decimal point has been moved to the left or to the right, according as the exponent is positive or negative. We therefore move the decimal point to the right if the exponent is positive, and to the left if the exponent is negative.

EXAMPLE 3. $2.46 \times 10^4 = 24,600$

EXAMPLE 4. $2.32 \times 10^{-4} = 0.000232$

Using Scientific Notation in Computation

An important application of scientific notation is found in estimating the results of computations involving very small or very large numbers. This is especially true if a slide rule is used, where the location of the decimal point is best done by estimation. Each number is rounded off to one or two digits and expressed in scientific notation. The following examples will illustrate the process.

EXAMPLE 5. Estimate the result of the following problem:

$$\frac{(0.0475)(51.95)(2.22)}{(20{,}985)(365.2)}$$

This problem may be estimated as

$$\frac{(5 \times 10^{-2})(5 \times 10^{1})(2)}{(2 \times 10^{4})(4 \times 10^{2})} = \frac{50}{8} \times 10^{-7} \approx 6 \times 10^{-7}$$

By actual computation, the result to 3 significant digits is 6.42×10^{-7}.

EXAMPLE 6. The sag, d, in feet of a certain suspension bridge cable is given by

$$d = \frac{(1.42)(1100^{2})}{(8)(12{,}000)}$$

This may be estimated as

$$d = \frac{(1.4)(1.1 \times 10^{3})^{2}}{(8)(1.2 \times 10^{4})}$$
$$= \frac{(1.4)(1.2 \times 10^{6})}{1 \times 10^{5}}$$
$$= 1.68 \times 10^{1}$$
$$= 16.8 \text{ (estimated value)}$$

The computed value to 3 significant digits is 17.9 feet.

EXERCISE 4.3

Scientific Notation

The following measurements are typical of the very large and very small quantities that occur in scientific literature. Express each measurement in scientific notation. All numbers are approximate.

1. 14,700,000 square miles. The area of the moon.
2. 30,000,000,000 centimeters per second. The velocity of light.
3. 440,000,000 years. One estimate of the age of the earth.
4. 0.000 011. The coefficient of linear expansion of steel.
5. 0.000 042 centimeter. The wavelength of violet light.
6. 0.000 000 03 centimeter. The length of the edge of a molecule.
7. 0.00129 gram. The weight of a cubic centimeter of air.
8. 230,000,000,000,000 horsepower. The energy received by the earth from the sun.

9. 0.000 000 000 02 centimeter. The wavelength of a gamma ray.
10. 197,000,000 square miles. The area of the earth's surface.
11. 4,300,000,000 miles. The distance of the planet Pluto from the sun.
12. 6,000,000,000,000,000,000,000 long tons. The mass of the earth.
13. 0.000 000 000 002. The number of ergs in one electron volt.

The following equivalents are written in scientific notation. Express each number in ordinary notation.

14. One kilometer equals 1×10^{13} Angstrom units.
15. One kilowatt hour equals 3.6×10^6 joules.
16. One erg equals 2.778×10^{-14} kilowatt hour.
17. One cubic centimeter equals 3.531×10^{-5} cubic feet.
18. One foot pound per minute equals 3.030×10^{-5} horse-power.
19. One Angstrom unit equals 1×10^{-8} centimeter.
20. One mile equals 1.609×10^5 centimeters.
21. One square kilometer equals 1.196×10^6 square yards.

Express the numbers in Problems 22 to 25 in scientific notation and estimate the result with sufficient accuracy to place the decimal point.

22. $\dfrac{380 \times 0.00291 \times 8.88}{195 \times 98.6 \times 0.0018}$

23. $\dfrac{1200 \times 840 \times 245}{590 \times 49,000}$

24. $\dfrac{152 \times 0.00275 \times 0.031}{304 \times 0.000820}$

25. $\dfrac{0.075 \times 1700 \times 0.896}{655}$

26. The tension in a belt transmitting power from a large motor is given by the formula
$$T = \frac{2.393 \times 394}{1.393}$$
Estimate the value of T.

27. The heat loss in a certain pipe is given by the formula
$$Q = \frac{2\pi \times 0.035 \times 35,000}{0.405}$$
Estimate the value of Q.

28. The temperature of a certain fluid flowing through a heater is given by the formula
$$T = \frac{520 \times 0.65 \times 242}{714 \times 0.72} + 190.$$
Estimate the value of T.

29. The electrical current in a certain coil is given by the formula
$$I = \frac{20 \times 16 \times 0.18 \times 1.28}{2\pi \times 30.}$$
Estimate the value of I.

30. The height of a certain tower is calculated by the formula

$$h = \frac{250 \times 0.30}{0.20 \times 0.86}$$

Estimate the value of h.

4.4 OPERATIONS WITH RADICALS

In Section 2.3 we discussed simple expressions involving radicals, such as $\sqrt[3]{27}$, $\sqrt{9}$, and $\sqrt[5]{-32}$. In section 4.3 we showed that equivalent expressions could be written using exponents in place of radicals. Thus

$$\sqrt[3]{27} = 27^{1/3} = 3$$
$$\sqrt{9} = 9^{1/2} = 3$$
$$\sqrt[5]{-32} = (-32)^{1/5} = -2$$

In general, we have the equivalent expressions

$$\sqrt[n]{b^m} = b^{m/n}$$

which are, of course, reversible; we can change from radicals to exponents, and from exponents to radicals. While any operation involving radicals may be carried out by working with equivalent expressions using exponents, it is convenient to develop laws for operating directly with radical expressions. We shall first state the following definition:

DEFINITION 4.6 $(\sqrt[n]{b})^n = b$

This definition follows immediately from the meaning previously given to radicals.[1] For if

$$\underbrace{x \cdot x \cdot x \cdots x}_{n \text{ factors}} = b \tag{1}$$

then

$$x = \sqrt[n]{b} \tag{2}$$

Substituting $\sqrt[n]{b}$ for x in Equation 1,

$$\underbrace{\sqrt[n]{b} \, \sqrt[n]{b} \, \sqrt[n]{b} \cdots \sqrt[n]{b}}_{n \text{ factors}} = b \tag{3}$$

That is,

$$(\sqrt[n]{b})^n = b \tag{4}$$

---

[1] This definition also follows from Definition 4.3 with $m = n$. Its frequent use leads us to restate it here as a separate definition.

EXAMPLE 1. $(\sqrt[3]{25})^3 = 25$

EXAMPLE 2. $(\sqrt[5]{2x})^5 = 2x$

We now state several theorems useful in operating with radicals; and restate, for convenience, Definition 4.3. The letters, m, n, and p, denote positive integers.

THEOREM 4.5. $\sqrt[np]{b^{mp}} = \sqrt[n]{b^m}$

THEOREM 4.6. $\sqrt[n]{ab} = \sqrt[n]{a}\ \sqrt[n]{b}$ $a > 0, b > 0$, when n is even.

THEOREM 4.7. $\sqrt[n]{a/b} = \dfrac{\sqrt[n]{a}}{\sqrt[n]{b}}$ $a > 0, b > 0$, when n is even.

DEFINITION 4.3 $\sqrt[n]{b^m} = (\sqrt[n]{b})^m$ ($b > 0$ if n is even). The examples which follow will indicate the usefulness of these theorems.

EXAMPLE 3. $\sqrt[6]{16} = \sqrt[6]{2^4} = \sqrt[3]{2^2} = \sqrt[3]{4}$, by Theorem 4.5. While $\sqrt[6]{16}$ cannot be evaluated by using Table 1, $\sqrt[3]{4}$ is readily found in Table 1 (Appendix) as 1.587.

EXAMPLE 4. $\sqrt[3]{120} = \sqrt[3]{8 \cdot 15} = \sqrt[3]{8} \cdot \sqrt[3]{15} = 2\sqrt[3]{15}$, by Theorem 4.6.   Note that $\sqrt[3]{120}$ does not appear in Table 1, but from the table $2\sqrt[3]{15} \approx 2(2.406) = 4.812$.

EXAMPLE 5. $\dfrac{2\sqrt{28}}{\sqrt{7}} = 2\sqrt{4} = 4$, by Theorem 4.7.

Note that Theorem 4.7 has been read from right to left in applying it to Example 5. The advantage of using this theorem is obvious when one considers the labor of evaluating the original expression.

EXAMPLE 6. $\sqrt[3]{125^2} = (\sqrt[3]{125})^2 = 5^2 = 25$, by Definition 4.3.

The advantage of using Definition 4.3 was previously noted in Example 9 of section 4.2.

Proof of Theorems

Theorems 4.5, 4.6, and 4.7 may be proved by writing each radical expression as an equivalent expression with exponents and applying the theorems and definitions for exponents.

THEOREM 4.5. $\sqrt[np]{b^{mp}} = b^{mp/np} = b^{m/n} = \sqrt[n]{b^m}$ $b > 0$ if n is even.

THEOREM 4.6. $\sqrt[n]{ab} = (ab)^{1/n} = a^{1/n}b^{1/n} = \sqrt[n]{a}\,\sqrt[n]{b}$ $a > 0, b > 0.$

THEOREM 4.7. $\sqrt[n]{a/b} = \left(\dfrac{a}{b}\right)^{1/n} = \dfrac{a^{1/n}}{b^{1/n}} = \dfrac{\sqrt[n]{a}}{\sqrt[n]{b}}$

The Simplest Form of a Radical

Examples 3 to 6 show how the laws of radicals could be used to simplify certain radical expressions, that is, to write them in a form easier to evaluate. As we shall see, however, that although this is frequently the case, the meaning assigned to the "simplest form" of a radical does not necessarily mean that a radical written in simplest form is easier to evaluate.

We shall consider a radical to be in simplest form when:

1. No integral factor can be removed from the radicand.
2. The radicand is an integral expression.
3. The radical does not appear in the denominator of a fraction.
4. The radical is of lowest order, that is, the index is the smallest possible integer.

EXAMPLE 7. $\sqrt{98} = \sqrt{49 \times 2} = \sqrt{49}\,\sqrt{2} = 7\,\sqrt{2}$, by Theorem 4.6. We see in this example that, using Table 1, $7\,\sqrt{2}$ requires the multiplication $7(1.414)$, while $\sqrt{98}$ can be read directly as 9.899. Thus in this case the simplest form of $\sqrt{98}$ is not the easiest to evaluate.

EXAMPLE 8. $\sqrt[3]{24} = \sqrt[3]{8 \times 3} = \sqrt[3]{8}\,\sqrt[3]{3} = 2\sqrt[3]{3}$, by Theorem 4.6.   Again, using Table 1, $2\sqrt[3]{3}$ is not easier to evaluate than $\sqrt[3]{24}$, although it is written in simplest form.

EXAMPLE 9. $\sqrt{3/7} = \sqrt{\dfrac{21}{49}} = \dfrac{\sqrt{21}}{\sqrt{49}} = \dfrac{\sqrt{21}}{7}$ or $\dfrac{1}{7}\,\sqrt{21}$, by Theorem 4.7 and the principle that a fraction is unchanged in value when both numerator and denominator are multiplied or divided by the same non-zero number. The number chosen as a multiplier, 7, was selected in order to make the denominator of the equivalent fraction a perfect square.

EXAMPLE 10. $\sqrt[3]{\dfrac{1}{2}} = \sqrt[3]{\dfrac{4}{8}} = \dfrac{\sqrt[3]{4}}{\sqrt[3]{8}} = \dfrac{\sqrt[3]{4}}{2}$ or $\dfrac{1}{2}\,\sqrt[3]{4}$. In this example both terms of the fraction $\dfrac{1}{2}$ were multiplied by 4, to make the denominator of the equivalent fraction, $\dfrac{4}{8}$, a perfect cube. Then Theorem 4.7 was applied. Note that $\sqrt[3]{\dfrac{1}{2}}$ cannot be evaluated from Table I, but $\sqrt[3]{4}$ is readily found.

EXAMPLE 11. $\dfrac{\sqrt{7}}{\sqrt{2}} = \dfrac{\sqrt{7}\sqrt{2}}{\sqrt{2}\sqrt{2}} = \dfrac{\sqrt{14}}{2}$ or $\dfrac{1}{2}\sqrt{14}$, by Definition 4.6.

Note that of the two equivalent forms, $\dfrac{\sqrt{7}}{\sqrt{2}}$, and $\dfrac{\sqrt{14}}{2}$, the latter is much easier to evaluate, since division by 2 may be done mentally. The process used in this example is called "rationalizing the denominator," since the radical is removed from the denominator in accordance with the rules for writing a radical in simplest form.

EXAMPLE 12. $\dfrac{\sqrt[3]{5}}{\sqrt[3]{9}} = \dfrac{\sqrt[3]{5}\sqrt[3]{3}}{\sqrt[3]{9}\sqrt[3]{3}} = \dfrac{\sqrt[3]{15}}{\sqrt[3]{27}} = \dfrac{\sqrt[3]{15}}{3}$ or $\dfrac{1}{3}\sqrt[3]{15}$.

Observe that both terms of the fraction were multiplied by $\sqrt[3]{3}$ to make the radicand of the new denominator, 27, a perfect cube. As in Example 11, $\dfrac{\sqrt[3]{15}}{3}$ is much simpler to evaluate than $\dfrac{\sqrt[3]{5}}{\sqrt[3]{3}}$.

EXAMPLE 13. $\sqrt[6]{25} = \sqrt[6]{5^2} = \sqrt[3]{5}$, by Theorem 4.5.

EXAMPLE 14. $\sqrt[4]{9} = \sqrt[4]{3^2} = \sqrt{3}$, by Theorem 4.5.

Note that the first form of each radical cannot be evaluated by using Table 1, but the second, or simplest form, may be evaluated directly from the table.

Addition of Radicals

Since only "like" or "similar" quantities may be added, we need the following definition:

DEFINITION 4.7. Similar radicals are radicals that have the same index and the same radicand.

EXAMPLE 15. $3 \sqrt{3}$, $-2 \sqrt{3}$, and $a\sqrt{3}$, are similar radicals.

EXAMPLE 16. $2 \sqrt[3]{81}$, $4 \sqrt[3]{24}$, and $\sqrt[6]{9}$, when reduced to their simplest form are $6 \sqrt[3]{3}$, $8 \sqrt[3]{3}$, and $\sqrt[3]{3}$, respectively, and are then similar radicals.

To find the sum of two or more radicals, reduce each radical to simplest form and combine similar radicals by adding their coefficients. We see here that one advantage of writing radicals in simplest form is that an expression involving sums of radicals may frequently be simplified, as in Example 17.

EXAMPLE 17. $2 \sqrt{2} + 5 \sqrt{8} - 3 \sqrt{98} =$
$2 \sqrt{2} + 10 \sqrt{2} - 21 \sqrt{2} =$
$(2 + 10 - 21) \sqrt{2} = -9 \sqrt{2}.$

EXAMPLE 18. $2 \sqrt{3} + 4 \sqrt{8} - 2 \sqrt{12} + 3 \sqrt{50} =$
$2 \sqrt{3} + 8 \sqrt{2} - 4 \sqrt{3} + 15 \sqrt{2} =$
$(2 - 4) \sqrt{3} + (8 + 15) \sqrt{2} =$
$-2 \sqrt{3} + 23 \sqrt{2}.$

Multiplication of Radicals

To find the product of two or more radicals with the same index, we use Theorem 4.6, simplifying the result if possible.

EXAMPLE 19. $(4 \sqrt{2})(3 \sqrt{12}) = 12 \sqrt{24} = 24 \sqrt{6}$

EXAMPLE 20. $(2 + 3 \sqrt{2})(2 - 3 \sqrt{2}) = 4 - 6 \sqrt{2} + 6 \sqrt{2} - 9 \sqrt{4} =$
$4 - 18 = -14.$

EXAMPLE 21. $(\sqrt[3]{4})(\sqrt[3]{50})(\sqrt[3]{5}) = \sqrt[3]{1000} = 10.$

To find the product of two or more radicals of different order, we use Theorem 4.5 to write them as radicals of the same order, and proceed as above.

EXAMPLE 22. $(\sqrt{2a})(\sqrt[3]{4a}) =$
$(\sqrt[6]{(2a)^3}) (\sqrt[6]{(4a)^2}) =$ $8a^3 \times 16a^2 =$
$\sqrt[6]{128a^5} = 2 \sqrt[6]{2a^5}.$ $128a^5 =$

Division of Radicals

To find the quotient of radicals having the same index, we use Theorem 4.7, simplifying the result if possible. If the radicand in the denominator is not an exact divisor of the radicant in the numerator, we use the process of rationalizing the denominator, as in Example 11 of this section, to obtain the quotient in simplest form.

EXAMPLE 23. $\dfrac{\sqrt{50}}{\sqrt{2}} = \sqrt{\dfrac{50}{2}} = \sqrt{25} = 5$

EXAMPLE 24. $\dfrac{\sqrt{10}}{\sqrt{3}} = \dfrac{\sqrt{10}\,\sqrt{3}}{\sqrt{3}\,\sqrt{3}} = \dfrac{\sqrt{30}}{3}$ or $\dfrac{1}{3}\sqrt{30}$.

EXAMPLE 25. $\dfrac{3 + \sqrt{2}}{3 - \sqrt{2}}$. We may rationalize the denominator by multiplying numerator and denominator by the radical $3 + \sqrt{2}$. Therefore

$$\frac{3 + \sqrt{2}}{3 - \sqrt{2}} = \frac{(3 + \sqrt{2})(3 + \sqrt{2})}{(3 - \sqrt{2})(3 + \sqrt{2})} = \frac{11 + 6\sqrt{2}}{9 - 2} = \frac{11 + 6\sqrt{2}}{7}$$

In general, it should be observed that since $(\sqrt{a} + \sqrt{b})(\sqrt{a} - \sqrt{b}) = a - b$, either factor of the given product is a rationalizing factor of the other.

EXERCISE 4.4

Operations with Radicals

Simplify each of the following radicals. All variables represent nonnegative numbers.

1. $\sqrt{128}$	2. $\sqrt{72}$	3. $\sqrt{500}$
4. $5\sqrt{20}$	5. $3\sqrt{28}$	6. $2\sqrt{162}$
7. $3\sqrt{80}$	8. $\dfrac{1}{5}\sqrt{150x^4}$	9. $3\sqrt{12x^3}$
10. $\sqrt[3]{16}$	11. $2\sqrt[3]{24}$	12. $3\sqrt[3]{54}$
13. $\dfrac{1}{3}\sqrt[3]{81}$	14. $\dfrac{1}{2}\sqrt[3]{40}$	15. $\dfrac{1}{2}\sqrt[3]{56x^3y^2}$
16. $\dfrac{2}{3}\sqrt[3]{108x^4}$	17. $2\sqrt[3]{54x^3y^4}$	18. $\sqrt[3]{-27}$

19. $\sqrt{1000}$ 20. $\sqrt[3]{-24x^3y^2}$ 21. $\sqrt[3]{2x^5y^3}$

22. $\sqrt[5]{-64}$ 23. $\sqrt[4]{243x^5y^6}$ 24. $\sqrt[4]{3x^5y^5}$

25. $\sqrt[5]{x^6y^7}$ 26. $\sqrt[3]{-250x^3y^2}$ 27. $\sqrt[4]{64xy^9}$

28. $\sqrt[9]{1000}$ 29. $\sqrt[4]{625}$ 30. $\sqrt[6]{9x^2}$

31. $\sqrt[4]{9x^2y^2}$ 32. $\sqrt[6]{81a^2}$ 33. $\sqrt[10]{32x^5}$

34. $\sqrt[4]{25x^2}$ 35. $\sqrt[6]{x^3y^6}$ 36. $\sqrt[6]{27x^3}$

37. $\sqrt[2n]{25a^2b^4c^6}$ 38. $\sqrt[3n]{a^nb^{2n}c^{3n}}$ 39. $\sqrt{\dfrac{2}{3}}$

40. $\sqrt{\dfrac{1}{2}}$ 41. $\sqrt{\dfrac{1}{5}}$ 42. $\sqrt{\dfrac{3}{8}}$

43. $\sqrt[3]{\dfrac{1}{4}}$ 44. $\sqrt{\dfrac{3}{16}}$ 45. $\sqrt[3]{\dfrac{1}{2}}$

46. $\sqrt[3]{\dfrac{3}{4}}$ 47. $\sqrt[3]{\dfrac{2}{25}}$ 48. $\sqrt[3]{\dfrac{2}{5}}$

49. $\sqrt[3]{\dfrac{1}{9}}$ 50. $\sqrt[7]{\dfrac{1}{64}}$ 51. $\sqrt[3]{\dfrac{2}{x}}$

52. $\sqrt[3]{\dfrac{3y}{x^2}}$ 53. $\sqrt{\dfrac{x}{y}}$ 54. $\sqrt[3]{\dfrac{x}{y}}$

55. $\sqrt[4]{\dfrac{2x}{y^3}}$ 56. $\sqrt[5]{\dfrac{1}{16x^2}}$ 57. $\sqrt[3]{\dfrac{5x}{2y}}$

58. $\sqrt{\dfrac{1}{15x}}$ 59. $\sqrt[3]{\dfrac{2x}{5y^3}}$ 60. $\sqrt[4]{\dfrac{1}{8x^2}}$

In Problems 61 to 69, simplify each radical and combine similar terms.

61. $\sqrt{2} + 3\sqrt{8} - 2\sqrt{18}$ 62. $\sqrt{12} + \sqrt{27} + \sqrt{48}$

63. $3\sqrt{32} + 5\sqrt{18} - \sqrt{12}$ 64. $3\sqrt{40} + \sqrt{250} - \sqrt{90}$

65. $3\sqrt{75x^3} + 2\sqrt{12x^3} - 3\sqrt{18x^3}$ 66. $3\sqrt[3]{16} + \sqrt[3]{2}$

67. $\sqrt[3]{54} + 2\sqrt[3]{128x^3}$ 68. $4\sqrt[3]{108x^5} + 2\sqrt[3]{256x^2} - 3\sqrt[3]{32x^8}$

69. $\sqrt{12x} - \sqrt{24x^3} + \sqrt{54x^3} - \sqrt{75x^5}$

Multiply the following radicals and simplify the product if possible.

70. $\sqrt{2} \cdot \sqrt{3}$ 71. $\sqrt{3x} \cdot \sqrt{3x}$ 72. $\sqrt{3} \cdot \sqrt{6}$

73. $2\sqrt{5} \cdot 2\sqrt{5}$ 74. $\sqrt{2} \cdot \sqrt{4} \cdot \sqrt{48}$ 75. $3\sqrt{3x} \cdot 2\sqrt{30x}$

76. $5\sqrt[3]{81} \cdot 3\sqrt[3]{2}$ 77. $\sqrt[3]{6} \cdot \sqrt[3]{6} \cdot \sqrt[3]{6}$ 78. $\sqrt[3]{4} \cdot \sqrt[3]{8}$

79. $\sqrt{3}(\sqrt{2} + \sqrt{3} - \sqrt{4})$ 80. $2\sqrt{3}(\sqrt{3} - \sqrt{2})$

Multiply the following radicals by first expressing them as radicals of the same order.

81. $\sqrt{5} \cdot \sqrt[3]{3}$ 82. $\sqrt{xy} \cdot \sqrt[3]{xy}$ 83. $\sqrt[3]{3} \cdot \sqrt{3}$ 84. $\sqrt[3]{2x} \cdot \sqrt[4]{2x^3y^3}$

85. $\sqrt[3]{2} \cdot \sqrt[4]{3}$ 86. $\sqrt{ab} \cdot \sqrt[5]{a^4b^4}$ 87. $\sqrt[3]{x^2} \cdot \sqrt[4]{x^3}$ 88. $\sqrt[3]{2} \cdot \sqrt[6]{6}$

89. $\sqrt[4]{4} \cdot \sqrt[6]{8}$ 90. $\sqrt{3a} \cdot \sqrt[3]{9a^2}$ 91. $\sqrt[3]{2x} \cdot \sqrt[4]{8x^3}$ 92. $\sqrt[4]{y} \cdot \sqrt[3]{y} \cdot \sqrt{y}$

93. $\sqrt{7} \cdot \sqrt[3]{11}$ 94. $\sqrt{2x} \cdot \sqrt[3]{2x^2}$ 95. $\sqrt{3x} \cdot \sqrt[3]{9x^2} \cdot \sqrt[6]{243x^5}$

Find the following products, simplifying the result when possible.

96. $(\sqrt{2} + 3)(\sqrt{2} - 3)$ 97. $(2\sqrt{2} - 3)(2\sqrt{2} + 3)$

98. $(2 + 3\sqrt{2})(2 - 3\sqrt{2})$ 99. $(2 - \sqrt{5})(2 - \sqrt{5})$

100. $(\sqrt{2} + 2\sqrt{3})(\sqrt{2} - 3\sqrt{3})$ 101. $(2\sqrt{5} + 2)(3\sqrt{5} - 6)$

102. $(\sqrt{2} + \sqrt{3})^2$ 103. $(\sqrt{3} + \sqrt{2})(\sqrt{3} - \sqrt{2})$

Find the following quotients, writing the results in simplest form.

104. $\dfrac{\sqrt{28}}{\sqrt{7}}$ 105. $\dfrac{\sqrt{24}}{\sqrt{6}}$ 106. $\dfrac{\sqrt{8}}{\sqrt{4}}$ 107. $\dfrac{\sqrt{2}}{\sqrt{3}}$ 108. $\dfrac{\sqrt{5}}{\sqrt{2}}$

109. $\dfrac{\sqrt{6}}{\sqrt{2x}}$ 110. $\dfrac{3\sqrt{7}}{2\sqrt{3x}}$ 111. $\dfrac{5\sqrt{15}}{4\sqrt{12}}$ 112. $\dfrac{2x}{\sqrt{3x}}$ 113. $\dfrac{2}{\sqrt{2}}$

114. $\dfrac{3x}{\sqrt{3}}$ 115. $\dfrac{\sqrt[3]{16}}{\sqrt[3]{2}}$ 116. $\dfrac{\sqrt[3]{54}}{\sqrt[3]{2}}$ 117. $\dfrac{\sqrt[3]{12}}{\sqrt[3]{4x}}$ 118. $\dfrac{\sqrt[3]{16x^2}}{\sqrt[3]{4x^2}}$

119. $\dfrac{4}{\sqrt{3} - \sqrt{2}}$ 120. $\dfrac{2}{\sqrt{5} - \sqrt{2}}$ 121. $\dfrac{2\sqrt{3}}{\sqrt{3} - \sqrt{2}}$ 122. $\dfrac{2 + \sqrt{3}}{2 - \sqrt{3}}$

123. $\dfrac{2}{\sqrt{5} + 1}$ 124. $\dfrac{3}{4 - \sqrt{3}}$ 125. $\dfrac{\sqrt{3}}{\sqrt{3} - 1}$ 126. $\dfrac{\sqrt{2} + 1}{\sqrt{2} - 1}$

127. $\dfrac{\sqrt{3} - 4}{\sqrt{3} + 2}$ 128. $\dfrac{\sqrt{10} - 3}{\sqrt{10} + 3}$ 129. $\dfrac{\sqrt{x} + 1}{\sqrt{x} - 1}$ 130. $\dfrac{\sqrt{x} - \sqrt{y}}{\sqrt{x} + \sqrt{y}}$

4.5 THE SET OF COMPLEX NUMBERS

Thus far we have carefully avoided such expressions as $\sqrt{-1}$, $\sqrt[4]{-16}$, and any even root of a negative number. It is clear that the set of real numbers is not adequate to give meaning to such expressions, for if we let $\sqrt{-1} = x$, where x is a real number, then $x^2 = -1$, by Definition 4.6. Since the square of any real number is positive, or zero, x cannot be a real number.

As in the case of exponents other than the positive integers, mathematicians have two choices: either to reject the equation $x^2 = -1$ as meaningless, or to accept the equation, and therefore accept $x = \sqrt{-1}$ as a solution. This, of course, means that $\sqrt{-1}$ must be accepted as a number. Great mathematicians as early as the seventeenth century recognized the existence of such numbers as necessary for the solution of certain equations, but refused to accept them as numbers. The term "imaginary" given to these expressions since they are not real, while in a sense an appropriate name, has unfortunate and unintended connotations. For who in his right mind would talk about, much less work with, an imaginary number? Eventually opposition to the idea of imaginary numbers vanished, as they became an important part in the mathematical theory of alternating current, the science of cartography, and many other areas of scientific knowledge. We can see the wisdom of the larger viewpoint of extending our number system to include imaginary numbers.

The Imaginary Unit *i*

In operating with imaginary numbers, it is convenient to represent the imaginary unit $\sqrt{-1}$ by the symbol i. Then for any imaginary number $\sqrt{-n}$ $(n > 0)$,

$$\sqrt{-n} = \sqrt{-1 \cdot n} = \sqrt{-1} \cdot \sqrt{n} = i\sqrt{n}$$

We are therefore led to the following definition.

DEFINITION 4.8. For an imaginary number, $\sqrt{-n}$ $(n > 0)$, $\sqrt{-n} = i\sqrt{n}$.

EXAMPLE 1. $\sqrt{-4} = i\sqrt{4} = 2i$.

EXAMPLE 2. $\sqrt{-3} = \sqrt{3}i$.

Operations with Imaginary Numbers

Imaginary numbers may be combined in the same manner as similar radicals. It is convenient, but not necessary, to express them in terms of i before adding.

EXAMPLE 3. $2\sqrt{-3} + 4\sqrt{-3} + 3\sqrt{-6} =$
$2\sqrt{3}i + 4\sqrt{3}i + 3\sqrt{6}i =$
$(6\sqrt{3} + 3\sqrt{6})i$.

Care must be used in multiplying imaginary numbers, since the laws developed for the product of real numbers do not hold for the product of imaginary numbers. Consider the product of two imaginary numbers

$$\sqrt{-m}\sqrt{-n}. \qquad (m > 0, n > 0)$$

We may be tempted to write this product as $\sqrt{mn}$, since for real numbers, $(-m)(-n) = mn$. If, however, we write each factor in terms of the imaginary unit i, then we have

$$\sqrt{m}i \cdot \sqrt{n}i = \sqrt{mn}\, i^2.$$

Since $i^2 = -1$, we therefore have the important result for the product of two imaginary numbers,

$$\sqrt{-m}\sqrt{-n} = -\sqrt{mn} \qquad (m > 0, n > 0)$$

EXAMPLE 4. $\sqrt{-2}\,\sqrt{-8} = -\sqrt{16} = -4.$

The quotient of two imaginary numbers, however, follows the usual rule of signs for real numbers.

EXAMPLE 5. $\dfrac{\sqrt{-8}}{\sqrt{-2}} = \dfrac{\sqrt{8}i}{\sqrt{2}i} = \sqrt{4} = 2$

EXAMPLE 6. $\dfrac{-\sqrt{-8}}{\sqrt{-2}} = \dfrac{-\sqrt{8}i}{\sqrt{2}i} = -\sqrt{4} = -2.$

Powers of the imaginary unit i exhibit an interesting pattern. By direct multiplication, we have

$$
\begin{array}{ll}
i = i & i^5 = i^4 \cdot i = i \\
i^2 = -1 & i^6 = i^4 \cdot i^2 = -1 \\
i^3 = -i & i^7 = i^4 \cdot i^3 = -i \\
i^4 = 1 & i^8 = i^4 \cdot i^4 = 1
\end{array}
$$

A little reflection will show that this pattern is repeated periodically, so that any integral power of i equals i, -1, $-i$, or 1.

EXAMPLE 7. $i^{15} = i^{12} \cdot i^3 = (1)(-i) = -i$

EXAMPLE 8. $i^{10} = i^8 \cdot i^2 = (1)(-1) = -1.$

The Set of Complex Numbers

A more general expression involving imaginary numbers leads to the set of *complex numbers*. Complex numbers are numbers of the form $a + bi$, where a and b are real numbers, which may be positive, negative, or zero. Thus

$$
\begin{array}{c}
3 + 4i \\
3 - 3i \\
3i = 0 + 3i \\
-4 = -4 + 0i
\end{array}
$$

are all complex numbers. It is clear from the above examples of complex numbers that the set of real numbers is a subset of the set of complex numbers. For any complex number $a + bi$, a is called the *real* part and bi the *imaginary* part. When $a = 0$, the complex number bi is called a *pure imaginary*.

For equality of complex numbers, we have the following definition.

DEFINITION 4.9. Two complex numbers, $a + bi$ and $c + di$ are equal if and only if $a = c$ and $b = d$.

EXAMPLE 9. $3 + 4i = x + iy$ implies that $x = 3$ and $y = 4$.

It follows from definition 4.9 that the complex number $a + bi$ equals zero if and only if $a = 0$ and $b = 0$.

EXAMPLE 10.   The complex number $(a - 2) + (b - 3)i$ equals zero if and only if $(a - 2) = 0$ and $(b - 3) = 0$, that is, $a = 2$ and $b = 3$.

Operations with Complex Numbers

The addition of two complex numbers is defined as follows.

DEFINITION 4.10. The sum of two complex numbers, $(a + bi) + (c + di)$, equals $(a + c) + (b + d)i$, that is, the sum of the real parts plus the sum of the imaginary parts.

EXAMPLE 11. $(3 + 4i) + (2 - 3i) = (3 + 2) + (4 - 3)i = 5 + i$.

The product of two complex numbers is found in the same manner as the product of two binomials.

DEFINITION 4.11. The product of two complex numbers, $a + bi$ and $c + di$ equals $(a + bi)\,(c + di) = ac + adi + bci + bdi^2 = (ac - bd) + (ad + bc)i$.

In finding a product it is generally easier to multiply directly rather than to use definition 4.11.

EXAMPLE 12. $(3 + 2i)(3 - 4i) = 9 - 12i + 6i - 8i^2 = 17 - 6i$.

Definitions 4.10 and 4.11 are formulated with a view to making the field properties (Section 1.3) valid for the set of complex numbers.   The following is one example that illustrates this point; additional examples are included as problems in Exercise 4.5.

EXAMPLE 13.   The multiplicative inverse of the complex number $a + bi$ is the complex number $\dfrac{1}{a + bi}$, since their product is 1. To write this number so as to indicate the real and imaginary parts we multiply numerator and denominator by $a - bi$. Then we shall have

$$\frac{1}{a + bi} = \frac{a - bi}{(a + bi)(a - bi)}$$

$$= \frac{a - bi}{a^2 - b^2 i^2}$$

$$= \frac{a - bi}{a^2 + b^2} \text{ (since } i^2 = -1)$$

$$= \frac{a}{a^2 + b^2} - \frac{b}{a^2 + b^2} i$$

The quantity $a - bi$, used in Example 13 is called the conjugate of $a + bi$, according to the following definition.

DEFINITION 4.12. The *conjugate* of the complex number $a + bi$ is $a - bi$, and the *conjugate* of $a - bi$ is $a + bi$.

EXAMPLE 14. The conjugate of $3 + 2i$ is $3 - 2i$. The conjugate of $3 - 2i$ is $3 + 2i$.

Since the product $(a + bi)(a - bi) = a^2 + b^2$, we see that the product of a complex number and its conjugate is a real number. Therefore, to find the quotient of two complex numbers we multiply both numerator and denominator by the conjugate of the denominator in order to separate the real and imaginary parts, as in Example 15.

EXAMPLE 15. $\dfrac{3 + 4i}{2 - 3i} = \dfrac{(3 + 4i)(2 + 3i)}{(2 - 3i)(2 + 3i)}$

$$= \frac{6 + 17i + 12i^2}{4 - 9i^2}$$

$$= \frac{-6 + 17i}{13} \text{ (since } i^2 = -1)$$

$$= \frac{-6}{13} + \frac{17}{13} i$$

Notice that the final result is written in the form $a + bi$.

EXERCISE 4.5

The Set of Complex Numbers

Express each of the following sums in terms of the imaginary unit i.

1. $6\sqrt{-3} + 3\sqrt{-12} - 2\sqrt{-27}$
2. $3\sqrt{-2} + 4\sqrt{-8} - 6\sqrt{-32}$
3. $3\sqrt{-2} + 4\sqrt{-3} + 4\sqrt{-8} - 2\sqrt{-12}$
4. $4i^3 + 3i - 2i^5 + 2i^7$
5. $(2i)^5 + (3i)^3 - (2i)^3 + 4i$
6. $(2\sqrt{-3})^3 + 2\sqrt{-3} + (2\sqrt{-1})^3$

Express each of the following products as a real or imaginary number.

7. $2\sqrt{-3} \cdot 3\sqrt{-2}$ 8. $3\sqrt{-3} \cdot \sqrt{-27}$ 9. $2\sqrt{-6} \cdot \sqrt{-4}$

10. $\sqrt{-3} \cdot \sqrt{-2} \cdot \sqrt{-5}$ 11. $\sqrt{5} \cdot \sqrt{-5}$ 12. $\sqrt[3]{-27} \cdot \sqrt[3]{-8}$

Express each of the following quotients as a real or imaginary number.

13. $\dfrac{\sqrt{-16}}{\sqrt{4}}$ 14. $\dfrac{\sqrt{-20}}{\sqrt{-5}}$ 15. $\dfrac{\sqrt{16}}{\sqrt{-4}}$

16. $\dfrac{\sqrt{28}}{\sqrt{-7}}$ 17. $\dfrac{\sqrt{-32}}{\sqrt{-2}}$ 18. $\dfrac{\sqrt{-15}}{\sqrt{5}}$

Find the values of x and y which makes each pair of complex numbers equal.

19. $(4 - x) + (2 + y)i; 3 + 2i$ 20. $(x + 2) + (y - 4)i; 3 - 2i$
21. $(x - 3) + (y + 3)i; 2 + 2i$ 22. $(x - 2a) + (y - 3b)i; a + bi$

Find the values of x and y which makes each complex number equal zero.

23. $(x - 4) + (y - 2)i$ 24. $(3x - 2) + (4y + 3)i$
25. $(2x + 1) - (4y + 1)i$ 26. $(4 - 3x) + (2 - 3y)i$
27. $(x^2 - 1) + (y^2 - 4)i$

Express the following sums as a single complex number.

28. $(3 + 2i) + (-3 + 4i)$ 29. $(3 - 4i) - (1 - 6i)$
30. $(12 + 2i) - (-7 + 3i)$ 31. $(4i + 1) - (3i - 2)$
32. $7 - (2 - 3i)$ 33. $(6 - 5i) - (3 - 2i)$
34. $6i - (3 + 2i)$ 35. $(x + yi) + (x - yi)$
36. $(x + yi) + (x + yi)$

Find the following products.

37. $(3 + i)(3 - i)$ 38. $(5 - 2i)(6 + 3i)$ 39. $(1 + 3i)(-2 - 2i)$
40. $(2 + i)^2$ 41. $(2 - i)^2$ 42. $(1 + i)(1 - 2i)$

43. $(\sqrt{3} - 2i)(\sqrt{3} + 2i)$ 44. $\sqrt{-2}\,(2 - \sqrt{-2})$

45. $\sqrt{3}\,(\sqrt{-3} + \sqrt{3})$ 46. $(\sqrt{3} + \sqrt{-2})(\sqrt{3} - \sqrt{-2})$

Express each quotient in the form $a + bi$.

47. $\dfrac{2}{i}$ 48. $\dfrac{-5}{i}$ 49. $\dfrac{2}{\sqrt{-3}}$ 50. $\dfrac{3}{2 + i}$ 51. $\dfrac{2}{3 - i}$ 52. $\dfrac{3i}{4 - i}$

53. $\dfrac{\sqrt{-2}}{1 + \sqrt{-2}}$ 54. $\dfrac{1 + 3i}{1 - 3i}$ 55. $\dfrac{3 + 2i}{2 + 3i}$ 56. $\dfrac{\sqrt{3} + \sqrt{-3}}{\sqrt{3} - \sqrt{-3}}$

57. Show that the complex number $-1 + i$ is a solution of the equation $x^2 + 2x + 2 = 0$.

58. Show that $-1 - i$ is also a solution to the equation of problem 57.

59. What is the additive inverse of the complex number $a + bi$?

60. What is the value of $2x^2 - 6x + 7$ when $x = \dfrac{3}{2} + \dfrac{\sqrt{5}}{2}\,i$?

61. Using example 28 of this exercise, verify that the commutative law of addition holds for complex numbers.

62. Using example 38 of this exercise, verify that the commutative law of multiplication holds for complex numbers.

63. Using the product $(1 + i)(1 - i)(1 + 2i)$, verify that the associative law of multiplication holds for complex numbers.

64. By adding the three factors of Problem 63, verify that the associative law of addition holds for complex numbers.

chapter 5

factoring and the solution of quadratic equations

THE SOLUTION OF QUADRATIC EQUATIONS, AS WELL AS many other processes in algebra, involves the factoring of algebraic expressions. We shall discuss some methods of factoring here. In the products

$$42 \times 31 = 1302$$

$$(x + 3)(x + 2) = x^2 + 5x + 6$$

42 and 31 are *factors* of 1302, and $x + 3$ and $x + 2$ are factors of $x^2 + 5x + 6$. More formally, we have the following definition.

DEFINITION 5.1. In the product $a \cdot b \cdot c \cdots = p$, the quantities $a, b, c, \cdots$ are factors of p.

The quantities $a, b, c, \cdots p$, may be numbers or algebraic expressions, as in the above examples.

Prime Factors

It is clear from the following examples that a number or algebraic expression may have more than one set of factors. Thus

$$30 = 6 \times 5$$
$$= 3 \times 10$$
$$= 2 \times 15$$
$$2x^3 - 17x^2 + 45x - 36 = (2x - 3)(x^2 - 7x + 12)$$
$$= (x - 3)(2x^2 - 11x + 12)$$
$$= (x - 4)(2x^2 - 9x + 9)$$

Careful examination of each set of factors will reveal that one of the two factors in each set of factors can itself be rewritten as the product of two factors. Thus

$$30 = 2 \times 3 \times 5$$
$$= 3 \times 2 \times 5$$
$$= 2 \times 3 \times 5$$

so that except for the order of the factors each factorization is alike. In a similar manner each factorization of $2x^3 - 17x^2 + 45x - 36$ can be rewritten as

$$2x^3 - 17x^2 + 45x - 36 = (2x - 3)(x - 3)(x - 4)$$

We observe that the three factors of 30, namely 2, 3, and 5 are prime numbers and are therefore called prime factors of 30. The three factors of the polynomial, $(2x - 3)$, $(x - 3)$, and $(x - 4)$ are prime factors of the polynomial since none of them can be expressed as the product of two or more polynomials. We may of course write

$$x - 3 = (\sqrt{x} + \sqrt{3})(\sqrt{x} - \sqrt{3})$$
$$2x - 3 = 2\left(x - \frac{3}{2}\right)$$

but we ordinarily restrict the factors to polynomials or monomials with integral coefficients, so that $x - 3$ and $2x - 3$ are considered prime for purposes of factoring. An expression such as $x^2 + x + 1$ is also prime, since it cannot be expressed as the product of two polynomial factors.

The above considerations lead to an important theorem of algebra:

THEOREM 5.1   A polynomial (or integer) has one and only one set of prime factors.[1]

---

[1] For a proof of this important theorem, see H. B. Fine, *College Algebra*, Dover, 1905, page 210.

Dependence of Factoring on Multiplication

If we desire to find the product 342×451, or the product $(2x - 3)(x - 1)$, we encounter no difficulty; the work may be tedious, but the process is direct, and it is easily verified that

$$342 \times 451 = 154{,}242$$
$$(2x - 3)(x - 1) = 2x^2 - 5x + 3$$

The related problem of finding the factors of a number or of a polynomial is not as direct or as easy. To find x and y so that

$$8687 = x \cdot y$$

or to write

$$9x^5 + 3x^4 - 21x^3 + x^2 + 10x - 2 = (\quad)(\quad)$$

that is, as the product of two factors, requires a process of systematic trial; there is no direct process as in multiplication. Only after some trial (and much experience!) of possible factors we do find that

$$8687 = 73 \times 119$$
$$9x^5 + 3x^4 - 21x^3 + x^2 + 10x - 2 = (3x^2 - 2)(3x^3 + x^2 - 5x + 1)$$

It should be clear from the foregoing discussion that the process of factoring depends heavily on multiplication, since the ultimate test of the correct choice of factors is that their product equals the original expression. We shall therefore turn our attention to methods of multiplying certain algebraic expressions more rapidly to reduce the labor of testing the factors we choose. Although there is no limit to the types of expressions that may be multiplied, we shall limit ourselves to the types of expressions that occur most frequently in elementary algebra.

5.1 SPECIAL PRODUCTS

We shall first list the "special products" to be considered in this section.

I. The product of a monomial and a polynomial.   By direct application of the distributive law

$$a(x + y + z) = ax + ay + az$$

II. The product of two binomials. By procedures discussed in Section 2.4, we have

$$(ax + by)(cx + dy) = acx^2 + (bc + ad)xy + bdy^2$$

III. Special cases of the product of two binomials occur frequently enough to warrant their inclusion here, although they may be found by the general method of formula II.

$$(ax + by)^2 = a^2x^2 + 2abxy + b^2y^2 \tag{a}$$

$$(ax - by)^2 = a^2x^2 - 2abxy + b^2y^2 \tag{b}$$

$$(ax + by)(ax - by) = a^2x^2 - b^2y^2 \tag{c}$$

IV. Products leading to the sum or difference of two cubes. By direct multiplication

$$(x + y)(x^2 - xy + y^2) = x^3 + y^3 \tag{a}$$

$$(x - y)(x^2 + xy + y^2) = x^3 - y^3 \tag{b}$$

In applying formulas I through IV it is important to recognize that they are merely *type* forms. Thus the product $(2a + 3b)(4a^2 - 6ab + 9b^2)$ may be identified as Type IV(a), with $2a$ replacing x and $3b$ replacing y. The product is therefore $(2a)^3 + (3b)^3 = 8a^3 + 27b^3$. The examples that follow will further illustrate this point.

EXAMPLE 1. $3m(2m^2 - 3mn + n^2) = 6m^3 - 9m^2n + 3mn^2$ Type I

EXAMPLE 2. $(2x + 3y)(3x - 4y) = 6x^2 + (9 - 8)xy - 12y^2$ Type II
$$= 6x^2 + xy - 12y^2$$

We may write the product of two binomials more rapidly by use of the following scheme, using Example 2 again for this purpose,

$$(2x + 3y)(3x - 4y) = 6x^2 - 8xy + 9xy - 12y^2$$
$$= 6x^2 + xy - 12y^2$$

In this scheme, the small numbers indicate the order of operation, which may be described as follows.

(a) The first term of the product is the product of the first term of each binomial.

(b) The second term is the sum of the products of the "outer" and "inner" terms of the two binomials.

(c) The third term is the product of the second terms of each binomial.

After a little practice the addition of the terms in step (b) should be done mentally.   The importance of this scheme for finding the product of two binomials lies in its application to the related problem of factoring a trinomial, and the student should become proficient in using it.

EXAMPLE 3. $(2x + 3y)(3x + 4y) = 6x^2 + 17xy + 12y^2$ Type II

EXAMPLE 4. $(4t - 5)(3t + 2) = 12t^2 - 7t - 10$ Type II

EXAMPLE 5. $(3x + 4y)^2 = 9x^2 + 24xy + 16y^2$ Type III (a)

As suggested earlier, $(3x + 4y)^2$ may be written as $(3x + 4y)(3x + 4y)$ and the product written as in Examples 3 and 4.

EXAMPLE 6. $(2t - 3)^2 = 4t^2 - 12t + 9$ Type III(b)

EXAMPLE 7. $(2t + 3)(2t - 3) = 4t^2 - 9$ Type III (c)

EXAMPLE 8. $(4 - 2w)(4 + 2w) = 16 - 4w^2$ Type III(c)

EXAMPLE 9. $(p + 2q)(p^2 - 2pq + 4q^2) = p^3 + (2q)^3 = p^3 + 8q^3$ Type IV

Some Additional Special Products

Certain products may be written so as to conform to the products stated previously. Examples of them will indicate the process.

TYPE II, EXAMPLE 10.

$$
\begin{aligned}
(x + y + 7)(x + y + 3) &= [(x + y) + 7][(x + y) + 3] \\
&= (x + y)^2 + 10(x + y) + 21 \\
&= x^2 + 2xy + y^2 + 10x + 10y + 21
\end{aligned}
$$

TYPE III, EXAMPLE 11.

$$
\begin{aligned}
(x + y + 2)(x - y - 2) &= [x + (y + 2)][x - (y + 2)] \\
&= x^2 - (y + 2)^2 \\
&= x^2 - y^2 - 4y - 4
\end{aligned}
$$

TYPE III, EXAMPLE 12. $(x - 3)(x^2 + 9)(x + 3) = (x^2 + 9)(x^2 - 9)$
$$= x^4 - 81$$

TYPE III, EXAMPLE 13.

$$(x + 2y - 3z)^2 = [(x + 2y) - 3z]^2$$
$$= (x + 2y)^2 - 6z\,(x + 2y) + 9z^2$$
$$= x^2 + 4xy + 4y^2 - 6xz - 12yz + 9z^2$$

EXERCISE 5.1

Special Products

Find the following products.

1. $ab(a^2 + b^2 - 1)$ 2. $2a(a + b - 2c)$ 3. $2\pi(R - r)$
4. $2\pi(r^2 - Rr + R^2)$ 5. $2xy(x^2 + 2xy + 2y^2)$ 6. $xy(xy^2 - xy + x^2y)$
7. $-2x(x + y - z)$ 8. $x^n(x^n - 1)$ 9. $x^{n-1}(x + x^{1-n})$
10. $abc(a - b - c)$

Find the following products. Combine the "inner and outer" products mentally.

11. $(2x + 3y)(x + 3y)$ 12. $(3x - 7y)(2x - 5y)$ 13. $(2t - 3)(2t + 5)$
14. $(2t - 3)(2t - 5)$ 15. $(x + 7)(2x + 7)$ 16. $(x + 7)(2x - 7)$
17. $(3x - 2y)(x + y)$ 18. $(3x + 2y)(x - y)$ 19. $(x - 7)(x - 3)$
20. $(x - 7)(x + 3)$ 21. $(3x + 2a)(x + 2a)$ 22. $(x - 2b)(x + b)$

Find the square of each of the following binomials.

23. $(2x + 3y)^2$ 24. $(3x - 4y)^2$ 25. $(2x - 3y)^2$ 26. $(x + 3y)^2$
27. $(4 + 3x)^2$ 28. $(4 - 3x)^2$ 29. $(2\pi r + h)^2$ 30. $(r + r')^2$
31. $(b_1 + b_2)^2$ 32. $(1 - 4x)^2$ 33. $(r - r')^2$

Find each product of the sum and difference of two terms.

34. $(3x - 2y)(3x + 2y)$ 35. $(3x - 4)(3x + 4)$ 36. $(2x + 4)(2x - 4)$
37. $(\pi r + h)(\pi r - h)$ 38. $(r + r')(r - r')$ 39. $(x^2 + 6)(x^2 - 6)$
40. $(x^2 - y^2)(x^2 + y^2)$ 41. $(2x^2 - 3y)(2x^2 + 3y)$

Find the missing term or terms so that the product will be the sum or difference of two cubes; then find the product.

42. $(a + b)(a^2 - \underline{} + b^2)$ 43. $(2a - b)(4a^2 + 2ab + \underline{})$
44. $(x + 3b)(x^2 - \underline{} + 9b^2)$ 45. $(x + \underline{})(x^2 - 2xy + 4y^2)$
46. $(2x - 3y)(4x^2 + \underline{} + 9y^2)$ 47. $(\underline{} + \underline{})(4a^2 - 6ab + 9b^2)$
48. $(3x - \underline{})(\underline{} + 12xy + \underline{})$

Find the product of the trinomials.

49. $(x + y + 7)(x + y + 3)$ 50. $(x + y - 2)(x + y + 2)$

51. $(x + y + 2)(x + y + 3)$ 52. $(x + y + 1)(x - y - 1)$

53. $(2s + t + 3)(2s - t - 3)$ 54. $(2m + n - 5)(2m + n + 6)$

55. $(3x + y - 1)(3x - y + 1)$ 56. $(2x + 2y + 3z)(2x + 2y + 4z)$

57. $(x + y + z)^2$ 58. $(x + y - z)^2$ 59. $(x - y + z)^2$

60. $(x - y - z)^2$ 61. $(2x + y + 1)^2$ 62. $(x - y + 3)^2$

63. From the product $(x + y + z)^2 = x^2 + y^2 + z^2 + 2xy + 2xz + 2yz$, write in words a rule for finding the square of a trinomial.

Find the following products of three factors.

64. $(n - 1)(n^2 + 1)(n + 1)$ 65. $(x + 2)(x - 2)(x^2 - 4)$

66. $(x + 1)(x - 1)(x^2 - 1)$ 67. $(x + 2)(x - 2)(x^2 + 4)$

Find the following squares or products, as in Problems 68 and 69.

68. $35^2 = (30 + 5)^2 = 900 + 300 + 25 = 1225.$

69. $38 \times 42 = (40 - 2)(40 + 2) = 1600 - 4 = 1596.$

70. 36^2 71. 29^2 72. 21^2 73. 57^2 74. 63^2

75. 91^2 76. 401^2 77. 399^2 78. 24×16 79. 21×19

80. 25×35 81. 62×58 82. 29×31 83. 210×190 84. 305×295

Find the missing factor in each of the following products.

85. $(x^{1/3} + y^{1/3})($ $) = x + y.$ *Hint.* write $x + y$ as $(x^{1/3})^3 + (y^{1/3})^3$

86. $(x^{1/3} - y^{1/3})($ $) = x - y$

87. $(x^{1/3} + 2)($ $) = x + 8$

88. $(x^{1/3} - 2)($ $) = x - 8.$

89. State in words a rule for determining the square of a binomial [Type III(a) and (b)].

90. State in words a rule for multiplying the sum and difference of two terms [Type III(c)].

5.2 FACTORING POLYNOMIALS

Although there is no general method of factoring any given polynomial, we may consider various types of polynomials in much the same manner that we considered various types of special products in Section 5.1.

Factoring Polynomials with a Common Monomial Factor

We shall first consider factoring polynomials each of whose terms have a common monomial factor.

EXAMPLE 1. $6x^2y - 3xy^2 + 3xy = 3xy(2x - y + 1)$

EXAMPLE 2. $2\pi r^2 + 2\pi rh = 2\pi r(r + h)$

Expressions of this type are quite easy to factor by direct application of the distributive law. It is always advisable to multiply the two factors (as in Example 1, Section 5.1) to insure that the factors have been correctly chosen. It is important that every polynomial which is to be factored be first tested for the presence of a common monomial factor before other types of factors are considered.

Factoring the Trinomial $ax^2 + bxy + cy^2$

Let us consider the factors of the polynomial $2x^2 - xy - 6y^2$. Since the terms contain no common monomial factor, we shall try to factor it as the product of two binomials (Type II, Section 5.1). Then we shall have

$$2x^2 - xy - 6y^2 = (ax + by)(cx + dy)$$

where a, b, c, and d have to be determined. It is clear from the method of finding the product of two binomials that ac must equal 2 and bd must equal -6. The possible factors are then

$$(2x - 6y)(x + y) = 2x^2 - 4xy - 6y^2$$
$$(2x + 6y)(x - y) = 2x^2 + 4xy - 6y^2$$
$$(2x + y)(x - 6y) = 2x^2 - 11xy - 6y^2$$
$$(2x - y)(x + 6y) = 2x^2 + 11xy - 6y^2$$
$$(2x - 3y)(x + 2y) = 2x^2 + xy - 6y^2$$
$$(2x + 3y)(x - 2y) = 2x^2 - xy - 6y^2$$
$$(2x + 2y)(x - 3y) = 2x^2 - 4xy - 6y^2$$
$$(2x - 2y)(x + 3y) = 2x^2 + 4xy - 6y^2$$

Each pair of factors produce the first term, $2x^2$, and the last term, $-6y^2$, of the given polynomial. This is because we chose only factors that would produce these terms. Of the eight possible pair of factors, only one, $(2x + 3y)(x - 2y)$, gives the correct middle term, $-xy$. We then have the result

$$2x^2 - xy - 6y^2 = (2x + 3y)(x - 2y)$$

which has been verified by multiplication. After a little practice, the student should be able to choose the correct pair of factors without writing down all of the possibilities. Clearly the middle term of the product is the key to the correct choice of factors.

EXAMPLE 3. Factor the polynomial $3x^2 - 11x + 6$. The polynomial contains no common monomial factor; we shall try to factor it as the product of two binomials. The possible factors are then

$$(3x - 1)(x - 6) = 3x^2 - 19x + 6$$
$$(3x - 6)(x - 1) = 3x^2 - 9x + 6$$
$$(3x - 2)(x - 3) = 3x^2 - 11x + 6$$
$$(3x - 3)(x - 2) = 3x^2 - 9x + 6$$

We first note that although the factors of the last term 6, may both be positive or both negative, the middle term is negative, that is, -11, and therefore we need try only the negative factors of 6. Since only the third pair of factors gives the correct middle term, we have the result

$$3x^2 - 11x + 6 = (3x - 2)(x - 3)$$

EXAMPLE 4. Factor the polynomial $18x^2 + 45x - 50$. The possible combinations which will give $18x^2$ for the first term and -50 for the last are numerous. Only one combination gives the correct middle term, $45x$, and the result is

$$18x^2 + 45x - 50 = (6x - 5)(3x + 10).$$

The correctness of the factoring should be verified by multiplication.

Factoring the Trinomial Square $a^2x^2 + 2abxy + b^2y^2$

Essentially, the polynomial $16x^2 + 24xy + 9y^2$ does not differ from those previously considered, and can be factored in the same manner as Examples 2 to 4. Noting, however, that the first and last terms are perfect squares, we try as our first combination

$$16x^2 + 24xy + 9y^2 = (4x + 3y)(4x + 3y) \text{ or } (4x + 3y)^2$$

Multiplying the two factors verifies that the factors are correct.

We note that a trinomial whose first and last terms are perfect squares need not be itself a perfect square. Thus

$$36x^2 - 97x + 36 = (9x - 4)(4x - 9); \textit{ not } (6x - 6)^2$$

which again emphasizes the fact that every factoring problem should be checked by multiplication. From the rule for the square of a binomial, the student will be asked in Exercise 5.2, Problem 57, how to determine in advance whether a trinomial is a perfect square.

EXAMPLE 5. $4x^2 - 12x + 9 = (2x - 3)(2x - 3) = (2x - 3)^2$

EXAMPLE 6. $9x^2 + 60x + 64 = (3x + 4)(3x + 16)$, and is therefore not a perfect square.

Factoring the Difference of Two Squares

As a direct consequence of the product $(ax + by)(ax - by) = a^2x^2 - b^2y^2$ [Type III(c)] we may write at once

$$16x^2 - 81 = (4x - 9)(4x + 9)$$

The result should be verified by multiplication.

EXAMPLE 7. $9x^2 - 49 = (3x + 7)(3x - 7)$

EXAMPLE 8. $16x^6 - 49y^4 = (4x^3 - 7y^2)(4x^3 + 7y^2)$

Factoring Polynomials with More than Two Factors

Certain polynomials may have more than two factors, and unless all of the factors are given, that is, the polynomial is factored into prime factors, the factoring is not considered complete. The following examples will show several polynomials of this type.

EXAMPLE 9. $3x^2 + 12x + 12 = 3(x^2 + 4x + 4) = 3(x + 2)(x + 2) = 3(x + 2)^2$

EXAMPLE 10. $2x^2 - 6x + 4 = 2(x^2 - 3x + 2)$
$$= 2(x - 2)(x - 1)$$

EXAMPLE 11. $18x^2 - 98y^2 = 2(9x^2 - 49y^2)$
$$= 2(3x - 7y)(3x + 7y)$$

EXAMPLE 12. $a^4 - 13a^2 + 36 = (a^2 - 9)(a^2 - 4)$
$$= (a - 3)(a + 3)(a - 2)(a + 2)$$

Only experience gained from solving many problems in factoring will develop proficiency in determining whether a polynomial has more than two factors; or, in fact, whether a polynomial has any factors at all.

EXERCISE 5.2

Factoring Polynomials

multiple of 3
1 - 39   43 - 54

Factor the following polynomials as the product of a monomial and a polynomial

1. $2x + 4y + 6z$ 2. $3ab + 2a^2b + 5ab^2$ 3. $7a^2 - 49ab$

4. $16a^2b - 24ab^2 + 8ab$ 5. $81a^2x - 9ax + 27ax^2$ 6. $a^2b^2 - 3a^3b^3 + 4a^4b^4$

7. $15x^3 + 10a^2x^2 - 15x$ 8. $6ax^2 + 15ax - 18a$ 9. $P + Prt$

10. $2x^3 - 4x^2y + 10xy^2$ 11. $6x^{2n} - 3x^{2n+1}$ 12. $a^{3n} - a^{2n} + a^n$

13. $2\pi Rh + 2\pi rh$ 14. $\pi r^2 + 2\pi r$ 15. $2\pi R - 2\pi r$

Factor the following trinomials as the product of two binomials

16. $x^2 + 3x + 2$ 17. $x^2 - 4x + 3$ 18. $2n^2 + 7n + 6$

19. $2a^2 + 9a + 9$ 20. $3x^2 - 8x + 4$ 21. $a^2 + a - 12$

22. $a^2 - a - 12$ 23. $2x^2 + 7xy + 3y^2$ 24. $2t^2 - 5ty - 3y^2$

25. $6x^2 + 13x - 5$ 26. $7x^2 - 41x - 6$ 27. $x^2 + 42x - 43$

28. $x^2 - 42x - 43$ 29. $t^2 - t - 30$ 30. $2x^2 + 5xy + 2y^2$

31. $6x^2 - 13x - 5$ 32. $2x^2 - x - 6$ 33. $2x^2 - 5xy + 3y^2$

34. $3x^2 + 4x + 1$ 35. $3x^2 - 7ax + 2a^2$ 36. $56 - 15x + x^2$

37. $a^2 + a - 110$ 38. $a^2 - 14a - 51$ 39. $x^2 - 11x - 152$

40. In Section 5.2, four of the possible eight factors of $2x^2 - xy - 6$ could have been immediately rejected. What are these factors and why can they be rejected?

41. In Example 3, Section 5.1, two of the four possible factors could have been immediately rejected. What are these factors and why can they be rejected?

Factor the following trinomial squares.

42. $a^2 + 4a + 4$ 43. $x^2 + 22x + 121$ 44. $16t^2 + 8t + 1$

45. $x^2 + 10xy + 25y^2$ 46. $16 - 8a + a^2$ 47. $4x^2 - 12xy + 9y^2$

48. $25t^2 - 20t + 4$ 49. $9x^2 + 30x + 25$ 50. $9y^2 - 66y + 121$

51. $9 - 6a + a^2$ 52. $x^2y^2 - 16xy + 64$ 53. $4x^2 + 4x + 1$

54. $x^2 - 26xy + 169y^2$ 55. $9x^2 - 30xy + 25y^2$ 56. $m^2 - 38m + 361$

57. State a rule for determining whether a trinomial is a perfect square. Use the expression $X^2 \pm 2XY + Y^2 = (X \pm Y)^2$ as an aid to stating the rule.

Determine, without factoring, which of the trinomials are perfect squares.

58. $x^2 + 3xy + 9y^2$ 59. $x^2 + 6xy + 9y^2$ 60. $4x^2 + 12xy + 9y^2$

61. $9x^2 + 145x + 16$ 62. $9x^2 + 24x + 16$ 63. $9x^2 - 24x + 16$

64. $9x^2 - 24x - 16$ 65. $4x^2 - 12xy - 9y^2$ 66. $16 - 40x + 25x^2$

67. $16x^2 - 50x + 36.$ 68. $16x^2 - 102x + 36$ 69. $16x^2 + 48x + 36$

Factor the following binomials as the product of the sum and difference of two terms.

70. $x^2 - y^2$ 71. $a^2 - 1$ 72. $4t^2 - 25r^2$ 73. $144a^2 - 49b^2$

74. $36c^2d^2 - 9$ 75. $x^2 - \dfrac{1}{9}$ 76. $2.25a^2 - 1.69b^2$ 77. $0.81x^2 - 1.96y^2$

Factor (if possible) the following polynomials.

78. $2x^2 - 2y^2 - 2z^2$ 79. $x^2 + x + 1$ 80. $x^2 + 2x + 1$

81. $2x^2 - x - 6$ 82. $2x^2 - x + 6$ 83. $x^2 + y^3$

84. $2x^2 + x - 6$ 85. $2x^2 - 6xy + 36y$ 86. $4x^2 - 28xy - 49y^2$

87. $4x^2 + 28xy - 49y^2$ 88. $4x^2 - 28xy + 49y^2$ 89. $4x^2 - 28xy - 48y^2$

90. $6x^2 - 9y^2$ 91. $6x^2 - 12xy + 9y^2$ 92. $6x^2 - 12xy - 6$

93. $49 - 16x^2$ 94. $49 + 16x^2$ 95. $9x^2 - 30xy + 25y^2$

96. $9x^2 - 30xy + 30y^2$ 97. $R^2 + r^2$ 98. $\pi r^2 + \pi R^2$

99. $x^2 + 2x + 2$ 100. $x^2 + x - 2$.

Factor completely the following polynomials.

101. $3x^2 - 12x + 12$ 102. $2x^2 + 4x - 6$.   103. $6a^2 - 54b^2$

104. $3x^2y - xy - 2y$ 105. $6x^2 + 34x + 20$ 106. $12x^2 - 12x - 144$

107. $4n^4 - 9n^2 - 9$ 108. $3n^2 - 3n$ 109. $5ax^4 - 20x^5$

110. $5x^3 - 20x^2 - 300x$ 111. $8x^4 - 26x^2 + 18$ 112. $3x^2 - 27y^2$

113. $bx^4 - bx^8$ 114. $2n^3 - 2n$ 115. $x^4 - 81y^4$

116. $2xy^2 + 28xy + 98x$ 117. $2a + ay - 3ay^2$ 118. $4y^4 - 92y^2 - 200$

5.3 ADDITIONAL FACTORING TECHNIQUES

We shall now consider factoring other polynomials; the process, as before, depends on related special products in Section 5.1.

Factoring the Sum or Difference of Two Cubes

From the products leading to the sum and difference of two cubes, Section 5.1, we may immediately write

$$a^3 + b^3 = (a + b)(a^2 - ab + b^2)$$
$$a^3 - b^3 = (a - b)(a^2 + ab + b^2)$$

The following examples will further illustrate factoring expressions of this type.

EXAMPLE 1. $x^3y^3 - 8 = (xy)^3 - (2)^3$
$$= (xy - 2)(x^2y^2 + 2xy + 4)$$

EXAMPLE 2.
$$8a^3 + 125b^3 = (2a)^3 + (5b)^3$$
$$= (2a + 5b)(4a^2 - 10ab + 25b^2)$$

EXAMPLE 3.
$$27x^3y^6 - 1 = (3xy^2)^3 - (1)^3$$
$$= (3xy^2 - 1)(9x^2y^4 + 3xy^2 + 1)$$

Factoring Polynomials with a Common Binomial Factor

Let us consider the factors of the polynomial $a(x + y) + b(x + y)$. By the closure law we may write

$$x + y = z$$

and, making this substitution in the given polynomial, we have

$$a(x + y) + b(x + y) = az + bz$$
$$= z(a + b)$$

Reversing the substitution, we then have

$$a(x + y) + b(x + y) = (x + y)(a + b)$$

which may be verified by multiplication. In practice we need not actually make the substitution; we have done so here to show that a common binomial factor may be treated in the same manner as a common monomial factor.

EXAMPLE 4.
$$2a + 4b + ma + 2mb = 2(a + 2b) + m(a + 2b)$$
$$= (a + 2b)(2 + m)$$

EXAMPLE 5.
$$ax - x - a + 1 = x(a - 1) - 1(a - 1)$$
$$= (a - 1)(x - 1)$$

Sometimes the order of the terms must be changed, as in Example 6, to make the factorization more apparent.

EXAMPLE 6.
$$12xy + 6 - 9x - 8y = 12xy - 9x - 8y + 6$$
$$= 3x(4y - 3) - 2(4y - 3)$$
$$= (4y - 3)(3x - 2)$$

Additional Methods of Factoring Polynomials

The following examples will illustrate how we may adapt the previous methods of factoring to certain polynomials.

EXAMPLE 7. $(x + y)^2 - 4 = (x + y)^2 - 2^2 = (x + y + 2)(x + y - 2)$.

Note that the quantity $(x + y)$ is treated as if it were a single term.

EXAMPLE 8. $x^2 - a^2 - 2ab - b^2 = x^2 - (a^2 + 2ab + b^2)$
$$= x^2 - (a + b)^2$$
$$= [x + (a + b)][x - (a + b)]$$
$$= (x + a + b)(x - a - b)$$

EXAMPLE 9. $x^2 + 4xy + 4y^2 + 3x + 6y + 2 = (x + 2y)^2 + 3(x + 2y) + 2$
$$= [(x + 2y) + 2][(x + 2y) + 1]$$
$$= (x + 2y + 2)(x + 2y + 1)$$

Note that in Example 9 we consider $(x + 2y)$ as a single term.

EXAMPLE 10. $x^2 - y^2 + x + y = (x - y)(x + y) + 1(x + y)$
$$= (x + y)(x - y + 1)$$

The result is obtained by observing that $(x + y)$ is a common binomial factor.

EXERCISE 5.3

Factoring Other Polynomials

Factor the following sums or differences of two cubes.

1. $a^3 - 8$ 2. $a^3 - 1$ 3. $x^3 + 27$ 4. $8x^3 + y^3$
5. $x^3y^3 - 1$ 6. $x^3y^3 + 1$ 7. $y^3 + 8x^3$ 8. $27x^3 - 64y^3$
9. $8x^3 - 125b^3$ 10. $8x^3 - 27y^3$ 11. $64x^3 + 125y^3$ 12. $x^3 + y^3z^3$
13. $(x + 2)^3 - 1$ *Hint.* Let $x + 2 = z$ 14. $(x + 2)^3 + 1$
15. $(2x + 1)^3 + 8$ 16. $(x - 1)^3 - 1$ 17. $(x + 2)^3 - 27$
18. $(x + 1)^3 - (y + 1)^3$

Factor the following polynomials as the product of two binomials.

19. $a^2 + ab + ac + bc$
21. $ax - bx - ay + by$
23. $6x^2 + 6xy - 2bx - 2by$
25. $6xy + 15y - 8x^2 - 20x$
27. $9ax - 6ay + 6bx - 4by$
29. $5ab - 5bc - a + c$
31. $a^2 - a + 2ab - 2b$
33. $6ab - 6 + a^2b - a$
35. $2am + bn + an + 2bm$

20. $3mp - np - 3mq + nq$
22. $5m + mn + 5n + n^2$
24. $ax - 3ay + 2bx - 6by$
26. $2a^2x + 6a^2y - 6ax^2 - 18axy$
28. $x^2 + bx - ax - ab$
30. $a^3 - a^2b + ab - b^2$
32. $2xy^2 + 5x - 10y^2 - 25.$
34. $ax + by + ay + bx$

Factor each polynomial as in Examples 7, 8, 9, and 10.

36. $(x + y)^2 - 1$ 37. $(a + b)^2 - 4$ 38. $(2x + 3)^2 - 9y^2$

39. $x^2 + 2x + 1 - y^2$ 40. $4t^2 - 12t + 9 - r^2$ 41. $x^2 - a^2 - 2a - 1$

42. $4a^2 + 4a + 1 - b^2$ 43. $x^2 - y^2 - x - y$

44. $x^2 + 2xy + y^2 + 2x + 2y + 1$ 45. $x^2 + y^2 - z^2 + 2xy$

46. $4a^2 - 9b^2 + 2a + 3b$ 47. $a^2 + 2ab + b^2 - m^2 + 2mm - n^2$

48. $a^3 - b^3 - a + b$ 49. $x^3 + y^3 + 2x + 2y$

50. $x^2 - y^2 + 6x + 6y$

Factor each of the following polynomials into their prime factors.

51. $2mx + 2my + 3nx + 3ny$ 52. $8a^3 + 1$

53. $m^2 - n^2 - m - n$ 54. $a^2 + 2ab + b^2 - c^2$

55. $a^2 + 4ab + 4b^2 - m^2 - 2mn - n^2$ 56. $a^3b^3 - 8$

57. $1 - x^2 - 2xy - y^2$ 58. $a^2 - x^2 + 2xy - y^2$ 59. $ac + cd - ab - bd$

60. $x^2 - m^2 + x - m$ 61. $(x + y)^3 - 8$ 62. $(x - y)^3 + 27$

63. $a^3 - a^2 + a - 1$ 64. $m^6 + 27$ 65. $3(a + 1)^2 - 8a - 8$

66. $x^4 - y^4$ 67. $x^6 - 64$ 68. $x^4 - 8x$

5.4 Quadratic Equations

If a ball is thrown upward with a velocity of 100 feet per second from the top of a building 30 feet above the ground, the approximate time t for the ball to reach the ground is a solution of the equation

$$16t^2 - 100t - 30 = 0 \tag{1}$$

Equation 1 is an example of a quadratic equation which we shall now define.

DEFINITION 5.1. A quadratic equation in a single variable is a polynomial equation of second degree. That is, the highest degree term in the variable is of second degree.

Examples of quadratic equations are

(a) $x^2 - 2x - 5 = 0$

(b) $3x^2 - 2x = 8$

(c) $3x^2 = 6$

(d) $2x^2 - 7x = 0$

(e) $3x^2 = 0$

Notice that in each of the equations above x appears to the second power, and no higher.

Standard Form of a Quadratic Equation

It is convenient to write the general quadratic equation in one variable with the right-hand member equal to zero in the form, called *standard form*,

$$ax^2 + bx + c = 0 \qquad a \neq 0 \tag{2}$$

The constants a, b, and c are real numbers and, in this discussion, will be rational numbers. The condition $a \neq 0$ insures that the equation is quadratic and not linear, while b and c may be positive, negative, or zero, as in the examples below. A quadratic equation which is not in standard form may be rewritten in this form. It is customary to have a, b, and c, integers, with $a > 0$, as in the following examples.

	Equation	*Standard Form*
(f)	$2x^2 - 3x = 5$	$2x^2 - 3x - 5 = 0$
(g)	$6x - 7 = 3x^2$	$3x^2 - 6x + 7 = 0$
(h)	$\frac{2}{3}x^2 - 6x + 5 = 0$	$2x^2 - 18x + 15 = 0$
(i)	$-2x^2 + 7x = 8$	$2x^2 - 7x + 8 = 0$
(j)	$4x^2 = 5x$	$4x^2 - 5x = 0$
(k)	$\dfrac{-x^2}{3} = 4$	$x^2 + 12 = 0$

Solution of the Quadratic Equation by Factoring

We shall now show that the solutions of a quadratic equation may be obtained by solving two related linear equations. Consider the equation

$$x^2 - 5x + 6 = 0 \tag{3}$$

Factoring the left-hand member, we have

$$(x - 3)(x - 2) = 0 \tag{4}$$

From Definition 1.8, Section 1.4, we may reasonably state the following principle:

The product of two factors is zero if and only if one or both of the factors equals zero. That is,

$$(a)(b) = 0 \text{ if and only if } a = 0 \text{ or } b = 0$$

The word "or" is used in the inclusive sense, that is, both a and b may equal zero. This principle then implies that

$$x - 3 = 0 \qquad \text{or} \qquad x - 2 = 0 \tag{5}$$

Equations 5 are both linear equations; their solutions are

$$x = 3 \qquad \text{or} \qquad x = 2 \tag{6}$$

If $x = 3$ is substituted in Equation 3, we have

$$9 - 15 + 6 = 0$$
$$0 = 0$$

If $x = 2$ is substituted in Equation 3, we have

$$4 - 10 + 6 = 0$$
$$0 = 0$$

Since both $x = 2$ and $x = 3$ satisfy the given equation, they are both solutions of the given equation, that is, $x = 2$ *and* $x = 3$ are roots of the equation.

Obviously the method of factoring applies only when the right-hand member of the equation is a factorable expression; that is, an equation such as

$$x^2 + 2x - 5 = 0$$

is not ordinarily solved by factoring, although it may be factored as

$$(x + 1 - \sqrt{6})(x + 1 + \sqrt{6}) = 0$$

The roots are then $-1 + \sqrt{6}$ and $-1 - \sqrt{6}$. The solution of quadratic equations which are not factorable will be treated in the next section.

We may now summarize the preceding discussion by the following procedure for solving factorable quadratic equations.

1. Write the equation in standard form.
2. Factor the left-hand member of the equation.
3. Set each factor equal to zero and solve the resulting linear equations.
4. Check the solution by substituting the roots thus found in the original equation.

EXAMPLE 1. Solve the equation $2x^2 - 7x + 6 = 0$.

(1) $2x^2 - 7x + 6 = 0$

(2) $(2x - 3)(x - 2) = 0$

(3) $2x - 3 = 0$, or $x - 2 = 0$

$$x = \frac{3}{2}, x = 2$$

(4) Substituting $x = \frac{3}{2}$ in the given equation,

$$2\left(\frac{3}{2}\right)^2 - 7\left(\frac{3}{2}\right) + 6 = 0$$

$$\frac{9}{2} - \frac{21}{2} + \frac{12}{2} = 0$$

$$0 = 0$$

Substituting $x = 2$ in the given equation,

$$2(2)^2 - 7(2) + 6 = 0$$
$$8 - 14 + 6 = 0$$
$$0 = 0$$

EXAMPLE 2. Solve the equation $4x^2 = 9x$.

$\quad$ (1) $4x^2 - 9x = 0$

$\quad$ (2) $x(4x - 9) = 0$

$\quad$ (3) $x = 0$, or $4x - 9 = 0$

$$x = 0, \ x = \frac{9}{4}$$

$\quad$ (4) Substituting $x = 0$ in the given equation,

$$4(0)^2 = 9(0)$$
$$0 = 0$$

$\quad$ Substituting $x = \dfrac{9}{4}$ in the given equation,

$$4\left(\frac{9}{4}\right)^2 = 9\left(\frac{9}{4}\right)$$
$$\frac{81}{4} = \frac{81}{4}$$

EXAMPLE 3. Solve the equation $4x^2 = 100$.

$\quad$ (1) $4x^2 - 100 = 0$

$\quad$ (2) $4(x - 5)(x + 5) = 0$

$\quad$ (3) $x - 5 = 0$, or $x + 5 = 0$

$$x = 5, \ x = -5.$$

$\quad$ (4) Substituting $x = 5$ in the given equation,

$$4(5)^2 = 100$$
$$100 = 100$$

$\quad$ Substituting $x = -5$ in the given equation,

$$4(-5)^2 = 100$$
$$100 = 100$$

EXAMPLE 4. Solve the equation $4x^2 = 4x - 1$.

$\quad$ (1) $4x^2 - 4x + 1 = 0$

$\quad$ (2) $(2x - 1)(2x - 1) = 0$

$\quad$ (3) $2x - 1 = 0, \ 2x - 1 = 0$

$$x = \frac{1}{2}, \ x = \frac{1}{2} \ \left(\text{Both roots are equal to } \frac{1}{2}\right)$$

$\quad$ (4) The student should verify that $\dfrac{1}{2}$ is a root of the equation.

In Example 2, the student may be tempted to divide both sides of the equation by x, the resulting equation then being $4x = 9$. The root of this equation is

$x = \dfrac{9}{4}$, as before, but the other root, $x = 0$, is lost. Note that Axiom 3.5 of Section 3.1 does not include multiplication or division by expressions which contain the variable. It should also be noted that a quadratic equation is considered to have two roots, even though they may be equal.

EXERCISE 5.4

Quadratic Equations

Which of the following equations are quadratic equations? Letters other than x and t are to be considered as constants.

1. $x^2 - 2x - 5 = 0$ 2. $9x - 17 = 0$ 3. $a^2x + bx = c$

4. $a^2x^2 + b^2x - c = 0$ 5. $3x^2 - 7 = 0$ 6. $ax^2 + b + c = 0$

7. $3t^2 - 3t - 6 = 0$ 8. $t^2 = 5t + 3$ 9. $t^2 + 17t = 16t$

10. $t^2 = 18$ 11. $t^3 - 3t^2 = 5$ 12. $a^3x^2 + b^3x = 5$

13. $ax^3 - b^2x^2 = c$ 14. $27t^2 - t = 1$ 15. $\dfrac{x^2}{4} = 5$

Rewrite the following equations in standard form.

16. $3x^2 - 3x = 3$ 17. $2x^2 - 4 = 3x$ 18. $4x - x^2 = 17$

19. $3x = x^2 - 5$ 20. $4x^2 = 5$ 21. $x^2 = 15 - 2x$

22. $-2x^2 - 13x = 5$ 23. $6x^2 = 13 - 2x$ 24. $17x = 12 - x^2$

25. $x^2 - \dfrac{1}{5} = 1$ 26. $\dfrac{1}{4}x^2 - \dfrac{1}{2}x = 2$ 27. $\dfrac{2}{3}x^2 - 3x + 1 = 0$

28. $0.2x^2 - 0.3x = 1.2$ 29. $0.04x^2 - 0.02x = 1$ 30. $2x^2 = 3x + \dfrac{1}{3}$

State the value of a, b, and c, in the following equations. If the equation is not in standard form, rewrite it in this form.

31. $2x^2 - 7x - 6 = 0$ 32. $2x^2 = 5x - 3$ 33. $3x = 7 - 4x^2$

34. $5x^2 - 5x - 5 = 0$ 35. $2x - 4 = 3x^2$ 36. $2x^2 = 81$

37. $2x^2 = -81$ 38. $3x^2 = 4x$ 39. $3x^2 - 4x = 0$

40. $3x^2 = 0$ 41. $x^2 = 6x$ 42. $4x - 3 = x^2$

43. $x^2 = 7x - 7$ 44. $4x - 3 = -x^2$ 45. $4x - 3x^2 = 2$

Solve each of the following equations by factoring. d $check$

46. $x^2 = 16$ 47. $x^2 - 49 = 0$ 48. $x^2 = 3x$

49. $x^2 - 7x = 0$ 50. $x^2 - 8x + 15 = 0$ 51. $x^2 + 2x - 15 = 0$

52. $x^2 - 4x + 4 = 0$ 53. $x^2 - 8x + 16 = 0$ 54. $x^2 = 6x - 9$

55. $x^2 = 13x + 30$ 56. $2x^2 - 7x = 15$ 57. $2x^2 + x = 15$

58. $8x^2 = -6x + 9$ 59. $6x^2 = 13x + 5$ 60. $2x^2 - 5x + 3 = 0$

61. What is the value of c in the standard form of the quadratic equation if one root equals zero?

Solve each of the following *cubic* equations by setting each of the three factors equal to zero.

62. $x^3 - 3x^2 + 2x = 0$ 63. $x^3 = 16x$ 64. $x^3 - 6x^2 = -9x$

65. $x^3 - 3x^2 - 4x + 12 = 0$, given that one factor is $x - 2$. (see hint below)

66. $x^3 - 6x^2 + 11x - 6 = 0$, given that one factor is $x - 1$. (see hint below)

> *Hint.* Divide the left hand member of the equation by the given factor, and express the quotient as the product of two factors.

5.5 THE QUADRATIC FORMULA AND ITS APPLICATIONS

The solution of quadratic equations by the method of factoring has two limitations. The first limitation is that it does not apply to equations such as $x^2 + 2x - 5 = 0$, where the left-hand member is not easily factored. A second limitation is that it applies to specific equations only, and therefore cannot furnish any information concerning the roots of the equation until they have been determined. For these reasons we seek to develop a method, or formula, which will apply to the general equation $ax^2 + bx + c = 0$, whether or not the left-hand member is readily factorable. The formula, which will express the roots in terms of a, b, and, c, will then provide information concerning these roots before their numerical values have been determined. This application of the formula will be discussed later in this section.

The Quadratic Formula

Our method of developing a formula for the solution of the quadratic equation will be to find the factors of the general quadratic equation

$$ax^2 + bx + c = 0 \tag{1}$$

and then apply the principle stated in Section 5.4 to determine the roots. In factoring the left-hand member of Equation 1 we shall slightly complicate the form of the equation, but the result will provide us with the desired formula.

From Equation 1, dividing by the constant a,

$$x^2 + \frac{b}{a}x + \frac{c}{a} = 0 \tag{2}$$

Adding and subtracting the quantity $\dfrac{b^2}{4a^2}$

$$x^2 + \frac{b}{a}x + \frac{b^2}{4a^2} - \frac{b^2}{4a^2} + \frac{c}{a} = 0 \tag{3}$$

The first three terms of Equation 3 now form a perfect trinomial square, and may be written as $\left(x + \dfrac{b}{2a}\right)^2$. The last two terms have a common denominator of $4a^2$, and may be written as $-\dfrac{b^2 - 4ac}{4a^2}$. Then Equation 3 may be written as

$$\left(x + \frac{b}{2a}\right)^2 - \frac{b^2 - 4ac}{4a^2} = 0 \tag{4}$$

Equation 4 may be written as the difference of two squares,

$$\left(x + \frac{b}{2a}\right)^2 - \left(\frac{\sqrt{b^2 - 4ac}}{2a}\right)^2 = 0 \tag{5}$$

In factored form, Equation 5 is

$$\left(x + \frac{b}{2a} + \frac{\sqrt{b^2 - 4ac}}{2a}\right)\left(x + \frac{b}{2a} - \frac{\sqrt{b^2 - 4ac}}{2a}\right) = 0 \tag{6}$$

If we now set each factor equal to zero, we have the related linear equations

$$x + \frac{b}{2a} + \frac{\sqrt{b^2 - 4ac}}{2a} = 0$$

$$x + \frac{b}{2a} - \frac{\sqrt{b^2 - 4ac}}{2a} = 0 \tag{7}$$

We may combine the solutions of Equations 7 into one equation,

$$x = \frac{-b \pm \sqrt{b^2 - 4ac}}{2a} \tag{8}$$

Equation 8 is known as the *quadratic formula*.

Using the Quadratic Formula

To solve a quadratic equation by means of the quadratic formula:

1. Write the equation in standard form.
2. Write the specific values of a, b, and c.
3. Substitute these values in the formula.
4. Simplify the result.

5. Find the roots by first using the plus sign and then the minus sign or vice versa.
6. Check each root in the original equation.

EXAMPLE 1. Solve the equation $2x^2 - 5x + 3 = 0$.

(1) $2x^2 - 5x + 3 = 0$

(2) $a = 2, b = -5, c = 3$

(3) $x = \dfrac{-(-5) \pm \sqrt{(-5)^2 - 4(2)(3)}}{2(2)}$

(4) $x = \dfrac{5 \pm \sqrt{1}}{4}$

(5) $x = \dfrac{5 + 1}{4} = \dfrac{3}{2}$, and $x = \dfrac{5 - 1}{4} = 1$

(6) Substituting $x = \dfrac{3}{2}$ in the given equation,

$$2\left(\dfrac{3}{2}\right)^2 - 5\left(\dfrac{3}{2}\right) + 3 = 0$$
$$0 = 0$$

Substituting $x = 1$ in the given equation,
$$2(1)^2 - 5(1) + 3 = 0$$
$$0 = 0$$

It may be noted that this particular equation could have been solved by the method of factoring.

EXAMPLE 2. Solve the equation $x^2 = 4x - 1$.

(1) $x^2 - 4x + 1 = 0$

(2) $a = 1, b = -4. c = 1$

(3) $x = \dfrac{-(-4) \pm \sqrt{(-4)^2 - 4(1)(1)}}{2(1)}$

(4) $x = \dfrac{4 \pm \sqrt{12}}{2} = 2 \pm \sqrt{3}$

(5) $x = 2 + \sqrt{3}$ and $x = 2 - \sqrt{3}$

(6) If these values of x are substituted in the original equation it will be found that they satisfy the given equation, so that $x = 2 + \sqrt{3}$ and $x = 2 - \sqrt{3}$ are roots of the equation.

If $\sqrt{3}$ is taken to be 1.732, the roots are approximately $(2 + 1.732) = 3.732$ and $(2 - 1.732) = 0.268$. The equation may be checked with these values of the roots, but the student should bear in mind that since these values are approximations, the check may not be exact.

EXAMPLE 3. Solve the equation $x^2 - x + 1 = 0$.

(1) $x^2 - x + 1 = 0$

(2) $a = 1, b = -1, c = 1$

(3) $x = \dfrac{-(-1) \pm \sqrt{(-1)^2 - (4)(1)(1)}}{2(1)}$

(4) $x = \dfrac{1 \pm \sqrt{-3}}{2}$

(5) $x = \dfrac{1 + \sqrt{-3}}{2}$ and $x = \dfrac{1 - \sqrt{-3}}{2}$

It is seen that the two roots are conjugate complex numbers, and may be written as $\dfrac{1}{2} + \dfrac{\sqrt{3}}{2} i$ and $\dfrac{1}{2} - \dfrac{\sqrt{3}}{2} i$. Substitution of each of these roots in the original Equation 1 will show that they satisfy the equation.

The Discriminant $b^2 - 4ac$

We have suggested earlier in this section that the quadratic formula provides information concerning the roots of the quadratic formula without actually solving the equation. One type of information concerning the nature of the roots is provided by the quantity $b^2 - 4ac$, known as the *discriminant* of the quadratic equation. Let us restate the quadratic formula

$$x = \frac{-b + \sqrt{b^2 - 4ac}}{2a}$$

and consider the role of the discriminant, $b^2 - 4ac$, in this formula,

1. Suppose $b^2 - 4ac > 0$. Since the radicand is then a positive number, the roots are real numbers. Moreover, two values of x are found by using both the positive and negative sign in the formula. Finally, if $b^2 - 4ac$ is a perfect square, the roots are also rational numbers. Example 4, which follows, illustrates this case.

2. Suppose $b^2 - 4ac = 0$. The addition or subtraction of zero in the formula does not affect the value of x, that is $\dfrac{-b}{2a}$. Therefore, in the case where $b^2 - 4ac = 0$, the roots of the quadratic equation are real and equal. Example 5 illustrates this case.

3. Suppose $b^2 - 4ac < 0$. Since the radicand is then a negative number, the roots are nonreal conjugate complex numbers (see Example 3). Example 6 illustrates this case.

The above discussion may be summarized as follows.

In the quadratic equation $ax^2 + bx + c = 0$, where a, b, and c are rational numbers:

1. If $b^2 - 4ac > 0$, the roots of the equation are real and unequal. If $b^2 - 4ac$ is a perfect square, they are also rational.
2. If $b^2 - 4ac = 0$, the roots of the equation are real, rational and equal.
3. If $b^2 - 4ac < 0$, the roots are nonreal conjugate complex numbers.

EXAMPLE 4.   Determine the character of the roots of the equation
$x^2 - 5x + 6 = 0$.

SOLUTION: The discriminant of the equation is $(-5)^2 - (4)(1)(6) = 1$. Hence the roots are real, unequal, and rational.

EXAMPLE 5.   Determine the character of the roots of the equation
$4x^2 - 12x + 9 = 0$.

SOLUTION: The discriminant of the equation is $144 - 144 = 0$. Hence the roots are real, equal, and rational.

EXAMPLE 6.   Determine the character of the roots of the equation
$2x^2 - x + 5 = 0$.

SOLUTION: The discriminant of the equation is $1 - 40 = -39$. Hence the roots are nonreal conjugate complex numbers.

The Sum and Product of the Roots

The quadratic formula, in addition to providing information concerning the character of the roots of the quadratic equation, also leads to a simple method of checking the solution without actually substituting the roots in the given equation.

If the quadratic formula is written in the form

$$x_1 = \frac{-b + \sqrt{b^2 - 4ac}}{2a}$$

$$x_2 = \frac{-b - \sqrt{b^2 - 4ac}}{2a}$$

where x_1 and x_2 are the roots of the equation, we may readily derive two important relations between the roots and coefficients of the equation. These relations, found by first adding and then multiplying the two roots, are

$$x_1 + x_2 = -\frac{b}{a}$$

$$x_1 \cdot x_2 = \frac{c}{a}$$

(9)

These relations may be more easily recalled if we write the equation in the form

$$x^2 + \frac{b}{a}x + \frac{c}{a} = 0$$

(10)

Thus, when the coefficient of x^2 in the quadratic equation equals 1, *the sum of the roots equals the negative of the coefficient of x, and the product of the roots equals the constant term.*

EXAMPLE 7.   Find the sum and product of the roots of the equation
$3x^2 - 2x + 1 = 0$.

SOLUTION: We first write the equation in the form

$$x^2 - \frac{2}{3}x + \frac{1}{3} = 0$$

We have at once

$$x_1 + x_2 = -\left(-\frac{2}{3}\right) = \frac{2}{3}$$

$$x_1 \cdot x_2 = \frac{1}{3}$$

Checking the Roots of a Quadratic Equation

EXAMPLE 8.   Solve and check the roots of the equation $2x^2 - 3x + 1 = 0$.

SOLUTION: $(2x - 1)(x - 1) = 0$

$$x = \frac{1}{2}$$

$$x = 1$$

Check. We write the equation as

$$x^2 - \frac{3}{2}x + \frac{1}{2} = 0$$

$\frac{1}{2} + 1 = \frac{3}{2}$, the negative of the coefficient of x

$\frac{1}{2}(1) = \frac{1}{2}$, the constant term

Forming a Quadratic Equation with Given Roots

While a quadratic equation may be determined from its given roots by reversing the process of the solution by factoring, the relations in Equations 9 are very convenient for this purpose. We shall show examples of each method.

EXAMPLE 9. Determine the quadratic equation whose roots are $\frac{1}{2}$ and $-\left(\frac{2}{3}\right)$.

SOLUTION: Method 1. $x = \frac{1}{2}$ $\qquad x = -\frac{2}{3}$

$$x - \frac{1}{2} = 0 \qquad x + \frac{2}{3} = 0$$

$$\left(x - \frac{1}{2}\right)\left(x + \frac{2}{3}\right) = 0$$

$$(2x - 1)(3x + 2) = 0$$

$$6x^2 + x - 2 = 0$$

Method 2. From the sum and product relations, we have

$$\frac{b}{a} = -\left(\frac{1}{2} - \frac{2}{3}\right) = \frac{1}{6}$$

$$\frac{c}{a} = \left(\frac{1}{2}\right)\left(-\frac{2}{3}\right) = -\frac{1}{3}$$

Then

$$x^2 + \frac{1}{6}x - \frac{1}{3} = 0, \text{ or}$$

$$6x^2 + x - 2 = 0$$

which is the required equation.

EXAMPLE 10. Determine the quadratic equation whose roots are $x = 2 + \sqrt{3}$ and $x = 2 - \sqrt{3}$.

SOLUTION: The second method is more convenient in this example:

$$-\frac{b}{a} = +(2 + \sqrt{3} + 2 - \sqrt{3}) = +4$$

$$\frac{c}{a} = (2 + \sqrt{3})(2 - \sqrt{3}) = 1$$

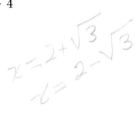

Then

$$x^2 - 4x + 1 = 0$$

which is the required equation.

EXERCISE 5.5

The Quadratic Formula

Solve the following quadratic equations by means of the formula. Check each solution by substituting the root in the given equation.

1. $2x^2 - 5x + 3 = 0$ 2. $6x^2 + 19x + 10 = 0$ 3. $2x^2 = 10 - x$
4. $4x^2 - 4x = 3$ 5. $5x^2 - 8 = 18x$ 6. $10x^2 - 9x + 2 = 0$
7. $2x^2 - 9x + 4 = 0$ 8. $4x^2 + 5x = 6$ 9. $x^2 - x - 6 = 0$
10. $4x^2 - 8x + 3 = 0$ 11. $x^2 - 7x = 0$ 12. $2x^2 - 3x = 0$

Solve the following quadratic equations by means of the formula. Express each root in radical form and then evaluate to three decimal places, using Table I in the Appendix. Check each solution by using the sum and product formulas in both radical and decimal values of the roots.

13. $2x^2 + 2x - 3 = 0$ 14. $x^2 + x - 3 = 0$ 15. $2x^2 + x - 4 = 0$
16. $2x^2 = 8x - 3$ 17. $x^2 + 4x = -2$ 18. $3x^2 + 2 = 8x$
19. $5x^2 = 2 - 5x$ 20. $4x^2 - 6x + 1 = 0$ 21. $x^2 = 3 - x$
22. $4x^2 + 4x = 1$ 23. $x^2 - 7x + 4 = 0$ 24. $2x^2 + 5x + 1 = 0$

Determine the character of the roots of the following equations

25. $2x^2 - 3x - 5 = 0$ 26. $3x^2 + 7x - 2 = 0$ 27. $x^2 - 8x + 16 = 0$
28. $4x^2 - 4x + 4 = 0$ 29. $x^2 - 3x + 7 = 0$ 30. $2x^2 - 4x + 4 = 0$
31. $2x^2 - 5x - 3 = 0$ 32. $2x^2 - 9x + 9 = 0$ 33. $x^2 + x + 1 = 0$
34. $x^2 - x + 1 = 0$ 35. $3x^2 - 7x + 11 = 0$ 36. $x^2 - 7 = 0$

37. From the quadratic formula, determine the condition for the roots of the quadratic equation $ax^2 + bx + c = 0$ to be equal but opposite in sign.

38. Determine the value of k so that the equation $9x^2 + 30x + k = 0$ has equal roots.

39. Determine the value of k so that the equation $x^2 - kx + 9 = 0$ has equal roots.

Form the quadratic equations which have the given roots.

40. $3, -2$ 41. $\dfrac{1}{2}, \dfrac{2}{3}$ 42. $\dfrac{2}{3}, -\dfrac{3}{5}$

43. $2, -5$ 44. $-\dfrac{2}{3}, -\dfrac{2}{3}$ 45. $35, \dfrac{4}{5}$

46. $3 + \sqrt{3}, 3 - \sqrt{3}$ 47. $2 + \sqrt{5}, 2 - \sqrt{5}$ 48. $-2 + \sqrt{6}, -2 - \sqrt{6}$

49. $1.7, -0.7$ 50. $2.3, -0.3$

5.6 EQUATIONS CONTAINING RADICALS

If both members of the equation

$$\sqrt{x + 2} = x - 4 \tag{1}$$

are raised to the second power, we have

$$x + 2 = x^2 - 8x + 16 \tag{2}$$

In standard form, Equation 2 is

$$x^2 - 9x + 14 = 0 \tag{3}$$

The solutions of Equation 3, obtained either by factoring or by the quadratic formula, are

$$\begin{aligned} x &= 7 \\ x &= 2 \end{aligned} \tag{4}$$

If we substitute these roots in Equation 1, that is, the original equation, we find that for $x = 7$

$$\sqrt{7 + 2} = 7 - 4$$
$$3 = 3$$

so that $x = 7$ is a root of Equation 1. For $x = 2$, however, we find that

$$\sqrt{2 + 2} \neq 2 - 4$$
$$2 \neq -2$$

so that $x = 2$ is not a solution of the original equation. A root obtained in this manner which does not satisfy the original equation is called an *extraneous* root. Obviously Equation 1 and Equation 4 are not equivalent.

The foregoing discussion illustrates a principle that we state without proof.

If both members of an equation are raised to the same power, the solution set of the original equation is a subset of the solution set of the resulting equation.

In effect this principle states that roots of the resulting equation will include all of the roots of the original equation and may include roots which do not satisfy the original equation, that is, extraneous roots.

The following example illustrates how extraneous roots are introduced in the process of squaring both members of an equation. Let the original equation be

$$x = 1 \tag{1}$$

Squaring both members of Equation 1, we obtain

$$x^2 = 1 \tag{2}$$

Obviously $x = -1$ satisfies Equation 2, but certainly does not satisfy Equation 1. This is because Equation 2 could also have been obtained by squaring both members of the equation

$$x = -1 \tag{3}$$

Therefore Equation 2 contains the roots of both Equation 1 and Equation 3, but the solutions of Equations 1 and 3 are quite different.

Several additional examples further illustrate the solution of equations containing radicals.

EXAMPLE 1.   Solve the equation $\sqrt{x^2 - 3x} = 2x - 6$.

SOLUTION: Squaring both members, we obtain

$$x^2 - 3x = 4x^2 - 24x + 36$$

Writing in standard form

$$3x^2 - 21x + 36 = 0$$

Dividing both members by 3, and factoring,

$$(x - 3)(x - 4) = 0$$

The roots are

$$x = 3, \qquad x = 4$$

Check: Substituting $x = 3$ in the original equation,

$$\sqrt{9 - 9} = 6 - 6$$
$$0 = 0$$

Substituting $x = 4$ in the original equation,

$$\sqrt{4} = 8 - 6$$
$$2 = 2.$$

Observe that both $x = 3$ and $x = 4$ satisfy the original equation, and there are no extraneous roots.

EXAMPLE 2. Solve the equation $\sqrt{11 - x} - \sqrt{x + 6} = 3$.

SOLUTION: The process of eliminating the radical is simpler if the equation is rewritten with one radical in each member before squaring.

$$\sqrt{11 - x} = 3 + \sqrt{x + 6}$$

Squaring both members

$$11 - x = 9 + 6\sqrt{x + 6} + x + 6$$

or

$$6\sqrt{x + 6} = -4 - 2x$$

Dividing both members by 2 and squaring

$$9(x + 6) = x^2 + 4x + 4$$

Writing in standard form,

$$x^2 - 5x - 50 = 0.$$

In factored form

$$(x - 10)(x + 5) = 0$$

The roots $x = 10$ and $x = -5$.

Check: Substituting $x = -5$ in the original equation

$$\sqrt{16} - \sqrt{1} = 3$$
$$3 = 3$$

Substituting $x = 10$ in the original equation

$$\sqrt{1} - \sqrt{16} \neq 3$$

or

$$1 - 4 = -3, \text{ not } 3$$

Observe that $x = -5$ satisfies the original equation, but $x = 10$ does not and is therefore an extraneous root.

EXAMPLE 3. Solve the equation

$$\sqrt{x} = 7 + \sqrt{x - 7}$$

SOLUTION: Squaring both members of the equation,

$$x = 49 + 14\sqrt{x - 7} + x - 7$$

Simplifying,

$$-3 = \sqrt{x - 7}$$

Squaring both members

$$9 = x - 7$$
$$x = 16$$

Checking the root by substitution in the given equation

$$\sqrt{16} \neq 7 + \sqrt{16 - 7}$$
$$4 \neq 7 + 3$$

Clearly $x = 16$ does not satisfy the given equation, and therefore the equation has no roots. The fact that the given equation has no roots could have been anticipated from the third equation above, $-3 = \sqrt{x - 7}$, since the positive root is indicated in the original equation.

EXERCISE 5.6

Equations Containing Radicals

In problems 1 to 12, test each number to the right of each equation as a possible solution of the equation.

1. $\sqrt{x^2 - 3x + 5} - \sqrt{x + 2} = 0 \ (1, 3)$ 2. $\sqrt{8x - 7} - x = 0 \ (7, 1)$

3. $\sqrt{4x^2 + 9} = 2x + 1 \ (2, -2)$ 4. $\sqrt{5x - 1} = 2\sqrt{x + 1} \ (5, 1)$

5. $\sqrt{6x - 8} = x \ (2, 4)$

6. $\sqrt{7 - 2x} - \sqrt{3 - x} = \sqrt{4 - x} \ (3, 4)$

7. $\sqrt{2x - 1} + 2 = \sqrt{2x + 11} \ \left(\dfrac{5}{2}, 2\right)$

8. $\sqrt{x + 4} + \sqrt{x + 16} = 2 \ (0, -4)$

9. $\sqrt{x - 4} + 9 = \sqrt{x + 5} \ (13, -5)$

10. $\sqrt{9x + 40} = 3\sqrt{x + 2} \ (9, 4)$

11. $\sqrt{x^2 + x + 5} - 2 = \sqrt{x^2 + x - 11} \ (-5, 4)$

12. $\sqrt{x + 1} + \sqrt{x - 2} = \sqrt{2x + 3} \ (-1, -2)$

Solve the following equations.

13. $\sqrt{8x - 7} = x + 1$ 14. $\sqrt{x + 3} = \sqrt{x^2 + 3x}$

15. $\sqrt{x + 2} = \sqrt{2x - 3}$ 16. $\sqrt{4x + 3} = \sqrt{6x + 2}$

17. $\sqrt{2x + 1} - \sqrt{x} = 1$ 18. $\sqrt{2x + 5} - \sqrt{x - 6} = 3$

19. $\sqrt{x} = x - 2$ 20. $\sqrt{4x^2 + 9} = 2x + 1$

21. $\sqrt{9x^2 - 5} = 3x - 5$ 22. $\sqrt{x + 4} = 2$

23. $2\sqrt{x - 1} = 3$ 24. $\sqrt{3x + 1} = x - 3$

25. $\sqrt{2x + 5} = \sqrt{x - 1} + 2$ 26. $\sqrt{2x + 21} = 2 - \sqrt{x + 7}$

27. $x + \sqrt{x - 5} = 11$ 28. $x + \sqrt{x^2 + 1} = 1$

29. $\sqrt{x} = 5 - \sqrt{x + 5}$ 30. $\sqrt{11 - x} - \sqrt{x + 6} = 3$

31. $\sqrt{x + 6} = \sqrt{x + 1} + 1$ 32. $\sqrt{x + 4} + \sqrt{9 - x} = 5$

5.7 APPLICATIONS OF QUADRATIC EQUATIONS

Many problems can be symbolically expressed as quadratic equations. The general method of solving such problems is quite similar to the method of solving problems expressed as linear equations, discussed in Section 3.5. We shall solve a variety of problems leading to quadratic equations in the examples which follow.

EXAMPLE 1. A square parcel of land has twice the area of a rectangular parcel whose frontage is 9 feet less and whose depth is 40 feet less. What are the dimensions of the square parcel of land?

SOLUTION: Let $x =$ the side of the square parcel of land. Then $x - 9$ is the frontage of the rectangular parcel, and $x - 40$ is the depth of the rectangular parcel. Since the area of the square parcel is x^2, and the area of the rectangular parcel is $(x - 9)(x - 40)$, the equation relating the two areas is then

$$x^2 = 2(x - 9)(x - 40) \tag{1}$$

$$x^2 = 2x^2 - 98x - 720 \tag{2}$$

or

$$x^2 - 98x - 720 = 0 \tag{3}$$

In factored form, we have

$$(x - 90)(x - 8) = 0 \tag{4}$$

So that

$$x = 90 \text{ and } x = 8.$$

It is clear from the statement of the problem that we must reject $x = 8$ as the side of the square parcel, since the dimensions of the rectangular parcel are 9 feet and 40 feet less. Therefore the dimensions of the square parcel are 90 feet by 90 feet, and those of the rectangular parcel are 81 feet by 50 feet. The reader may easily verify that the areas will then be in the ratio of two to one, as required in the problem.

EXAMPLE 2. The corners of a 2-inch square are cut off so as to form a regular octagon. What is the length of the piece to be cut off?

SOLUTION: In Figure 5.1 we let x equal the length to be cut off. From the figure we see that the side of the octagon is then equal to $2 - 2x$. Since the small triangles formed at each corner are right triangles, we have, from the Pythagorean theorem,

$$x^2 + x^2 = (2 - 2x)^2 \tag{1}$$

Equation 1 reduces to

$$x^2 - 4x + 2 = 0 \tag{2}$$

Using the quadratic formula, the roots of Equation 2 are

$$x = 2 - \sqrt{2}, \quad \text{and} \quad x = 2 + \sqrt{2}$$

We must reject the second root, $2 + \sqrt{2}$, since the part cut off cannot be greater than the entire side. Therefore the size of the piece cut off is $2 - \sqrt{2}$, or approximately 0.586 inches.

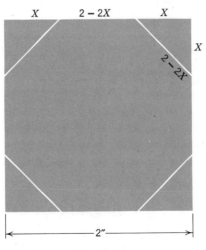

Figure 5.1

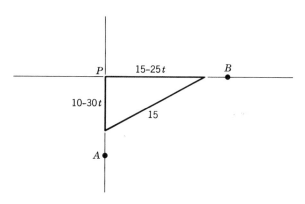

Figure 5.2

Example 2 may also be solved by the use of a linear equation, if the hypotenuse of the corner cut off is expressed as $x \sqrt{2}$ instead of $2 - 2x$. In problem 23 of Exercise 5.7 the student will be asked to solve the problem in this manner.

EXAMPLE 3. Two straight railroad tracks cross at right angles to each other at point P (Figure 5.2). A freight train starts at point A on the first track, 10 miles from P, traveling toward P at 30 miles per hour. At the same time a second freight train starts from point B on the second track, 15 miles from P, traveling toward P at 25 miles per hour. If both trains started at 12 noon, at what time will they be 15 miles apart?

SOLUTION: From the formula

$$\text{distance} = \text{rate} \times \text{time},$$

at the end of t hours the first train will have traveled $30t$ miles, and the second train will have traveled $25t$ miles. The distance apart, 15 miles, is the hypotenuse of a right triangle (Figure 5.2) whose sides are $15 - 25t$ and $10 - 30t$. From the Pythagorean theorem, we have

$$(10 - 30t)^2 + (15 - 25t)^2 = 15^2 \tag{1}$$

Equation 1 reduces to

$$61t^2 - 54t + 4 = 0 \tag{2}$$

Using the quadratic formula, the roots of Equation 2 are approximately

$$t = 0.082 \text{ and } 0.803$$

Both values of t are expressed in hours. In minutes, the time is $60(0.082) = 5$ minutes (approximately), and $60(0.803) = 48$ minutes (approximately). Hence

chapter 6

fractions

IN THIS CHAPTER WE SHALL BE PRIMARILY CONCERNED with fractions that are the quotients of two polynomials. These fractions are called rational algebraic expressions. A fraction will represent a real number for all values of the variables or variables which do not make the denominator of the fraction zero. Values of the variables that make the denominator zero are said to be inadmissible values because if they were used the value of the fraction would be undefined. Consider the fractions

$$\frac{3}{x+5}, \qquad \frac{x+2}{x^2-1}, \qquad \frac{2x-3}{x^2-5x+6}, \qquad \frac{2x-y}{x-y}$$

The first fraction is not defined for $x = -5$, the second fraction is not defined for $x = 1$ or $x = -1$, the third is not defined for $x = 2$ or $x = 3$, and the last fraction is not defined for $x = y$. These values are the inadmissible values of the variables; notice that the last fraction has an infinite number of inadmissible values of the variables.

6.1 EQUIVALENT FRACTIONS

Two fractions that always represent the same number are called equivalent fractions or equal fractions. Because the value of an algebraic fraction changes as the value of the variable changes, it is necessary to state that equal fractions *always* represent the same number.

THEOREM 6.1. If the fractions $\frac{a}{b}$ and $\frac{c}{d}$ are equivalent fractions, then $ad = bc$. Conversely, if $b \neq 0$ and $d \neq 0$ and $ad = bc$, then $\frac{a}{b} = \frac{c}{d}$.

PROOF:

$$\frac{a}{b} = \frac{c}{d} \qquad \text{Given}$$

$$bd\left(\frac{a}{b}\right) = bd\left(\frac{c}{d}\right) \qquad \text{If equals are multiplied by equals, the products are equal.}$$

$$adb\left(\frac{1}{b}\right) = bcd\left(\frac{1}{d}\right) \qquad \text{Commutative Property of Multiplication}$$

Recall that

$$b\left(\frac{1}{b}\right) = d\left(\frac{1}{d}\right) = 1 \qquad \text{Multiplicative Inverses}$$

Then

$$ad = bc$$

The converse of this theorem can be proved by reversing the order of the steps in the proof of the theorem. The importance of Theorem 6.1 is that it can be utilized to prove the most important theorem of fractions (theorem 6.2).

THEOREM 6.2.   THE FUNDAMENTAL THEOREM OF FRACTIONS

If both the numerator and the denominator of a fraction are multiplied or divided by the same quantity (not zero), the resulting fraction is equivalent to the original fraction.

PROOF:

$$\frac{a}{b} \overset{?}{=} \frac{ka}{kb} \qquad \text{To see if these fractions are equivalent, we use Theorem 1}$$

$$a(kb) \overset{?}{=} b(ka) \qquad \text{Substitution in Theorem 6.1 of } c = ka \text{ and } d = kb$$

$$abk = abk \qquad \text{Commutative and Associative Laws of Multiplication}$$

$$\frac{a}{b} = \frac{ka}{kb} \qquad \text{By converse of Theorem 6.1}$$

While in the proof above both numerator and denominator were multiplied by k, this proof is sufficient for both parts of the theorem, that is, multiplication and division. The only restriction on k is that it is not zero; therefore, since k can be considered the multiplicative inverse of a number n, multiplying by k would be the same as dividing by n.

One application of the Fundamental Theorem of Fractions is the reduction of fractions to lowest terms by dividing all common factors from the numerator and denominator. Another application is the changing of fractions to equivalent fractions when it is necessary to write several fractions with the same denominators. This will be considered in detail in Section 6.3.

The first step in an attempt to reduce a fraction to lowest terms is to factor both the numerator and denominator in terms of prime factors. All common factors are then divided out.

Note: Only common factors can be divided out, common terms can not be divided from the numerator and denominator.

EXAMPLE 1. Reduce $\dfrac{3x - 6}{x^2 - 4}$ to lowest terms.

$$\frac{3x - 6}{x^2 - 4} = \frac{3(x - 2)}{(x - 2)(x + 2)}$$

$$= \frac{3}{x + 2} \qquad \text{The numerator and denominator were divided by } x - 2.$$

EXAMPLE 2. Reduce $\dfrac{x^2 - 5x + 4}{x^2 - 7x + 12}$ to lowest terms.

$$\frac{x^2 - 5x + 4}{x^2 - 7x + 12} = \frac{(x - 1)(x - 4)}{(x - 3)(x - 4)}$$

$$= \frac{x - 1}{x - 3} \qquad \text{The numerator and the denominator were both divided by } x - 4.$$

It is possible to get different forms for answers to problems involving fractions. Consider for example $\dfrac{a}{b} = \dfrac{-a}{-b} = -\dfrac{-a}{b} = -\dfrac{a}{-b}$; it should be obvious that the first form is the most desirable form. Although the other fractions are all equal to the first fraction, an answer left in any form other than $\dfrac{a}{b}$ would not be in the simplest form.

Another example of a fraction in different forms is: $\dfrac{2}{1 - x} = \dfrac{-2}{x - 1} = -\dfrac{2}{x - 1}$. Whether one form is more desirable than the others in this example is a matter of opinion. However, one should be able to change from one form to another. The second fraction can be obtained from the first by multiplying both numerator and denominator by -1 and then changing the order of the terms in the denominator. The third form can be obtained from the first by changing the sign of the fraction and multiplying the denominator by -1. The general rule is that if the sign of the fraction is changed either the numerator or the denominator is multiplied by -1.

EXAMPLE 3. Reduce $\dfrac{4x - 20}{50 - 2x^2}$ to lowest terms.

$$\frac{4x - 20}{50 - 2x^2} = \frac{4(x - 5)}{2(25 - x^2)}$$

$$= \frac{2(2)(x - 5)}{2(5 - x)(5 + x)}$$

$$= \frac{-2(2)(5 - x)}{2(5 - x)(5 + x)}$$

$$= -\frac{2}{x + 5}$$

After factoring, both the numerator and denominator were divided by $2(5 - x)$, then the sign of the fraction was changed and the numerator was multiplied by -1 to obtain the final form of the answer.

EXERCISE 6.1

Equivalent Fractions

Reduce the following fractions to lowest terms.

1. $\dfrac{6x - 8}{15x - 20}$

2. $\dfrac{5y + 3}{15y + 9}$

3. $\dfrac{2x + 12}{3x + 18}$

4. $\dfrac{4y - 24}{3y - 18}$

5. $\dfrac{4x - 16}{x^2 - 16}$

6. $\dfrac{5y + 25}{y^2 - 25}$

7. $\dfrac{3x + 6}{x^2 - 4}$

8. $\dfrac{2y - 16}{y^2 - 64}$

9. $\dfrac{x^2 + 2x - 3}{x^2 - 5x + 4}$

10. $\dfrac{y^2 + y - 6}{y^2 - 2y - 15}$

11. $\dfrac{x^2 + 3x - 10}{x^2 + 9x + 20}$

12. $\dfrac{y^2 - 7y + 12}{y^2 + 2y - 24}$

13. $\dfrac{2x^2 + x - 6}{2x^2 + 3x - 9}$

14. $\dfrac{2y^2 - 7y + 5}{2y^2 - 3y - 5}$

15. $\dfrac{3x^2 - 11x + 6}{3x^2 - 17x + 10}$

16. $\dfrac{4y^2 + y - 3}{4y^2 - 11y + 6}$

17. $\dfrac{x^3 - x}{x^3 - 2x^2 - 3x}$

18. $\dfrac{y^3 - 4y}{y^3 - 5y^2 + 6y}$

19. $\dfrac{x^3 + x}{x^3 - 3x^2 + 2x}$

20. $\dfrac{y^3 - y^2 - 2y}{y^3 + y}$

21. $\dfrac{8x^2 + 6x + 1}{10x^2 + 11x + 3}$

22. $\dfrac{6y^2 + 7y + 2}{6y^2 + y - 2}$

23. $\dfrac{6x^2 - 5x - 6}{3x^2 + 11x + 6}$

24. $\dfrac{9y^2 - 3y - 2}{6y^2 - 7y - 3}$

25. $\dfrac{4x^2 + 8x - 96}{2x^2 - 2x - 24}$

26. $\dfrac{6y^2 - 150}{3y^2 + 9y - 30}$

27. $\dfrac{x^4 - x}{x^4 + x^3 + x^2}$

28. $\dfrac{y^4 + y}{y^4 - y^2}$

29. $\dfrac{3x^3 - 81}{2x^2 + 6x + 18}$

30. $\dfrac{2y^3 - 54}{3y^2 + 9y + 27}$

In Problems 31–40 simplify if possible and indicate all values of the variable for which the fraction is not defined.

31. $-\dfrac{2}{-b}$

32. $\dfrac{1 - n}{-3}$

33. $-\dfrac{-a}{a - 2}$

34. $-\dfrac{b}{2 - b}$

35. $-\dfrac{3 - x}{x + 5}$

36. $\dfrac{x - 3}{-(x + 4)}$

37. $\dfrac{7 - x}{-(3 + x)}$

38. $-\dfrac{-(3 - x)}{-(x - 5)}$

39. $-\dfrac{x + 3}{-(x - 1)}$

40. $-\dfrac{-(1 + x)}{x^2 - 1}$

In Problems 41–50, change each fraction to an equivalent fraction with the denominator as indicated to its right.

41. $\dfrac{3x}{y}, \dfrac{}{xyz}$

42. $\dfrac{5}{x}, \dfrac{}{x^3}$

43. $\dfrac{x + 2}{y}, \dfrac{}{xy^2}$

44. $\dfrac{x + 1}{x - 1}, \dfrac{}{x^2 - 3x + 2}$

45. $\dfrac{3x}{x + 1}, \dfrac{}{x^2 - 1}$

46. $\dfrac{x - 3}{x + 2}, \dfrac{}{x^2 + x - 2}$

47. $\dfrac{3n}{m + n}, \dfrac{}{n^2 - m^2}$

48. $\dfrac{5}{3 - x}, \dfrac{}{x^2 - 3x}$

49. $\dfrac{5x}{x - y}, \dfrac{}{y^2 - x^2}$

50. $\dfrac{2}{3 - x}, \dfrac{}{x^2 - 4x + 3}$

6.2 LEAST COMMON MULTIPLE (LCM)

The least common multiple or lowest common multiple of two or more integers is the smallest integer that is exactly divisible by each of the given integers. Consider the set of integers 2, 3, 5, 6; the least common multiple of this set of integers is 30. That is, 30 is the smallest integer that is exactly divisible by 2, 3, 5, and 6. When the integers of the set are small, the least common multiple can usually be determined by inspection. With numbers such as 12, 27, 32, and 36 the LCM cannot easily be determined by inspection. We shall use these numbers to illustrate a procedure used to find the LCM for this set. First, the numbers are expressed as the product of prime factors:

$$12 = 2^2(3)$$
$$27 = 3^3$$
$$32 = 2^5$$
$$36 = 2^2 3^2$$

The LCM must contain all of the prime numbers listed in the various factored forms, in this case 2 and 3. Furthermore, each of these primes must have the largest exponent it has in any of the factored forms. The exponents of 2 are 2, 2, and 5; the exponents of 3 are 1, 2, and 3. The largest exponent that 2 has is 5 and the largest exponent that 3 has is 3. The LCM of 12, 27, 32, and 36 is $2^5(3^3)$ or 864.

EXAMPLE 1. Find the LCM of 12, 18, 21, 25, and 35.

$12 = 2^2(3)$, $18 = 2(3^2)$, $21 = 3(7)$, $25 = 5^2$, $35 = 5(7)$
$$LCM = 2^2(3^2)(5^2)(7)$$
$$= 6300$$

EXAMPLE 2. Find the LCM of 26, 39, and 66.

$26 = 2(13)$, $39 = 3(13)$, $66 = 2(3)(11)$
$$LCM = 2(3)(11)(13)$$
$$= 858$$

We shall now extend the definition of least common multiple to polynomials. Read the definition below very carefully to see if you can determine how it differs from the previous definition of LCM of integers.

DEFINITION 6.1 LEAST COMMON MULTIPLE FOR POLYNOMIALS: The LCM for two or more polynomials is the polynomial of lowest degree that is exactly divisible by each of the polynomials.

Although it is not easily apparent from the definition, an LCM for polynomials is not necessarily unique; that is, there may be more than one acceptable polynomial which can be considered as the LCM. To illustrate a case of dual LCM's consider the polynomials $1 - x$ and $1 + x$. Neither of these expressions can be factored; they are both prime, so their product $1 - x^2$ is an LCM. However, $x^2 - 1$ is also exactly divisible by both of the polynomials $1 - x$ and $1 + x$. Both $x^2 - 1$ and $1 - x^2$ are acceptable as an LCM.

To avoid such dual results, the LCM's as they will be determined in this section, will be the form in which the coefficient of the term of highest degree in each factor is positive.

EXAMPLE 1. Find the LCM of: $x^2 + 2x + 1$, $x^2 - 1$, and $x^2 - 3x + 2$.

$x^2 + 2x + 1 = (x + 1)^2$, $x^2 - 1 = (x - 1)(x + 1)$,
$x^2 - 3x + 2 = (x - 1)(x - 2)$
LCM $= (x + 1)^2 (x - 1)(x - 2)$

As in the examples with integers, the LCM must contain all of the prime factors and each prime factor must contain the largest exponent it has in any of the factored forms.

EXAMPLE 2. Find the LCM of: $(x - 1)^2$, $(1 - x)^3$, $1 - x^3$.

$(x - 1)^2 = (x - 1)^2$
$(1 - x)^3 = [-1(x - 1)]^3 = (-1)^3(x - 1)^3 = -(x - 1)^3$
$1 - x^3 = (-1)(x^3 - 1) = - (x - 1)(x^2 + x + 1)$
LCM $= (x - 1)^3(x^2 + x + 1)$

Notice in the factoring of the second and the third polynomials that -1 was factored from the expressions first. This was done so that the terms of highest degree in the factors would have positive coefficients.

EXAMPLE 3. Find the LCM of: $6x^2 + 24x + 24$, $4x^2 - 8x - 12$, and $3x^2 + 9x + 6$.

$6x^2 + 24x + 24 = 6(x^2 + 4x + 4) = (3)(2)(x + 2)^2$
$4x^2 - 8x - 12 = 4(x^2 - 2x - 3) = (2^2)(x + 1)(x - 3)$
$3x^2 + 9x + 6 = 3(x^2 + 3x + 2) = 3(x + 1)(x + 2)$
LCM $= (2^2)(3)(x + 2)^2(x + 1)(x - 3)$

EXERCISE 6.2

Least Common Multiple

Find the least common multiple of each of the following sets of numbers.

1. 6, 10, 15	2. 12, 15, 20
3. 6, 11, 33	4. 11, 15, 55
5. 30, 35, 42	6. 35, 40, 56
7. 20, 27, 45	8. 24, 45, 50
9. 18, 48, 56	10. 24, 63, 98

Find the least common multiple of each of the following sets of algebraic expressions.

11. $4x, 2x^2, x^3$ 12. $3y, 9y^2, y^3$

13. $4x^2y^3, 6xy^2, xy^4$ 14. $12x^3y, 6xy^2, 3xy$

15. $8x^3, 12xy^2, 6y$ 16. $4xy^4, 3x^2y, 8xy^2$

17. $3x + 3, 2x + 2$ 18. $4y + 8, 6y + 12$

19. $5x - 10, 3x - 6$ 20. $6y - 3, 8y - 4$

21. $x + 2, x^2 + x - 2$ 22. $y - 4, y^2 - y - 12$

23. $x^2 - 1, x^2 + 2x + 1$ 24. $y^2 - 4y + 4, y^2 - 4$

25. $x^2 + 4x + 4, x^2 + 4, x^2 + 5x + 6$

26. $y^2 - 4y, y^2 - 16, y^2 + 2y - 8$

27. $x^2 - 3x, 3x^2 - 27, 2x + 6$

28. $y^2 + 2y, y^2 + 4y + 4, y^3 - y^2$

29. $x^3, x^3 + 1, x^2 - 1, x^2 + x$

30. $y^3, y^3 - 8, y^2 - 4, y^2 + 2y$

31. $4 - x^2, x^2 + 5x + 6, 3x - 6$

32. $x^2 + 7x + 12, 9 - x^2, 2x - 6$

33. $6 + x - x^2, 3x - 9, x^2 + 3x + 2$

34. $x^2 - 7x + 10, x^2 - 4x - 5, 10 - 2x$

35. $6 - 9x, 3x^2 - 12, x^2 + 5x - 14$

36. $x^2 - 12x + 32, 8 - 2x, 4x - 32$

37. $3 + x - 2x^2, 2 - x - 3x^2, 6x^2 - 13x + 6$

38. $36 - 5x - x^2, 9 - 3x, x^2 - 7x + 12$

39. $x^2 + 2x + 1, x^2 - 2x + 1, 1 - x^3$

40. $y^2 + 4y, 3y - 6, 8 - y^3$

6.3 OPERATIONS WITH FRACTIONS

When values are assigned to the variables of an algebraic fraction, the algebraic fraction is naturally changed to a numerical fraction. Therefore, the procedures we employ for the fundamental operations with algebraic fractions must yield results that are consistent with the results of the computation with numerical fractions. By consistent results, we mean that if a value is assigned to the variable thus changing the algebraic fractions to numerical fractions and then the indicated operations are performed with the numerical fractions the result will be the same as when the operations are performed with the algebraic fraction and then the resulting fraction is evaluated by using the same value of the variable.

To assure consistent results we therefore use the same procedures for the fundamental operations with algebraic fractions as we use for the corresponding operations with numerical fractions.

Addition and Subtraction of Fractions

Before two or more fractions can be combined by addition or subtraction, it is necessary to change the fractions to equivalent fractions which have the same denominators. The most efficient denominator to use, the lowest common denominator (LCD), is the least common multiple of the denominators. Once the lowest common denominator is determined, each of the fractions must be converted to an equivalent fraction by using the Fundamental Theorem of Fractions.

The sum (or difference) of two fractions with a common denominator may be determined as follows: the numerator of the sum (or difference) is the sum (or difference) of the numerators and the denominator is the common denominator. Symbolically this dual statement can be expressed as

$$\frac{a}{c} + \frac{b}{c} = \frac{a+b}{c}$$

for the sum and

$$\frac{a}{c} - \frac{b}{c} = \frac{a-b}{c}$$

for the difference. The answer obtained by properly combining the numerators should then be examined to see if it can be reduced to a simpler form.

EXAMPLE 1. Add $\dfrac{2}{x-3}$ and $\dfrac{5}{x+2}$. Neither of the denominators is factorable; therefore, the LCD is the product of the denominators.

$$\frac{2}{x-3} + \frac{5}{x+2} = \frac{2(x+2)}{(x-3)(x+2)} + \frac{5(x-3)}{(x-3)(x+2)} \quad \text{Fundamental Theorem of Fractions}$$

$$= \frac{2x+4+5x-15}{(x-3)(x+2)} \quad \text{Rule for Addition of Fractions}$$

$$= \frac{7x-11}{(x-3)(x+2)} \quad \text{Combining Terms}$$

The numerator is not factorable, so the result can not be reduced.

EXAMPLE 2. Subtract $\dfrac{2x-3}{x^2-3x+2}$ from $\dfrac{2-x}{x^2-2x+1}$. First we must determine the LCD.

$$x^2 - 3x + 2 = (x-1)(x-2)$$
$$x^2 - 2x + 1 = (x-1)^2$$

Therefore, the LCD $= (x-1)^2(x-2)$

$$
\begin{aligned}
\frac{2-x}{x^2-2x+1} - \frac{2x-3}{x^2-3x+2} &= \frac{(2-x)(x-2)}{(x-1)^2(x-2)} - \frac{(2x-3)(x-1)}{(x-1)^2(x-2)} \\
&= \frac{-x^2+4x-4-(2x^2-5x+3)}{(x-1)^2(x-2)} \\
&= \frac{-3x^2+9x-7}{(x-1)^2(x-2)} \\
&= -\frac{3x^2-9x+7}{(x-1)^2(x-2)}
\end{aligned}
$$

The numerator is not factorable so the fraction can not be reduced. Either of the last two fractions could be given as the answer.

EXAMPLE 3. Combine the following fractions:

$$\frac{3}{x^2-3x+2} + \frac{1}{x^2-5x+6} - \frac{2}{x^2-4x+3}$$

From the factored forms of the denominators:

$$x^2 - 3x + 2 = (x-1)(x-2),$$
$$x^2 - 5x + 6 = (x-2)(x-3),$$
$$x^2 - 4x + 3 = (x-1)(x-3);\text{ the LCD can be seen to be}$$
$(x-1)(x-2)(x-3).$

$$
\begin{aligned}
\frac{3}{x^2-3x+2} + \frac{1}{x^2-5x+6} - \frac{2}{x^2-4x+3} &= \frac{3(x-3)}{\text{LCD}} + \frac{1(x-1)}{\text{LCD}} - \frac{2(x-2)}{\text{LCD}} \\
&= \frac{(3x-9)+(x-1)-(2x-4)}{\text{LCD}} \\
&= \frac{2x-6}{\text{LCD}} \\
&= \frac{2(x-3)}{(x-1)(x-2)(x-3)} \\
&= \frac{2}{(x-1)\,(x-2)}
\end{aligned}
$$

Notice that in this example after the fractions were combined, the numerator was factorable and both the numerator and the denominator were divided by $x - 3$ to obtain the simplest form of the answer. Final answers should always be in simplest form, that is, all common factors should be divided from the numerator and denominator.

Multiplication of Fractions

Just as the procedure for addition and subtraction of algebraic fractions is the same as for numerical fractions, the procedure for finding the product of algebraic fractions is the same as that used to find the product of numerical fractions. That is, the product of two fractions has for its numerator the product of the numerators and for its denominator the product of the denominators.

However, in practice we do not immediately proceed to multiply the numerators and multiply the denominators; instead, we factor the numerators and denominators first and then divide out those factors that are present in both the numerator and the denominator.

EXAMPLE 4.   Find the product of $\dfrac{x^2 - x}{x^2 - x - 2}$ and $\dfrac{x - 2}{x^2}$.

$$\frac{x^2 - x}{x^2 - x - 2} \cdot \frac{x - 2}{x^2} = \frac{x(x - 1)(x - 2)}{(x - 2)(x + 1)\,x^2} \qquad \text{by factoring}$$

$$= \frac{x - 1}{(x + 1)\,x} \qquad \begin{array}{l}\text{by dividing out common} \\ \text{factors } x \text{ and } x - 2\end{array}$$

$$= \frac{x - 1}{x^2 + x}$$

EXAMPLE 5.   Multiply $\dfrac{y^2 + 3y + 2}{y - 3}$ by $\dfrac{y^2 - 7y + 12}{y^2 + y - 2}$.

$$\left(\frac{y^2 + 3y + 2}{y - 3}\right)\left(\frac{y^2 - 7y + 12}{y^2 + y - 2}\right) = \frac{(y + 1)(y + 2)(y - 3)(y - 4)}{(y - 3)(y + 2)(y - 1)} \qquad \text{factoring}$$

$$= \frac{(y + 1)(y - 4)}{y - 1} \qquad \begin{array}{l}\text{dividing out common} \\ \text{factors } (y + 2) \text{ and} \\ (y - 3)\end{array}$$

$$= \frac{y^2 - 3y - 4}{y - 1}$$

Either of the last two fractions may be accepted as correct results. The answers supplied at the end of the book are usually given in factored form.

Division of Fractions

To find the quotient of two fractions we multiply the dividend by the reciprocal of the divisor. That is,

$$\frac{a}{b} \div \frac{c}{d} = \frac{a}{b} \times \frac{d}{c} = \frac{ad}{bc}$$

We can readily verify the above rule for division of fractions by using the general definition of a quotient, namely, $N \div D = Q$, if and only if $N = DQ$. In our case, $N = \dfrac{a}{b}$, $D = \dfrac{c}{d}$, and $Q = \dfrac{ad}{bc}$. Substituting these quantities in $N = DQ$, we have

$$\frac{a}{b} = \left(\frac{c}{d}\right) \cdot \left(\frac{ad}{bc}\right)$$

By dividing out the common factors c and d from the numerator and denominator, we have the identity $\dfrac{a}{b} = \dfrac{a}{b}$. Thus we have verified our rule for the division of one fraction by another.

It is obvious that this rule for division of fractions is merely another form of the rule for division of numerical fractions: invert the divisor and then multiply.

EXAMPLE 6. Divide $\dfrac{2x - 8}{x + 1}$ by $\dfrac{3x^2 - 12x}{x^2 - 1}$.

$$\frac{2x - 8}{x + 1} \div \frac{3x^2 - 12x}{x^2 - 1} = \frac{2x - 8}{x + 1} \cdot \frac{x^2 - 1}{3x^2 - 12x} \qquad \text{Rule for Division of Fractions}$$

$$= \frac{2(x - 4)}{x + 1} \cdot \frac{(x + 1)(x - 1)}{3x(x - 4)} \qquad \text{factoring and dividing out common factors}$$

$$= \frac{2(x - 1)}{3x}.$$

EXAMPLE 7. Divide $\dfrac{2y^2 - 11y + 12}{6y^2 - 6y - 12}$ by $\dfrac{3y^2 - 14y + 8}{2y^2 - 6y + 4}$.

$$\frac{2y^2 - 11y + 12}{6y^2 - 6y - 12} \div \frac{3y^2 - 14y + 8}{2y^2 - 6y + 4} = \frac{2y^2 - 11y + 12}{6y^2 - 6y - 12} \cdot \frac{2y^2 - 6y + 4}{3y^2 - 14y + 8}$$

$$= \frac{(2y - 3)(y - 4)}{6(y - 2)(y + 1)} \cdot \frac{2(y - 2)(y - 1)}{(3y - 2)(y - 4)}$$

dividing out common factors

$$= \frac{(2y - 3)(y - 1)}{3(y + 1)(3y - 2)}.$$

EXERCISE 6.3

Operations with Fractions

In Problems 1–40 combine the following fractions. Simplify answers when possible.

1. $\dfrac{5}{12} + \dfrac{3}{12} - \dfrac{1}{12}$

2. $\dfrac{4}{9} + \dfrac{3}{9} - \dfrac{5}{9}$

3. $\dfrac{4}{x} + \dfrac{7}{x} - \dfrac{5}{x}$

4. $\dfrac{5}{2y} + \dfrac{3}{2y} + \dfrac{1}{2y} - \dfrac{7}{2y}$

5. $\dfrac{2}{3x} + \dfrac{1}{2x} + \dfrac{5}{6x}$

6. $\dfrac{5a}{12b} + \dfrac{4a}{3b} + \dfrac{3a}{4b}$

7. $\dfrac{7}{12y} - \dfrac{5}{6y} - \dfrac{2}{3y}$

8. $\dfrac{11}{10x} - \dfrac{3}{5x} - \dfrac{1}{2x}$

9. $3 + \dfrac{1}{2x} - \dfrac{1}{3x}$

10. $4 - \dfrac{1}{3b} + \dfrac{1}{2b}$

11. $\dfrac{2}{x+1} + \dfrac{3}{x-2}$

12. $\dfrac{5}{y-1} + \dfrac{2}{y+2}$

13. $\dfrac{5}{x-3} - \dfrac{2}{x-2}$

14. $\dfrac{7}{y-4} - \dfrac{5}{y-3}$

15. $\dfrac{3}{x} - \dfrac{2}{x^2} - \dfrac{1}{x^3}$

16. $\dfrac{4}{y} - \dfrac{3}{y^2} - \dfrac{1}{y^3}$

17. $\dfrac{6}{x} + \dfrac{3}{2x^2} - \dfrac{5}{3x^3}$

18. $\dfrac{7}{3y} - \dfrac{3}{2y^2} + \dfrac{4}{y^3}$

19. $\dfrac{x+1}{x} - \dfrac{x+2}{x^2} + \dfrac{x+3}{x^3}$

20. $\dfrac{y-1}{y} + \dfrac{y+2}{y^2} - \dfrac{y-3}{y^3}$

21. $\dfrac{3}{x+1} + \dfrac{5}{2x+2} + \dfrac{7}{3x+3}$

22. $\dfrac{4}{3x-1} - \dfrac{5}{6x-2} + \dfrac{1}{9x-3}$

23. $\dfrac{2}{2x-3} - \dfrac{4}{4x-6} - \dfrac{6}{6x-9}$

24. $\dfrac{3}{2y+3} - \dfrac{1}{4y+6} - \dfrac{5}{6y+9}$

25. $\dfrac{4}{2x+1} + \dfrac{3}{x+2}$

26. $\dfrac{5}{3y-1} + \dfrac{2}{y-2}$

27. $\dfrac{6}{x-2} + \dfrac{3}{2x-1}$

28. $\dfrac{7}{2y+1} + \dfrac{4}{y+2}$

29. $\dfrac{8}{2x-3} - \dfrac{8}{x+2}$

30. $\dfrac{7}{4y+1} - \dfrac{3}{2y-3}$

31. $\dfrac{1}{x-1} + \dfrac{2}{x+1} - \dfrac{1}{x^2-1}$

32. $\dfrac{3}{y-2} + \dfrac{2}{y+2} - \dfrac{2}{y^2-4}$

33. $\dfrac{1}{x-2} + \dfrac{2}{x+3} + \dfrac{3}{x^2+x-6}$

34. $\dfrac{2}{y+2} + \dfrac{1}{y-3} + \dfrac{4}{y^2-y-6}$

35. $\dfrac{2x+3}{x-2} + \dfrac{x-1}{x+1} + \dfrac{3x}{2x-4}$

36. $\dfrac{3y-2}{y+1} + \dfrac{2y+1}{y-3} + \dfrac{y-1}{2y+2}$

37. $\dfrac{3}{x-y} + \dfrac{2}{x+3y} + \dfrac{5}{2x-2y}$

38. $\dfrac{4}{a-2b} + \dfrac{3}{2a-b} + \dfrac{2}{4a-2b}$

39. $\dfrac{4}{x-2} + \dfrac{1}{x+1} - \dfrac{5}{x^2-2x}$

40. $\dfrac{6}{y^2-3y} + \dfrac{3}{y-3} - \dfrac{2}{y-2}$

In Problems 41–75 perform the indicated operations and simplify results when possible.

41. $\dfrac{5}{13} \times \dfrac{26}{55}$

42. $\dfrac{5}{9} \times \dfrac{18}{45}$

43. $\dfrac{7}{17} \times \dfrac{34}{49}$

44. $\dfrac{6}{7} \times \dfrac{14}{27}$

45. $\dfrac{3a}{4b} \times \dfrac{20b}{a}$

46. $\dfrac{6a}{11b} \times \dfrac{33b}{2a}$

47. $\dfrac{16x^2}{y^3} \times \dfrac{5y}{24x^6}$

48. $\dfrac{25y^3}{x^2} \times \dfrac{3x^5}{45y^6}$

49. $\dfrac{5x+10}{3y} \times \dfrac{9y^2}{3x+6}$

50. $\dfrac{4a-6b}{13b} \times \dfrac{39b^3}{6a-9b}$

51. $\dfrac{3x^2y}{2x-7} \times \dfrac{4x-7}{12xy^2}$

52. $\dfrac{15ab^3}{3a-5} \times \dfrac{6a-5}{25a^3b}$

53. $\dfrac{3x-6}{x^2+1} \times \dfrac{x+2}{x^2-4}$

54. $\dfrac{x^2-1}{x^2-4} \times \dfrac{x-2}{x-1}$

55. $\dfrac{x^2-3x+2}{x^2+5x+4} \times \dfrac{x^2+6x+8}{x^2-4}$

56. $\dfrac{y^2-y-2}{4y^2-4} \times \dfrac{8y+8}{3y-3}$

57. $\dfrac{2x^2-3x-2}{2x^2-5x-3} \times \dfrac{3x^2-10x+3}{3x^2-7x+2}$

58. $\dfrac{6x^2+x-1}{2x^2-5x-3} \times \dfrac{x^2-5x+6}{3x^2-7x+2}$

59. $\dfrac{y^2-4y-5}{y^2+3y+2} \times \dfrac{y^2-y-6}{y^2-2y-15}$

60. $\dfrac{a^2-ab-2b^2}{a^2+ab-2b^2} \times \dfrac{a^2-b^2}{a^2-4b^2}$

61. $\dfrac{x^3-8y^3}{x^2-4xy+4y^2} \times \dfrac{x^2-4y^2}{3x+6y}$

62. $\dfrac{a+b}{a^3-b^3} \times \dfrac{a^2+ab+b^2}{(a+b)^2}$

63. $\dfrac{x^3+27y^3}{x+9y} \times \dfrac{x-2y}{x^2+xy-6y^2}$

64. $\dfrac{x^2 - 1}{x^2 - x + 1} \times \dfrac{x^3 - 1}{(x - 1)^2}$

65. $\dfrac{16a^2b}{7cd} \div \dfrac{4ab^2}{21c^2d^3}$

66. $\dfrac{x^2 - 16}{x + 3} \div \dfrac{4x - 16}{3x^2 + 9x}$

67. $\dfrac{2x^2 + 3x - 2}{2x^2 - 3x + 1} \div \dfrac{x^2 - 5x + 6}{x^2 - 4x + 3}$

68. $\dfrac{2x^2 - 7x + 3}{2x^2 - 5x + 3} \div \dfrac{3x^2 - 9x}{4x^3 - 6x^2}$

69. $\dfrac{16x^2 - 64}{9x^2 + 18x + 9} \div \dfrac{x^2 + 1}{3x + 3}$

70. $\dfrac{9x^2 - 36}{x^2 + 1} \div \dfrac{3x + 6}{x^4 - 1}$

71. $\dfrac{3y^2 + 11y + 6}{6y^2 + 7y + 2} \div \dfrac{8y^2 + 18y + 9}{8y^2 + 10y + 3}$

72. $\dfrac{6x^2 - 13x + 6}{2x^2 + 15x + 18} \div \dfrac{3x^2 + 7x - 6}{4x^2 - 9}$

73. $\dfrac{y^3 - 1}{y^2 - 1} \div \dfrac{y^2 + y + 1}{y^2 + 2y + 1}$

74. $\dfrac{x^4 - 16}{x + 2} \div \dfrac{x^2 + 4}{x^2 - 4x + 4}$

75. $\dfrac{y^3 + 1}{y^2 + 1} \div \dfrac{3y^2 + 6y + 3}{2y + 2}$

6.4   COMPLEX FRACTIONS

Although some of the problems of the previous section may have seemed difficult, all of the fractions we have dealt with thus far are called simple fractions. We shall now discuss complex fractions. Complex fractions are fractions that have one or more fractions in the numerator or the denominator or in both the numerator and denominator.

Examples of complex fractions are

$$\frac{\dfrac{1}{2}}{5}, \quad \frac{1}{\dfrac{2}{5}}, \quad \frac{\dfrac{3x}{y}}{\dfrac{x^3}{y}}, \quad \frac{\dfrac{x^2}{3y}}{\dfrac{1}{9y^2 - 6y}}$$

and

$$\frac{\dfrac{1}{x} + \dfrac{1}{y}}{\dfrac{1}{x^2} - \dfrac{1}{y^2}}$$

In printed material the main fraction line is distinguished by the bold face line (heavier line). In written work it is customary to use a longer line to distinguish the main fraction line from the other fraction lines. Unless you are careful to identify the main fraction line, the meaning of a complex fraction may be ambiguous. To illustrate this, consider the first two examples in the list of complex fractions:

$\dfrac{\frac{1}{2}}{5}$ means that $\dfrac{1}{2}$ is to be divided by 5. The simplified form of this fraction is obviously $\dfrac{1}{10}$.

$\dfrac{1}{\frac{2}{5}}$ means 1 is to be divided by $\dfrac{2}{5}$. This is equal to $\dfrac{5}{2}$.

One should expect that an answer left in the form of a complex fraction is not the most desirable form. We will now propose two methods of simplifying complex fractions.

The first method is to write both the numerator and the denominator of the complex fraction as single fractions. Once this is accomplished we can then use the procedure for dividing one fraction by another and simplify the result.

EXAMPLE 1. Simplify the complex fraction $\dfrac{\frac{1}{2} + \frac{1}{3}}{\frac{1}{4} + \frac{1}{5}}$.

$$\frac{\frac{1}{2} + \frac{1}{3}}{\frac{1}{4} + \frac{1}{5}} = \frac{\frac{3}{6} + \frac{2}{6}}{\frac{5}{20} + \frac{4}{20}} \qquad (1)$$

$$= \frac{\frac{5}{6}}{\frac{9}{20}} \qquad (2)$$

$$= \frac{5}{6} \times \frac{20}{9} \qquad (3)$$

$$= \frac{50}{27} \qquad (4)$$

In Step 1 we wrote the fractions in the numerator with a common denominator and did the same for the fractions in the denominator.

In Step 2 we combined the fractions in the numerator and combined the fractions in the denominator.

In Step 3 we inverted the divisor and changed the operation to multiplication. Dividing both numerator and denominator by 2 we obtain the simplified form of the original complex fraction.

EXAMPLE 2. Simplify the complex fraction $\dfrac{\dfrac{1}{x} - \dfrac{1}{y}}{\dfrac{1}{x^2} - \dfrac{1}{y^2}}$.

$$\frac{\dfrac{1}{x} - \dfrac{1}{y}}{\dfrac{1}{x^2} - \dfrac{1}{y^2}} = \frac{\dfrac{y}{xy} - \dfrac{x}{xy}}{\dfrac{y^2}{x^2y^2} - \dfrac{x^2}{x^2y^2}}$$

$$= \frac{\dfrac{y - x}{xy}}{\dfrac{y^2 - x^2}{x^2y^2}}$$

$$= \frac{y - x}{xy} \cdot \frac{x^2y^2}{y^2 - x^2}$$

$$= \frac{(y - x)(xy)(xy)}{xy(y - x)(y + x)}$$

$$= \frac{xy}{y + x}$$

Both of these examples used the same procedure in arriving at the simplified form of the complex fraction. This procedure can always be used to simplify complex fractions but it is not the best method available. A better method (generally faster and less subject to errors) is to multiply both the numerator and the denominator of the main fraction by the LCM of all the denominators in both the numerator and denominator. We shall illustrate this method by using the same complex fractions that we used in Examples 1 and 2.

EXAMPLE 3. Simplify $\dfrac{\dfrac{1}{2} + \dfrac{1}{3}}{\dfrac{1}{4} + \dfrac{1}{5}}$.

The denominators are 2, 3, 4, and 5. The LCM is 60. Multiply every term of the numerator and every term of the denominator by 60.

$$\frac{\dfrac{1}{2} + \dfrac{1}{3}}{\dfrac{1}{4} + \dfrac{1}{5}} = \frac{30 + 20}{15 + 12}$$

$$= \frac{50}{27}$$

EXAMPLE 4. Simplify $\dfrac{\dfrac{1}{x} - \dfrac{1}{y}}{\dfrac{1}{x^2} - \dfrac{1}{y^2}}$.

The LCM of x, y, x^2 and y^2 is $x^2 y^2$.

$$\frac{\dfrac{1}{x} - \dfrac{1}{y}}{\dfrac{1}{x^2} - \dfrac{1}{y^2}} = \frac{xy^2 - x^2 y}{y^2 - x^2}$$

$$= \frac{xy(y - x)}{(y - x)(y + x)}$$

$$= \frac{xy}{y + x}$$

EXAMPLE 5. Simplify $\dfrac{\dfrac{1}{x - 1} - \dfrac{1}{x - 2}}{\dfrac{1}{x - 2} - \dfrac{1}{x - 3}}$.

The LCM of $x - 1$, $x - 2$, and $x - 3$ is the product of the three binomials.

$$\text{LCM} = (x - 1)(x - 2)(x - 3)$$

$$\frac{\dfrac{1}{x - 1} - \dfrac{1}{x - 2}}{\dfrac{1}{x - 2} - \dfrac{1}{x - 3}} = \frac{(x - 3)\,[(x - 1)(x - 2)]\left[\dfrac{1}{x - 1} - \dfrac{1}{x - 2}\right]}{(x - 1)\,[(x - 2)(x - 3)]\left[\dfrac{1}{x - 2} - \dfrac{1}{x - 3}\right]}$$

We can see that the factor $x - 3$ is not needed to eliminate the fractions in the numerator. So we shall keep this as a factor of the product of the quantities within the brackets.

Likewise, $x - 1$ will be kept as a factor of the product of the two quantities within the brackets in the denominator. Then

$$\frac{\dfrac{1}{x - 1} - \dfrac{1}{x - 2}}{\dfrac{1}{x - 2} - \dfrac{1}{x - 3}} = \frac{(x - 3)\,[(x - 2) - (x - 1)]}{(x - 1)\,[(x - 3) - (x - 2)]}$$

$$= \frac{(x - 3)\,[-1]}{(x - 1)\,[-1]}$$

$$= \frac{x - 3}{x - 1}.$$

EXERCISE 6.4

Complex Fractions

Simplify the complex fractions:

1. $\dfrac{\dfrac{1}{2} - \dfrac{1}{3}}{\dfrac{1}{2} - \dfrac{1}{4}}$

2. $\dfrac{\dfrac{2}{3} - \dfrac{1}{2}}{\dfrac{3}{4} - \dfrac{1}{2}}$

3. $\dfrac{\dfrac{1}{4} - \dfrac{1}{6}}{\dfrac{1}{6} - \dfrac{1}{12}}$

4. $\dfrac{\dfrac{1}{3} - \dfrac{1}{6}}{\dfrac{1}{4} + \dfrac{1}{8}}$

5. $\dfrac{\dfrac{1}{2a} - \dfrac{1}{b}}{\dfrac{2}{3a} + \dfrac{1}{b}}$

6. $\dfrac{\dfrac{1}{3x} - \dfrac{1}{y}}{\dfrac{1}{2x} + \dfrac{2}{y}}$

7. $\dfrac{\dfrac{1}{2x} + \dfrac{1}{2y}}{\dfrac{1}{4x^2} - \dfrac{1}{4y^2}}$

8. $\dfrac{\dfrac{1}{x} - \dfrac{1}{y}}{\dfrac{1}{x^2} + \dfrac{1}{y^2}}$

9. $\dfrac{\dfrac{1}{x} + \dfrac{1}{x+1}}{\dfrac{1}{x+1} + \dfrac{1}{x+2}}$

10. $\dfrac{\dfrac{1}{x-2} - \dfrac{1}{x-3}}{\dfrac{1}{x-4} - \dfrac{1}{x-3}}$

11. $\dfrac{\dfrac{1}{x^2} + \dfrac{1}{xy} + \dfrac{1}{y^2}}{\dfrac{1}{x^3} - \dfrac{1}{y^3}}$

12. $\dfrac{\dfrac{1}{b^2} - \dfrac{1}{ab} + \dfrac{1}{a^2}}{\dfrac{1}{a^3} + \dfrac{1}{b^3}}$

13. $\dfrac{\dfrac{1}{x} - \dfrac{1}{x-1}}{\dfrac{1}{x-1} + \dfrac{1}{x-2}}$

14. $\dfrac{\dfrac{1}{a} + \dfrac{1}{a+1}}{\dfrac{1}{a+1} - \dfrac{1}{a+2}}$

15. $\dfrac{\dfrac{1}{x} + \dfrac{2}{x^2} + \dfrac{1}{x^3}}{\dfrac{1}{x} - \dfrac{1}{x^3}}$

16. $\dfrac{\dfrac{4}{y} + \dfrac{12}{y^2} + \dfrac{9}{y^3}}{\dfrac{4}{y} - \dfrac{9}{y^3}}$

17. $\dfrac{16 - \dfrac{4}{x} + \dfrac{1}{x^2}}{64 + \dfrac{1}{x^3}}$

18. $\dfrac{9 - \dfrac{3}{y} + \dfrac{1}{y^2}}{27 + \dfrac{1}{y^3}}$

19. $\dfrac{1 - \dfrac{1}{x^6}}{\dfrac{1}{x^2} + \dfrac{1}{x^4} + \dfrac{1}{x^6}}$

20. $\dfrac{\dfrac{1}{y^3} - \dfrac{1}{y^5} + \dfrac{1}{y^7}}{\dfrac{1}{y} + \dfrac{1}{y^7}}$

6.5 FRACTIONAL EQUATIONS

An equation that contains one or more fractions which have the unknown in the denominator is called a fractional equation. For example, $\dfrac{3}{x} + 5 = 7$ is a fractional equation, but $\frac{3}{4}x - 2 = 14$ is not a fractional equation.

The first step in the solution of a fractional equation is to multiply both members of the equation by the least common denominator of all the fractions of the equation. Since every denominator is an exact divisor of the LCD, this will produce an equation that is free of fractions.

This new equation may be linear, quadratic, or of higher degree. However, the problems of this section have been chosen so that only linear or quadratic equations will result from the multiplication by the LCD.

The multiplication of an equation by a factor that contains the unknown may not always produce an equation that is equivalent to the original. The new equation may have solutions that are not solutions of the original equation. The extra root or roots are called extraneous roots and the new equation is then said to be a redundant equation.

The fact that new roots may be introduced by the multiplication by the LCD can be seen from the following example.

EXAMPLE 1. Solve $\dfrac{3}{x - 1} + \dfrac{2}{x + 1} = \dfrac{6}{x^2 - 1}$.   (1)

Multiplying both members of the equation by the LCD. $(x^2 - 1)$ we obtain Equation 2:

$$3(x + 1) + 2(x - 1) = 6 \qquad (2)$$
$$3x + 3 + 2x - 2 = 6$$
$$5x = 5$$
$$x = 1$$

Substituting $x = 1$ into Equation 2, we can readily see that it is a solution of that equation. However, $x = 1$ is not an admissible value of x for Equation 1; therefore, $x = 1$ is not a solution of Equation 1. It is an extraneous root that was introduced by the multiplication by the LCD. The original equation does not have a solution.

EXAMPLE 2.   Solve $\dfrac{3}{x - 1} + \dfrac{1}{x - 2} = \dfrac{5}{(x - 1)(x - 2)}.$ $\qquad\qquad$ (1)

Multiplying both members of the equation by the LCD $(x - 1)(x - 2)$, we obtain

$$3(x - 2) + x - 1 = 5$$
$$3x - 6 + x - 1 = 5$$
$$4x - 7 = 5$$
$$4x = 12$$
$$x = 3$$

Substituting $x = 3$ into the original equation

$$\frac{3}{2} + 1 = \frac{5}{(2)(1)}$$
$$\frac{5}{2} = \frac{5}{2}$$

we find $x = 3$ satisfies the original equation.

EXAMPLE 3.   Solve $\dfrac{x}{x - 2} + \dfrac{x - 1}{2} = x + 1.$

Multiplying both members by $2(x - 2)$ we obtain

$$2x + (x - 1)(x - 2) = 2(x + 1)(x - 2)$$
$$2x + x^2 - 3x + 2 = 2x^2 - 2x - 4$$
$$x^2 - x - 6 = 0 \qquad\qquad \text{Solving by factoring}$$
$$(x - 3)(x + 2) = 0$$
$$x = 3, x = -2$$

Since both of these solutions are admissible values of x, they both should satisfy the original equation.

Check for $x = 3$:

$$\frac{3}{1} + \frac{2}{2} = 3 + 1$$
$$3 + 1 = 3 + 1$$

Check for $x = -2$:

$$\frac{-2}{-4} + \frac{-3}{2} = -2 + 1$$

$$\frac{1}{2} + \frac{-3}{2} = -1$$

$$-1 = -1$$

EXAMPLE 4. Solve $\dfrac{x + 1}{x^2 - 5x + 6} + \dfrac{x + 2}{x^2 - 7x + 12} = \dfrac{6}{x^2 - 6x + 8}$.

$$\frac{x + 1}{(x - 2)(x - 3)} + \frac{x + 2}{(x - 3)(x - 4)} = \frac{6}{(x - 2)(x - 4)}$$

The LCD is $(x - 2)(x - 3)(x - 4)$. Multiplying every term of the equation by the LCD we have:

$$(x + 1)(x - 4) + (x + 2)(x - 2) = 6x - 18$$
$$x^2 - 3x - 4 + x^2 - 4 = 6x - 18$$
$$2x^2 - 3x - 8 = 6x - 18$$
$$2x^2 - 9x + 10 = 0$$
$$(2x - 5)(x - 2) = 0$$
$$x = \frac{5}{2}, \; x = 2$$

$x = 2$ is an extraneous root, since it is not an admissible value for the original equation. (It makes two of the denominators zero.) $x = \dfrac{5}{2}$ is an admissible value of x for the original equation and is a solution if it will satisfy the original equation.

Check: $x = \dfrac{5}{2}$

$$\frac{\dfrac{7}{2}}{\left(\dfrac{1}{2}\right)\left(-\dfrac{1}{2}\right)} + \frac{\dfrac{9}{2}}{\left(-\dfrac{1}{2}\right)\left(-\dfrac{3}{2}\right)} = \frac{6}{\left(\dfrac{1}{2}\right)\left(-\dfrac{3}{2}\right)}$$

$$\frac{14}{-1} + \frac{18}{3} = \frac{24}{-3}$$

$$-14 + 6 = -8$$

$$-8 = -8$$

In these four examples of fractional equations we found that multiplying by the LCD resulted in either a linear or a quadratic equation. The resulting equation may be equivalent to the original equation or it may be redundant with respect to the original equation.

EXERCISE 6.5

Fractional Equations

Solve each of the following equations.

1. $\dfrac{4}{x} + \dfrac{5}{x} + \dfrac{7}{x} = 8$

2. $\dfrac{5}{x} + \dfrac{6}{x} + \dfrac{7}{x} = 6$

3. $\dfrac{3}{x-2} + 5 = \dfrac{28}{x-2}$

4. $\dfrac{7}{x+3} + \dfrac{x}{x+3} = 5$

5. $\dfrac{3}{x} + \dfrac{5}{x-1} = \dfrac{13}{x^2-x}$

6. $\dfrac{4}{x} - \dfrac{2}{x-2} = \dfrac{6}{x^2-2x}$

7. $\dfrac{1}{x} - \dfrac{2}{x-3} = \dfrac{3}{x^2-3x}$

8. $\dfrac{3}{x+1} - \dfrac{2}{x^2-1} - \dfrac{4}{x-1} = 0$

9. $x + \dfrac{1}{x-3} = \dfrac{11}{x-3}$

10. $x + \dfrac{2}{x+2} - \dfrac{30}{3x+6} = 0$

11. $\dfrac{1}{x} + \dfrac{2}{x+2} - 1 = 0$

12. $\dfrac{5}{x} - \dfrac{1}{x^2} = 6$

13. $\dfrac{x}{x+3} + \dfrac{4}{x-2} - \dfrac{27}{x^2+x-6} = 0$

14. $\dfrac{5}{x-2} + \dfrac{x}{x+1} - \dfrac{9}{x^2-x-2} = 0$

15. $\dfrac{3}{x+2} - \dfrac{4}{x-3} + \dfrac{16}{x^2-x-6} = 0$

16. $\dfrac{5}{x+1} - \dfrac{3}{x+2} - \dfrac{3}{x^2+3x+2} = 0$

17. $\dfrac{x}{x+3} + \dfrac{4}{x-2} - \dfrac{15}{x^2+x-6} = 0$

18. $\dfrac{x}{2x+3} - \dfrac{2}{x-2} + \dfrac{15}{2x^2-x-6} = 0$

19. $\dfrac{x+1}{x+2} - \dfrac{x+3}{x+4} = 0$

20. $\dfrac{3x}{x-1} + \dfrac{x}{2x+2} - \dfrac{2}{2x^2-2} = 0$

21. $\dfrac{x-3}{x+1} - \dfrac{2x-3}{x+5} + \dfrac{x^2-3}{x^2+6x+5} = 0$

22. $\dfrac{x+2}{x-1} + \dfrac{x-4}{2x} - \dfrac{7}{3} = 0$

23. $\dfrac{5x}{x-1} - \dfrac{7x}{x-2} + \dfrac{2x}{x-3} = 0$

24. $\dfrac{x-1}{2x^2-5x+3} + \dfrac{2x+1}{2x-3} = 0$

25. $\dfrac{x}{x-8} - \dfrac{3}{x+8} = \dfrac{48}{x^2-64}$

26. $\dfrac{5x}{x} - \dfrac{3x}{x-1} - \dfrac{2x}{x+1} = 0$

27. $\dfrac{4}{x-2} + \dfrac{x}{2-x} = 3$

28. $\dfrac{x}{4-x} + \dfrac{8}{x-4} = 3$

29. $\dfrac{3}{x+2} - \dfrac{4}{x+4} + \dfrac{2}{x+3} - \dfrac{2x}{(x+2)(x+3)(x+4)} = 0$

30. $\dfrac{2}{x-2} - \dfrac{5}{x-6} + \dfrac{4}{x-4} + \dfrac{7x}{(x-2)(x-4)(x-6)} = 0$

6.6 APPLICATIONS OF FRACTIONAL EQUATIONS

Proportions

A ratio is a method of comparing the magnitudes of two quantities by their quotient. For example, the ratio of 15 inches to 36 inches is

$$\frac{15 \text{ inches}}{36 \text{ inches}} \qquad \text{or} \qquad \frac{5}{12}$$

The ratio of a to b is the quotient $\dfrac{a}{b}$.

The equality of two ratios such as $\dfrac{a}{b} = \dfrac{c}{d}$ is called a proportion. The elements a and d are called extremes and the elements b and c are called the means.

Some of the important properties of proportions will be stated now. The proofs of these properties will be left as exercises for the student.

If $\dfrac{a}{b} = \dfrac{c}{d}$, then properties 1–6 are valid.

Property 1. $ad = bc$ (the product of the extremes is equal to the product of the means)

Property 2. $\dfrac{b}{a} = \dfrac{d}{c}$ (proportion by inversion)

Property 3. $\dfrac{a}{c} = \dfrac{b}{d}$ (proportion by alternation)

Property 4. $\dfrac{a + b}{b} = \dfrac{c + d}{d}$ (proportion by composition)

Property 5. $\dfrac{a - b}{b} = \dfrac{c - d}{d}$ (proportion by subtraction)

Property 6. $\dfrac{a + b}{a - b} = \dfrac{c + d}{c - d}$ (proportion by composition and subtraction)

The solution of problems involving proportions frequently necessitates the solution of fractional equations as will be illustrated by the following examples.

EXAMPLE 1. Find the height of a tree which casts a shadow 20 feet long at the same time a vertical yard stick casts a shadow 30 inches long.

SOLUTION: The heights are directly proportional to the lengths of their shadows. If we let

H represent the height of the tree

h represent the height of the yardstick

S represent the length of the shadow of the tree

s represent the length of the shadow of the yard stick

then

$$\frac{H}{h} = \frac{S}{s}$$

$$\frac{H}{36 \text{ inches}} = \frac{20 \text{ feet}}{30 \text{ inches}}$$

$$H = \frac{6}{5} \times 20 \text{ feet}$$

hence

$$H = 24 \text{ feet}$$

EXAMPLE 2. On a map, $\dfrac{3}{16}$ inch represents 10 miles. What would be the length of a line on the map which represents 96 miles?

SOLUTION: The lengths of line segments on the map are proportional to the actual distances on the earth. If L represents the length of the line segment on the map corresponding to a distance of 96 miles, then

$$\frac{\dfrac{3}{16}}{L} = \frac{10}{96}$$

$$\frac{3}{16}(96) = 10L \qquad\qquad \text{by property 1}$$

$$L = \frac{18}{10}$$

hence

$$L = 1\tfrac{4}{5} \text{ inches.}$$

Although problems dealing with proportions usually involve the solution of rather simple equatiors, other types of problems frequently lead to fractional equations of greater difficulty.

Other Applications

EXAMPLE 3. If a container contains a mixture of 5 gallons of white paint and 11 gallons of brown paint, how much white paint must be added to the container so that the new mixture will be two-thirds white paint?

SOLUTION: If we let x represent the number of gallons of white paint to be added, then

$$5 + x$$

will be the number of gallons of white paint in the final mixture, and

$$16 + x$$

will be the number of gallons of paint. The ratio of these two quantities is equal to $\frac{2}{3}$. The proportion is

$$\frac{5 + x}{16 + x} = \frac{2}{3}$$

$$15 + 3x = 32 + 2x \qquad \text{by property 1}$$

$$3x - 2x = 32 - 15$$

$$x = 17 \text{ gallons}$$

Check: The final mixture would contain $5 + x = 22$ gallons of white paint, and the total volume would be $16 + x = 33$ gallons.

$$\frac{\text{Volume of white paint}}{\text{Total volume of paint}} = \frac{22 \text{ gal}}{33 \text{ gal}} = \frac{2}{3}$$

EXAMPLE 4. Two planes with speeds of 600 miles (in still air) each make a trip of 990 miles. They take off at the same time and fly in opposite directions. One has a head wind and the other a tail wind. The plane flying with a tail wind lands 20 minutes before the other plane. What is the wind velocity?

SOLUTION: If we let r represent the wind velocity in miles per hour, then the speeds of the planes are:

$$600 + r \qquad \text{speed of plane with tail wind}$$
$$600 - r \qquad \text{speed of plane with head wind}$$

Solving the distance formula,

$$d = rt \text{ for } t,$$

we obtain $t = \frac{d}{r}$. The time for the slower plane is

$$\frac{990}{600 - r}$$

and for the faster plane the time is

$$\frac{990}{600 + r}.$$

Since the difference in time is $\frac{1}{3}$ hour, we have

$$\frac{990}{600 - r} - \frac{990}{600 + r} = \tfrac{1}{3}.$$

$$3(990)(600 + r) - 3(990)(600 - r) = \frac{1}{3}(3)(600 + r)(600 - r)$$

$$3(990)(2r) = 360{,}000 - r^2$$

$$r^2 + 5940r - 360{,}000 = 0$$

$$(r - 60)(r + 6000) = 0$$

$$r - 60 = 0 \qquad\qquad\qquad r + 6000 = 0$$

$$r = 60 \text{ mph} \qquad\qquad\qquad r = -6000 \text{ mph}$$

The value -6000 mph can not be considered a solution since it was implied in the problem that the wind velocity was positive. Also a wind speed of 6000 mph is extremely unlikely.

Check: If the wind speed is 60 mph., the planes will have velocities of 540 mph and 660 mph. The difference of the times of flight is

$$\frac{990}{540} - \frac{990}{600} = \frac{11}{6} - \frac{3}{2}$$

$$= \frac{11}{6} - \frac{9}{6}$$

$$= \frac{1}{3} \text{ hour}$$

EXAMPLE 5. The sum of a number and its reciprocal is $\dfrac{65}{28}$. What is the number?

SOLUTION: Let x represent the number, then the reciprocal is $\dfrac{1}{x}$.

$$x + \frac{1}{x} = \frac{65}{28}$$

$$28x^2 + 28 = 65x$$

$$28x^2 - 65x + 28 = 0$$

$$(7x - 4)(4x - 7) = 0$$

$$7x - 4 = 0 \qquad\qquad\qquad 4x - 7 = 0$$

$$x = \frac{4}{7} \qquad\qquad\qquad x = \frac{7}{4}$$

Note: The two possible values of the number are reciprocals so a single check will suffice to show the number could be either $\frac{4}{7}$ or $\frac{7}{4}$.

Check: $\quad \dfrac{4}{7} + \dfrac{7}{4} = \dfrac{16}{28} + \dfrac{49}{28}$

$$= \frac{65}{28}$$

EXAMPLE 6. When two resistances are installed in an electric circuit in parallel, the reciprocal of the resistance of the system is equal to the sum of the reciprocals of the parallel resistances. If r_1 and r_2 represent the resistances installed and R the resistance of the system, then

$$\frac{1}{R} = \frac{1}{r_1} + \frac{1}{r_2}$$

What single resistance is the equivalent of resistances of 10 ohms and 25 ohms wired in parallel? If $r_1 = 10$ ohms and $r_2 = 25$ ohms, then

$$\frac{1}{R} = \frac{1}{10} + \frac{1}{25}$$

$$\frac{1}{R} = \frac{10}{100} + \frac{4}{100}$$

$$\frac{1}{R} = \frac{14}{100}$$

$$R = \frac{100}{14}$$

$$= \frac{52}{7} = 7.43 \text{ ohms}$$

EXERCISE 6.6

Applications of Fractional Equations

In Problems 1–6, prove the properties of proportions. By starting with the proportion $\dfrac{a}{b} = \dfrac{c}{d}$, prove:

1. Property 1. $ad = bc$

2. Property 2. $\dfrac{b}{a} = \dfrac{d}{c}$

3. Property 3. $\dfrac{a}{c} = \dfrac{b}{d}$

4. Property 4. $\dfrac{a + b}{b} = \dfrac{c + d}{d}$ (*Hint*: Add the same amount to both members of the equation.)

5. Property 5. $\dfrac{a - b}{b} = \dfrac{c - d}{d}$ (*Hint*: Subtract the same amount from both members of the equation).

6. Property 6. $\dfrac{a + b}{a - b} = \dfrac{c + d}{c - d}$ (*Hint*: Use properties 4 and 5 or proportions and a postulate of equality.)

7. If a four-foot post casts a shadow $2\frac{1}{2}$ ft long at the same time a tree casts a shadow 55 ft long, how tall is the tree?

8. A six-foot man casts a shadow five feet long at the same time a tower casts a shadow 67 feet long. How tall is the tower?

9. On a drawing, the scale used is: "1 inch represents 8 ft." If a part is 37 feet long, what would be the length of this part in the drawing?

10. Two towns are located $2\dfrac{3}{16}$ inches apart on a map. If the scale on the map is "1 inch represents 32 miles," what is the actual distance between the towns?

In problems 11–14, r_1 and r_2 represent resistances connected in parallel and R is the resistance of the circuit.

11. If $r_1 = 10$ ohms and $r_2 = 100$ ohms, find R.

12. If $r_1 = 50$ ohms and $r_2 = 50$ ohms, find R.

13. If $r_1 = 1000$ ohms and $R = \dfrac{1000}{11}$ ohms, find r_2.

14. Two equal resistors are to be connected in parallel to obtain a resistance of 150 ohms. Find the resistance of each resistor.

15. A man can travel by canoe 6 miles upstream and return in 4 hours. In still water he can travel 4 miles per hour. What is the speed of the current?

16. If a boat can travel 20 miles upstream and return in 4 hours, 10 minutes, in a stream with a current of two miles per hour, what is the speed of the boat in still water? How long would the round trip take if there were no current?

17. The sum of a number and its reciprocal is $\dfrac{89}{40}$. Find the number.

18. The sum of a number and its reciprocal is $\dfrac{97}{36}$. Determine the number.

19. For a thin convex lens the focal length (F) can be determined from the distance from the object to the lens (b) and the distance from the lens to the image (m) by using the following formula:

$$\frac{1}{F} = \frac{1}{b} + \frac{1}{m}.$$

What is the focal length of a lens if when the object is 5 ft from the lens the image is 2 in. from the lens?

20. Use the formula of Problem 19 to determine the focal length of a lens which will produce an image 2 cm from the lens when the object is 1 m from the lens.

chapter 7

the function concept

7.1 INTRODUCTION AND NOTATION

ONE OF THE MOST USEFUL AND PERVASIVE CONCEPTS IN mathematics is that of function. Before developing a formal definition of this important concept, we consider several illustrations.

Suppose that an investor has a portfolio of common stocks designated as the set $S = \{a, c, k, m, q, t, v\}$. At the end of a market day, we can associate with each common stock a closing price from a set P, a set of rational numbers graduated in eighths of a dollar. Such a correspondence is illustrated by Figure 7.1.

Notice that all elements of S are different, and that each is associated with one and only one element of the set P. This correspondence can be represented by the following set of pairs, which we designate as the set F.

$$F = \left\{ \left(a, 17\tfrac{1}{2}\right), \left(c, 34\tfrac{1}{4}\right), \left(k, 5\tfrac{3}{4}\right), \left(m, 112\tfrac{1}{2}\right), \left(q, 5\tfrac{3}{4}\right), \left(t, 5\tfrac{3}{4}\right), \left(v, 28\tfrac{3}{8}\right) \right\}$$

In this representation the first element of each pair is understood to be in set S and the second element of each pair is understood to be in set P. Since the order in which the elements of each pair are listed is of consequence, these pairs are called *ordered pairs*. The notion of ordered pairs may be defined as follows.

DEFINITION 7.1 An *ordered pair* of elements, indicated by the notation (a, b), is a pair of elements in which the meaning associated with each element

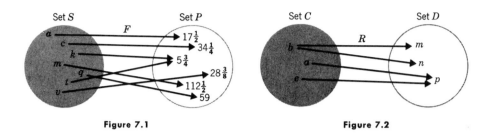

Figure 7.1   Figure 7.2

depends on its position in the pair. Two ordered pairs (a, b) and (c, d) are equal if and only if $a = c$ and $b = d$. This implies, in particular, that $(a, b) \neq (c, d)$ when $a \neq c$.

In the set F the meaning associated with each element by virtue of its position is that of belonging respectively to set S or set P. It is apparent that in this illustration any given pair (a, b) is not equal to (b, a), since the two sets S and P do not intersect. If, however, two sets had some elements in common, such as the numbers 3 and 8, then by Definition 7.1, $(3, 8) \neq (8, 3)$.

The notion of a set of ordered pairs is so broad and fundamental in pure and applied mathematics that it is given a special name, as indicated in the following definition.

DEFINITION 7.2   Any set of ordered pairs is a *relation*.

Since F is a set of ordered pairs, it is a relation. It has, however, some additional properties of interest to us. We note that all first elements of the ordered pairs in F are different, and that each first element is associated with one and only one second element. A relation that meets these additional qualifications is called a *function*. Therefore, the relation F is a function.

By way of contrast, we now consider a relation that is *not* a function. The correspondence between elements of sets C and D (Figure 7.2) produces the following set of ordered pairs:

$$R = \{(b, m), (b, n), (a, p), (c, p)\}$$

The relation R is not a function because in two of the ordered pairs the first components are the same, that is, the element b does not correspond to one and only one element of the second set.

The illustrations are formalized in the following definition of a function.

DEFINITION 7.3   A *function* is a set of ordered pairs in which the first components are all different. The *domain* of the function is the set of all first components of the ordered pairs, and the *range* of the function is the set of all second components of the ordered pairs.

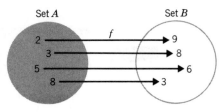

Figure 7.3

As a further example of a function, consider the set of ordered pairs:

$$f = \{(2, 9), (3, 8), (5, 6), (8, 3)\}$$

The function defined by this set of ordered pairs is illustrated in Figure 7.3. The domain of the function is the set $A = \{2, 3, 5, 8\}$ and the range of the function is the set $B = \{3, 6, 8, 9\}$. We can symbolize this function by the notation $f: A \to B$, which is interpreted as "the function f from set A to set B." Each element of set B is said to be the *image* of the corresponding member of set A. Thus 9 is said to be the image of 2 under f. We can also say that f maps the element 2 to the element 9, or that $f(2) = 9$. Similarly, 6 is the image of 5, or $f(5) = 6$, and so on.

Notice that in Figure 7.3 the images are all different. Therefore, not only does each element of set A correspond to a single element of set B but, conversely, each element of set B corresponds to a single element of set A. Any function that exhibits this special property is known as a one-to-one function. Thus, the function f illustrated in Figure 7.3 is a one-to-one function, but the function F illustrated in Figure 7.1 is not a one-to-one function.

In many applied situations, it is impractical or impossible to list all the ordered pairs of a particular function. We therefore need some other means to describe a function. At times a verbal statement, or a graph is useful. Usually, however, the goal of a mathematical description of a function is an equation. For example, the function illustrated in Figure 7.2 can be described by

$$F = \{(x, y) \,|\, y = 11 - x\}$$

where x is an element of set A and y is the corresponding element of set B. This equation will produce the given ordered pairs

$$F = \{(2, 9), (3, 8), (5, 6), (8, 3)\}$$

and, if we do not restrict the domain to set A, it may be used to produce as many ordered pairs as we please.

When a function is expressed as an equation, it is instructive to liken the idea of the function to the operation of a computer. In Figure 7.4, the diagram illustrates a computer programmed to perform a sequence of operations as defined by the equation. Whenever the first component x of an ordered pair is fed into

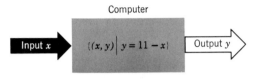

Figure 7.4

the computer, it performs the operation $11 - x$ to produce the corresponding second component of the ordered pair. Thus for an input $x = 7$, the computer would perform the operation of substracting 7 from 11 to produce an output $y = 4$. Therefore, $(7, 4)$ is one of the ordered pairs of the function. Additional ordered pairs can be generated by merely feeding into the computer the desired values of x.

A little reflection will indicate that numerous important examples of functions occur naturally in the world about us. The speed with which a freely falling object strikes the ground is related, through a set of ordered pairs, to its initial height. Similarly, the amount of voltage drop in an electric line is related to the length of the line, the decrease in radioactivity of a substance varies with the passage of the centuries, and the length of a steel span changes with its temperature. In each case there exists a correspondence between the elements of two sets which can be expressed as a set of ordered pairs such that just one element of a second set is associated with each element of a first set.

The meaningful examination of such relations requires some familiarity with the use of certain mathematical symbols. They are part of the language of mathematics. It is important to be able to read them correctly, understand their meanings, and use them in mathematical operations. The following are some of the more common notational conventions used to express the idea of function.

1. The symbol $f: A \rightarrow B$ is read "the function from A to B," or "the function f maps the elements of set A to the elements of set B." This notation always implies that set A is the domain of f and set B is the range of f. Similarly, $f: x \rightarrow x^2 + 7$ is read "the function from x to $x^2 + 7$."

2. The notation $f = \{(x, y) \mid y = x^2 + 7\}$ is read "the function f is the set of all ordered pairs (x, y) such that $y = x^2 + 7$." The domain is the set of x values and the range is the set of corresponding y values.

3. Perhaps the most usual notation, and the one we shall generally use in this book, is the symbol $f(x)$ which is read "f of x," or "the value of the function at x." Beginning students should recognize the distinction between the symbols f and $f(x)$. The symbol f represents a function, that is, a rule which enables one to associate the elements of two sets; it is not an element of either set. The symbol $f(x)$, on the other hand, is an element of one of the sets under consideration; specifically, it is the image of x under the particular correspondence defined by the function. Thus the statement

$$f(x) = x^2 + 7$$

can be read "the value of $x^2 + 7$ at x." Then $f(3)$, for example, is the value of the function at $x = 3$, that is,

$$f(3) = 3^2 + 7 = 16$$

Therefore, 16 is the image of 3 under the function $x^2 + 7$.

The symbol y is frequently used to represent the image of x, and in such cases the symbols y and $f(x)$ are interchangeable so that we could also write

$$y = f(x) = x^2 + 7$$

It is clear that y and $f(x)$ are symbols for the image of x, and that the function itself is the set of ordered pairs which results from matching each x with its image. In common practice, however, we frequently abbreviate this to the expression that y *is a function of* x. The symbol y is also referred to as the *dependent variable*, and in this context x is called the *independent variable*.

Although the symbols x, y, f, $f(x)$, F, and $F(x)$ are used most often, other variations will suggest themselves as being appropriate to a particular situation. The following examples illustrate some common uses of functional notation.

EXAMPLE 1. The area of a circular region is a function of its radius because for each value of the radius r, the corresponding area $A(r)$ is determined by the equation

$$A(r) = \pi r^2$$

The domain is the set of positive real numbers and the range of $A(r)$ is the corresponding set of positive real numbers. The independent variable is r; the dependent variable is $A(r)$.

EXAMPLE 2. If $g(x) = x^2 + 5x - 3$, find $g(-7)$.

SOLUTION: $g(-7) = (-7)^2 + 5(-7) - 3 = 49 - 35 - 3 = 11$.

EXAMPLE 3. If $f(t) = 6t + 13$, find $f(5) - f(4)$.

SOLUTION: $f(5) = 6 \cdot 5 + 13 = 43; f(4) = 6 \cdot 4 + 13 = 37$
$f(5) - f(4) = 43 - 37 = 6$

EXAMPLE 4. Show that $f(a) = f(-a)$ if $f(x) = x^2 + 3$.

SOLUTION: $f(a) = a^2 + 3$
$f(-a) = (-a)^2 + 3 = a^2 + 3 = f(a)$

EXAMPLE 5. Describe the domain and range of the function
$f = \{(x, y) \,|\, y = \sqrt{9 - x^2}\}$ if x and y are real numbers.

SOLUTION: Since the square root of a negative number is not a real number, the domain is restricted to those values of x which make the radicand positive or zero. Therefore x^2 cannot exceed 9 which means that x cannot exceed 3 or be less than -3. A convenient way to express this is to write $-3 \leq x \leq 3$, which is read "x is greater than or equal to -3 and less than or equal to 3." This is the domain of the function. To determine the range of the function we note that the largest value of y occurs when $x = 0$. Then $y = \sqrt{9 - 0} = 3$. Likewise, the smallest value of y occurs when $x = 3$ or $x = -3$. Then $y = \sqrt{9 - 9} = 0$. Therefore, the range of y can be written in the form $0 \leq y \leq 3$.

EXERCISE 7.1

The Function Concept: Introduction and Notation

Which of the following sets is a function?

1. $\{(3, 1), (6, 2), (9, 3), (-3, -1)\}$
2. $\{(2, 2), (5, 2), (2, 5), (5, 5)\}$
3. $\{(1, 2), (2, 2), (1, 3)\}$
4. $\{(-4, 0), (0, -4), (4, 0), (8, -4), (-8, 0)\}$
5. $\{(2, -3), (-2, 3), (3, -2), (-3, 2)\}$
6. $\{(9, 3), (9, -3), (16, 4), (16, -4), (25, 5), (25, -5)\}$

A set of ordered pairs is formed by mapping the elements of set A to those of set B. Determine whether the resulting relation is generally a one-to-one function, a many-to-one function, or is not a function.

7. $A = \{\text{college students}\}$, $B = \{\text{college teachers}\}$
8. $A = \{\text{real numbers}\}$, $B = \{\text{points on a number line}\}$
9. $A = \{\text{"major league" baseball players}\}$, $B = \{\text{"major league" baseball clubs}\}$
10. $A = \{\text{children}\}$, $B = \{\text{mothers}\}$
11. $A = \{\text{children}\}$, $B = \{\text{ancestors}\}$
12. $A = \{\text{authors of textbooks}\}$, $B = \{\text{textbooks}\}$
13. $A = \{\text{odd numbers}\}$, $B = \{\text{squares of odd numbers}\}$
14. $A = \{\text{cities in the U.S.}\}$, $B = \{\text{states in the U.S.}\}$

15. A = {perimeter of a square}, B = {area of a square}

16. A = {natural numbers}, B = {integers}. *Hint*: Consider the interesting relation $i = \frac{1}{2}n$ if n is even and $i = \frac{1}{2}(1 - n)$ if n is odd, where n is a natural number and i is the corresponding integer.

Choose the one phrase that best completes each of the following statements.

17. The number of nails to a pound can be expressed as a function of (a) the size of each nail, (b) the relative hardness of each nail, (c) the weight of each nail.

18. The area of a triangle with a fixed altitude can be expressed as a function of (a) its base, (b) its perimeter, (c) its vertex angle.

19. The time it takes for a radio-controlled projectile from the earth to reach a given planet on a direct-path trajectory is a function of (a) its velocity upon leaving the earth's atmosphere, (b) its average velocity from take-off to landing, (c) its velocity at the midpoint of its journey.

20. The volume of a given amount of gas at a given temperature is a function of (a) its chemical composition, (b) its weight, (c) its pressure.

Evaluate each of the following expressions for the function $f(x) = 3x + 5$. (Problems 21–29).

21. $f(7)$ 　　　　　　　 22. $f(6)$ 　　　　　　　 23. $\dfrac{f(7) - f(6)}{7 - 6}$

24. $f(2)$ 　　　　　　　 25. $f(-2)$ 　　　　　　 26. $\dfrac{f(2) - f(-2)}{2 - (-2)}$

27. $f(-3)$ 　　　　　　 28. $f(-10)$ 　　　　　 29. $\dfrac{f(-3) - f(-10)}{(-3) - (-10)}$

30. Is there anything in the results of Problems 23, 26, and 29 as they relate to the given function which suggests further investigations? Can you formulate a hypothesis based on these results?

Evaluate each of the following expressions for the function $f(x) = -2x + 7$.

31. $f(11)$ 　　　　　　 32. $f(4)$ 　　　　　　　 33. $\dfrac{f(11) - f(4)}{11 - 4}$

34. $f(8)$ 　　　　　　　 35. $f(0)$ 　　　　　　　 36. $\dfrac{f(8) - f(0)}{8 - 0}$

Describe the domain and the range of each of the following functions if both x and $f(x)$ are real numbers (Problems 37–42).

37. $f(x) = 2x + 9$ 　　　 38. $f(x) = -x$ 　　　　 39. $f(x) = 3x^2$

40. $f(x) = \sqrt{64 - x}$ 　 41. $f(x) = \sqrt{x^2 - 1}$ 　 42. $f(x) = \sqrt{1 - x^2}$

43. Any function for which $f(x) = f(-x)$ is called an *even function*. Show that $f(x) = x^4 - 5x^2 + 2$ is an even function, and give one other example of an even function.

44. Any function for which $f(x) = -f(-x)$ is called an *odd function*. Show that $f(x) = x^3 + 2x$ is an odd function, and give one other example of an odd function.

Determine the value of $f(3), f(1), f(-1), f(-3)$ for each of the following functions and describe the function as (a) even, (b) odd, or (c) neither (Problems 45–50).

45. $3x^2 - 5$ 46. $-x^2$ 47. $2x^3 + 7$

48. $2x^3$ 49. $-x^3 + 2x$ 50. $x^3 + x^2 + x + 1$

51. The distance in feet which a freely falling object travels is 16 times the square of the time of motion expressed in seconds. (a) Express the relation between the distance s and the time t by means of a formula. (b) Evaluate $f(3)$. What does it represent? (c) Evaluate $f(3) - f(2)$. What does this difference represent?

52. The base of a triangle is 5 units more than its height. If its height is x, (a) write the formula that describes the relation between the area of the triangle, A, and its height, x. (b) What is the domain of this function? Find the value of $f(6)$. What does it represent?

7.2 RECTANGULAR COORDINATE SYSTEM

A graph frequently provides an unusually clear and comprehensive view of a function. Such representation is most commonly based on the Cartesian system of rectangular coordinates, which was introduced by the French philosopher and mathematician René Descartes in 1637. It turned out to be one of the most brilliant and fruitful ideas in the history of mathematics. The essence of the idea is that a one-to-one correspondence can be established between a set of *ordered pairs of real numbers* and a set of *points in a plane*. One important consequence is that an intimate interdependence emerges between algebra (the science of numbers) and geometry (the science of space).

The system is a simple one, based on the following agreements.

1. Two real number lines, called the *coordinate axes*, are constructed perpendicular to each other as in Figure 7.5. The horizontal axis is usually called the *x-axis* and the vertical axis is usually called the *y-axis*. The point of intersection of the axes is called the *origin* and is usually denoted by 0.

2. The plane determined by the coordinate axes is called the *coordinate plane* or the *xy-plane*. The axes divide the coordinate plane into four parts called *quadrants*. These are numbered, counterclockwise, I, II, III, and IV as shown in Figure 7.5.

3. The line coordinate of a point on the *x*-axis to the right of the origin is taken as positive; the line coordinate of a point to the left of the origin is taken as negative. Similarly, a point on the *y-axis* above the origin has a positive co-

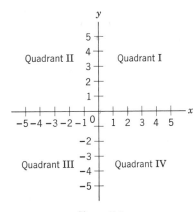

Figure 7.5

Figure 7.6

ordinate and a point below the origin has a negative coordinate. Ordinarily the same unit of length is used on both axes, although in some cases it is convenient to do otherwise.

4. Each ordered pair of numbers determines a point in the coordinate plane and, conversely, each point in the plane determines an ordered pair of numbers. The ordered pair is written in the form (x, y) where the first component of the pair corresponds to the reading along the x-axis, and the second component corresponds to the reading along the y-axis. The first component is also called the *x-coordinate* or the *abscissa* of the point, and the second component is also called the *y-coordinate* or *ordinate* of the point.

5. Locating a point in the system is referred to as *plotting* the point, and the plotted point is called the graph of the ordered pair.

EXAMPLE 1. Plot the points $(1, -2)$ and $(5, 1)$ in the xy-plane.

SOLUTION: The point $(1, -2)$ is 1 unit to the right of the origin and 2 units below the x-axis. Therefore it is located at point A in Figure 7.6. The point $(5, 1)$ is located at point B, 5 units to the right of the origin and 1 unit above the x-axis.

EXAMPLE 2. What ordered pair corresponds to point C in Figure 7.6?

SOLUTION: The abscissa of point C is 0 and its ordinate is 2. Therefore, the ordered pair is $(0, 2)$.

EXAMPLE 3. If points $A, B,$ and C of Figure 7.6 are three vertices of a parallelogram, what are the coordinates of the fourth vertex in the third quadrant?

SOLUTION: There are three possible locations for a fourth vertex. In quadrant III the vertex is the intersection of lines parallel to AB and BC, respectively. Since point C is 5 units to the left of point B and 1 unit above it, the required vertex D will be 5 units to the left of point A and 1 unit above it. Its coordinates are $(-4, -1)$.

EXAMPLE 4. What are the coordinates of the midpoint of a line segment joining $P(-2, 1)$ and $Q(6, 4)$?

SOLUTION: Plot the points P and Q, as illustrated in Figure 7.7. The midpoint of PQ is also the midpoint of the hypotenuse of right triangle PQR where R is at $(6, 1)$. Therefore the height QR of the triangle is 3 and its base PR is 8. Since a line through the midpoint of the hypotenuse of a triangle and parallel to its base bisects the remaining side of the triangle, the ordinate of the midpoint is $2\frac{1}{2}$. Similarly, its abscissa is 2. Therefore, the coordinates of the midpoint M are $(2, 2\frac{1}{2})$.

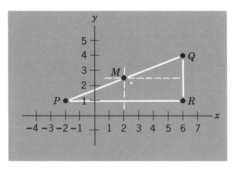

Figure 7.7

EXERCISE 7.2

Rectangular Coordinate System

Name the quadrant or quadrants for which each of the following statements is true (Problems 1–7).

1. The coordinates of each point have unlike signs.

2. The abscissa is negative and the ordinate is positive.

3. x and y have like signs.   4. The ordinate is positive.

5. $x < 0$ 6. $y < 0$ 7. $x > 0, y < 0$

8. Draw a line through the points $M(-3, 4)$ and $N(7, -2)$. Which of the following points also appear to lie on the line: $(-6, 6)$, $(-5, 6)$, $(2, 1)$, $(0, 3)$, $(3, 0)$, $(12, -5)$?

Plot each of the following sets of points. Then join the successive points of each set by straight lines and identify the geometric figure which is formed.

9. $(0, 0)$, $(-3, 5)$, $(5, 3)$ 10. $(0, -2)$, $(4, -3)$, $(1, 2)$, $(-3, 3)$

11. $(9, 2)$, $(1, 4)$, $(0, 0)$, $(8, -2)$ 12. $(0, 0)$, $(14, 4)$, $(5, 7)$, $(-2, 5)$

13. $(0, 0)$, $(3, 9)$, $(12, 6)$, $(9, -3)$

Plot the following pairs of points, locate the midpoint of the line segment joining the pair of points, and determine the coordinates of each midpoint (Problems 14–19).

14. $(2, 3)$, $(6, 11)$ 15. $(0, 0)$, $(8, 4)$ 16. $(-5, 5)$, $(3, 9)$

17. $(7, -6)$, $(-1, 0)$ 18. $(-11, 8)$, $(-1, -2)$ 19. $(-4, -7)$, $(10, 3)$

Using the results of Problems 14–19:

20. (a) How is the abscissa of the midpoint related to the abscissas of the two given end points? (b) How is the ordinate of the midpoint related to the ordinates of the two given end points?

21. Without plotting the points, what is the midpoint of the line segment joining the points $(2, 7)$ and $(22, -17)$?

22. What is the midpoint of the line segment joining the points (x_1, y_1) and (x_2, y_2)?

23. (a) Draw a line through the points $(6, 3)$ and $(-8, -4)$. (b) Verify that the points $(4, 2)$ $(0, 0)$, and $(-2, -1)$ also lie on the line. (c) What are the coordinates of several other points on the line? (d) Express the relation between the ordinate and abscissa of each point in the form of a verbal statement. (e) Express the relation between the ordinate and abscissa of each point in the form $y = f(x)$. (f) If this line were extended, would it pass through the point $(-96, -49)$? Give a reason for your answer.

24. (a) Draw a line through the points $(-3, 6)$ and $(5, -10)$. (b) List the coordinates of several other points on the line. (c) If y represents the ordinate of any one of these points, and x represents the corresponding abscissa, express the relation of these ordered pairs in the form $y = f(x)$. (d) Does this relation appear to hold true when x is not an integer? (e) Can you predict whether the point $(137, -274)$ would lie on the line? Support your answer.

25. Referring to Figure 7.8, line segment AB joins $A(3, 2)$ and $B(15, 7)$. (a) What are the coordinates of point C if AC and BC are parallel to the respective axes? (b) What is the length of the base of right triangle ABC? (c) What is the height BC? (d) Using the Pythagorean theorem, what is the length AB?

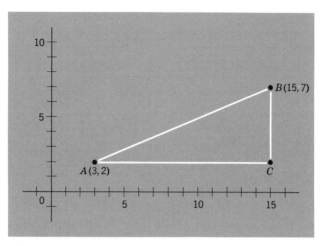

Figure 7.8

Using the Pythagorean theorem, as in Problem 25, determine the length of the line segment joining the following pairs of points (Problems 26–29).

26. $(3, 1)$ and $(15, 6)$

27. $(2, 3)$ and $(10, 9)$

28. $(1, -1)$ and $(-3, 2)$

29. $(0, 0)$ and $(3, 2)$

30. Prove that the triangle whose vertices are $A(5, 2)$, $B(-1, 5)$, and $C(-4, -1)$ is isosceles, that is, show that the lengths of two of its sides are equal.

7.3 GRAPHIC REPRESENTATION OF FUNCTIONS

We have noted that a function is a set of ordered pairs such that the first components are all different. If the domain and range of a function are real numbers, then the set of ordered pairs can be represented by a set of points in the xy-plane such that each point corresponds to one of the ordered pairs. This set of points is called the graph of the function. Thus the graph of the function

$$y = f(x) \tag{1}$$

is the set of points whose coordinates satisfy Equation 1.

The set of points may lie on a straight line. If this is so we can, of course, draw only a convenient portion of the line. Or the set of points may lie on a curve, in which case we usually approximate the graph by drawing a smooth curve through the points we choose to plot.

The following procedures illustrate some common approaches to plotting the graph of a given function.

1. Point-by-Point Plotting

This is a rather direct approach to graphing—simply selecting a succession of points to determine the general characteristics of the curve, supplemented by as many intermediate points as are needed to refine specific portions of the curve. In this context, selecting a succession of points means selecting, at will, the abscissas of the desired points, calculating the corresponding ordinates, and arranging the resulting ordered pairs in a tabular listing. The two examples that follow illustrate the steps in this procedure.

EXAMPLE 1. Graph the function $y = 9 - \dfrac{x}{2}$.

SOLUTION: Choosing even values of x in the interval $0 \leq x \leq 10$, we determine the ordered pairs listed in the following table.

x	0	2	4	6	8	10
y	9	8	7	6	5	4

Plotting these points, as illustrated in Figure 7.9, the graph appears to be a straight line passing through the first, second, and fourth quadrants. (The fact that it is a straight line will be proved in Section 7.4). Although we have plotted a limited number of points, the coordinates of each point on the line will satisfy the equation $y = 9 - \dfrac{x}{2}$ and, conversely, each ordered pair which satisfies the equation will determine a point on the line.

EXAMPLE 2. Draw a graph of the set of ordered pairs which satisfy the function $f(x) = x^2 - 7$.

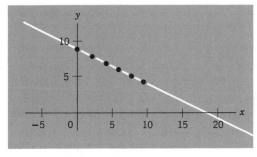

Figure 7.9

SOLUTION: The following table lists a sufficient sequence of ordered pairs to determine the general nature of the curve:

x	0	1	2	3	4	-1	-2	-3	-4
$y = f(x)$	-7	-6	-3	2	9	-6	-3	2	9

Plotting these points, we obtain the curve illustrated in Figure 7.10. The domain of the function is the set of real numbers. The range of the function appears to be limited to real numbers equal to or greater than -7. To determine whether -7 is indeed the lower limit of the range, it is possible to investigate the value of y for values of x as close to $x = 0$ as we please. The points $A(-4, 9)$ and $B(4, 9)$ in Figure 7.10 are said to be symmetric with respect to the y-axis. Similarly, C and D, E and F, and G and H are symmetric with respect to the y-axis.

2. Intercepts

The selection of plotted points in determining the graph of a function need not be entirely random. As will be illustrated in Example 3, it is possible to select points in such a way that fewer points are needed and yet the fundamental characteristics of the curve are determined with greater accuracy and clarity. Among the most important of these points are the points at which the curve crosses the coordinate axes, called the *intercepts* of the curve. Of course, if the curve does not cross an axis, that intercept does not exist.

The y-intercept is found by setting $x = 0$ in the function $y = f(x)$ and solving for y. This is usually a simple matter and can be ascertained by verifying the y-intercepts in Examples 1 and 2. Similarly, the x-intercept is found by setting $y = 0$ and solving for x. This may lead to a first degree equation as in Example 1, or a quadratic equation as in Example 2, or it may lead to higher degree equations in more complicated functions.

3. Symmetry

The points (x, y) and $(-x, y)$ are symmetric with respect to the y-axis. Therefore, any function for which $f(x) = f(-x)$ will result in a graph which is symmetric with respect to the y-axis. We note that for Example 2,

$$f(x) = x^2 - 7$$
$$f(-x) = (-x)^2 - 7 = x^2 - 7 = f(x)$$

Therefore, the curve is symmetric with respect to the y-axis. Knowing this, we could merely plot the portion of the curve for $x \geq 0$ and draw the mirror image of the curve for $x < 0$. The symmetry is evident in Figure 7.10.

Similarly, the points (x, y) and $(-x, -y)$ are symmetric with respect to the origin, that is, the origin will bisect any line through it joining two points on the curve. Therefore, if the replacement of (x, y) with $(-x, -y)$ leaves the equation unchanged, the graph will be symmetric with respect to the origin. The following example illustrates this type of symmetry.

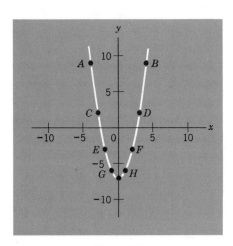

Figure 7.10

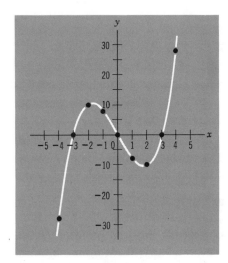

Figure 7.11

EXAMPLE 3. Graph the function $y = x^3 - 9x$.

SOLUTION: Choosing values of x in the interval $-4 \leq x \leq 4$, we have

x	−4	−3	−2	−1	0	1	2	3	4
y	−28	0	10	8	0	−8	−10	0	28

Notice that for each ordered pair (x, y) listed in the table there exists a pair $(-x, -y)$ which also satisfies the equation, indicating symmetry with respect to the origin. To prove that this is true for all points on the curve, we substitute $(-x, -y)$ for (x, y) in the given equation and show that the equation is unchanged. Thus

$$-y = (-x)^3 - 9(-x) = -x^3 + 9x$$

or, multiplying each member by -1,

$$y = x^3 - 9x$$

which is the original equation.

The curve is illustrated in Figure 7.11. The domain and range of the function have no restrictions in the set of real numbers. The curve has three x-intercepts at $x = -3$, $x = 0$, $x = 3$, and it has a single y-intercept at $y = 0$.

4. Domain and Range

In graphing a function, an investigation of the domain and range may provide important information about portions of the coordinate plane to which the graph is confined. For example, we noted that in graphing $y = x^2 - 7$ (see Example 2) the range of the function appeared to be limited to $y \geq -7$. This is algebraically apparent if we solve the given equation for x^2:

$$x^2 = y + 7$$

Since expressions equal to a perfect square cannot be negative, it follows that

$$y + 7 \geq 0$$

Therefore

$$y \geq -7$$

The following example summarizes and further illustrates the graphing procedures we have discussed.

EXAMPLE 4. Discuss the graph of the function $y = \dfrac{12}{x^2}$.

SOLUTION: *Intercepts:* Since division by zero is not defined, there is no y-intercept. Similarly, there is no x-intercept, *Symmetry:* The curve is symmetric with respect to the y-axis since $f(x) = f(-x)$. *Domain:* There is no limitation on x, except that $x \neq 0$. *Range:* Since $x^2 = \dfrac{12}{y}$, y must be positive. Therefore, the curve exists only in the first and second quadrants. *Plotting:* We note that, in the first quadrant, as x increases y decreases. Several points to illustrate this are listed in the following table.

x	0.5	1	2	3	$\cdots$	10
y	48	12	3	1.3	$\cdots$	0.12

After plotting these points, and tracing the curve in the first quadrant, the second branch is drawn in quadrant II, using the principle of symmetry. The curve is illustrated in Figure 7.12.

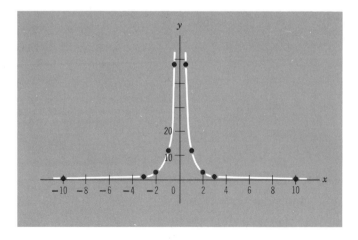

Figure 7.12

EXERCISE 7.3

Graphic Representation of Functions

What are the coordinates of the point which is symmetric to the given point with respect to (a) the y-axis, (b) the origin?

1. $(7, 2)$ 2. $(-3, 5)$ 3. $(2, -9)$

4. $(-1, -3)$ 5. $(4, 0)$ 6. $(0, -8)$

7. $(13, -1)$ 8. $(-6, -6)$ 9. (a, b)

10. $(a, -b)$ 11. $(-a, b)$ 12. $(-a, -b)$

Without graphing, discuss the symmetry (if any) of the curve defined by each of the following functions.

13. $y = 3x$ 14. $y = 2x + 3$ 15. $y = 3x^2$

16. $y = 3x^2 + 2$ 17. $y = -x$ 18. $y = -3x^2 + 7$

19. $y = x^3$ 20. $y = x^3 - 5$ 21. $y = \dfrac{1}{x^3}$

Without plotting, determine the intercepts (if any) of the curve defined by each of the following functions.

22. $y = x + 4$ 23. $2x + 3y = 12$ 24. $x - 4y = 20$

25. $y = x^2 - 25$ 26. $x^2 + y = 4$ 27. $y = 5x$

28. $xy = 5$ 29. $y = x^2 - 3x + 2$ 30. $y = x^2 + 7x + 10$

Sketch and discuss the graph of each of the following functions with respect to intercepts, symmetry, domain, and range.

31. $y = 2x + 1$ 32. $y = 3x - 2$ 33. $y = -x - 5$

34. $y = -2x$ 35. $3x - 2y = 6$ 36. $y = \dfrac{6}{x}$

37. $y = -x^3$ 38. $y = -\dfrac{1}{x^2}$ 39. $y = 3x^2$

40. $y = x^2 - 4$ 41. $y = x^3 - 4x$ 42. $y = x^2 + 2x - 3$

7.4   THE LINEAR FUNCTION

A linear function is one that can be expressed in the form

$$y = mx + b$$

where m and b are constants. Such functions are extremely useful because of their simplicity and because they occur very frequently in applications. Thus the formula

$$F = \tfrac{9}{5} C + 32$$

which relates Fahrenheit and centigrade readings of temperature is clearly a linear function, as is also the common formula for the circumference of a circle,

$$C = 2\pi r$$

In business applications, the simple interest formula

$$A = prt + p$$

is a linear function of the form $A = f(t)$, when the expressions pr and p are constants. Similarly, many other physical laws, geometric relations, and business applications can be expressed as linear functions. By studying properties of the general function $y = mx + b$ we can discover certain characteristics common to all such functions. This illustrates the claim, sometimes made, that the abstractness of mathematics is one of its most important virtues.

Graph of the Linear Function

It is proved in analytic geometry that the graph of the equation $y = mx + b$ is a straight line. This is the reason for the name "linear function." Although "line" is usually taken to be one of the undefined terms of Euclidean geometry, everyone intuitively feels he knows what is meant by "straight line." This notion is intimately related to the idea of direction of a line. One way of specifying direction is given in the following definition.

DEFINITION 7.3   Given two points $P_1(x_1, y_1)$ and $P_2(x_2, y_2)$, the slope of the line segment connecting the two points is $\dfrac{y_2 - y_1}{x_2 - x_1}$, $(x_2 \neq x_1)$. The graphic interpretation of slope is illustrated in Figure 7.13. The slope of specific line segments, illustrated in Figure 7.14, are computed as follows.

$$\text{slope of } AB = \frac{2 - 2}{10 - 3} = 0 \qquad\qquad \text{slope of } AF = \frac{-2 - 2}{7 - 3} = -1$$

$$\text{slope of } AC = \frac{5 - 2}{9 - 3} = \frac{1}{2} \qquad\qquad \text{slope of } AG = \frac{-7 - 2}{6 - 3} = -3$$

$$\text{slope of } AD = \frac{7 - 2}{8 - 3} = 1 \qquad\qquad \text{slope of } AH = \frac{-3 - 2}{4 - 3} = -5$$

$$\text{slope of } AE = \frac{8 - 2}{5 - 3} = 3$$

Thus we observe that the slope of a horizontal line is zero, and that as the slope increases the line appears to rotate counterclockwise toward a limiting vertical position. Similarly, as the slope decreases through negative values (line segments AF, AG, and AH), the line appears to rotate clockwise toward a limiting vertical

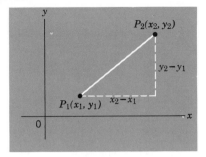

Figure 7.13

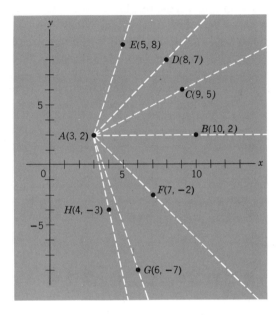

Figure 7.14

position. The slope, therefore, becomes a numerical index associated with the specific direction of a given line. The slope of a vertical line is undefined.

Another useful interpretation of the numerical value of slope is that it represents the number of units y changes per unit change in x. Thus, for the line AC, a slope of $\frac{1}{2}$ means that y increases $\frac{1}{2}$ unit for each unit increase in x. Similarly, for the line AG, a slope of -3 means that y decreases 3 units for each unit increase in x. It is left for the reader to verify that this interpretation is a direct consequence of the geometric properties of similar triangles.

We are now in a position to investigate the slope of the line defined by the equation $y = mx + b$. The procedure is fundamentally algebraic. If we select

$P_1(x_1, y_1)$ and $P_2(x_2, y_2)$ to be any two points on the graph, then each of these ordered pairs must satisfy the given equation. Therefore,

$$y_2 = mx_2 + b$$
$$y_1 = mx_1 + b$$

Then

$$\frac{y_2 - y_1}{x_2 - x_1} = \frac{(mx_2 + b) - (mx_1 + b)}{x_2 - x_1} = \frac{m(x_2 - x_1)}{x_2 - x_1} = m$$

Thus we have not only demonstrated that the slope of the line segment joining any two points on the graph is constant, but that this constant is the value m in the equation $y = mx + b$.

With this discovery, it is natural to inquire whether the remaining constant, b, also has any direct relation to the graph of the function. We note that when $x = 0$, $y = b$. Therefore, b represents the y-intercept of the graph of the function, that is, the graph intersects the y-axis at the point $(0, b)$. In summary, the graph of $y = mx + b$ is a straight line whose slope is m and whose y-intercept is b.

EXAMPLE 1. Discuss the graph of the function $y = -3x + 4$.

SOLUTION: The graph is a straight line since it is of the form $y = mx + b$. The line intersects the y-axis at the point $(0, 4)$ and has a slope of -3. This means that y decreases 3 units as x increases 1 unit anywhere along the line.

EXAMPLE 2. What is the equation of the line through the point $(3, 5)$ whose slope is 2?

SOLUTION: Let $P(x, y)$ be any point on this line other than $(3, 5)$. Using the definition of slope we have

$$2 = \frac{y - 5}{x - 3}$$
$$2x - 6 = y - 5$$
$$y = 2x - 1$$

This equation is satisfied by the coordinates $(3, 5)$ and represents a line with a slope of 2.

EXAMPLE 3. The two points $P_1(1, -2)$ and $P_2(4, 1)$ determine a line. What is the equation of the line?

SOLUTION: The slope of the line segment connecting the two points is

$$m = \frac{1 - (-2)}{4 - 1} = \frac{3}{3} = 1$$

Now the problem has been reduced to that of Example 2, that is, we know the slope and at least one point on the line. Therefore, following the procedure of Example 2, let $P(x, y)$ be any point on the line. Then the slope between the points P and P_1 (or, alternatively, between P and P_2) must be 1. Therefore,

$$1 = \frac{y - (-2)}{x - 1}$$
$$x - 1 = y + 2$$
$$y = x - 3$$

The required equation is $y = x - 3$. Note that both of the given points satisfy this equation.

EXAMPLE 4. The following table was constructed by reading the coordinates of selected points on a graphed line. Determine the equation of the line.

x	−2	−1	0	1	2	3
y	5	3	1	−1	−3	−5

SOLUTION: For each interval in the table, as x increases 1 unit, y decreases 2 units. Therefore, the slope of the line connecting these points is -2. The y-intercept is given as $(0, 1)$. Therefore, the required equation is one which represents a straight line with a slope of -2 and y-intercept of 1, that is, $y = -2x + 1$. It can be verified that each listed ordered pair will satisfy this equation.

The Linear Function $ax + by = c$

The linear function often appears in the form $ax + by = c$, $b \neq 0$. For example, $6x + 2y = 1$ is a linear function. To rewrite this equation in the familiar form $y = mx + b$, we can solve the given equation for y as follows:

$$6x + 2y = 1$$
$$2y = -6x + 1$$
$$y = -3x + \frac{1}{2}$$

Therefore, the graph of $6x + 2y = 1$ is a straight line whose slope is -3 and whose y-intercept is $\frac{1}{2}$.

In the same way, the general equation $ax + by = c$, $b \neq 0$, can be expressed in the form $y = mx + b$. Again solving for y, we have

$$ax + by = c$$
$$by = -ax + c$$
$$y = -\frac{a}{b}x + \frac{c}{b}$$

which is of the form $y = mx + b$, where the slope $m = -\dfrac{a}{b}$ and the y-intercept is $\dfrac{c}{b}$.

Since a straight line is determined by any two points, the graph of $ax + by = c$ can usually be drawn conveniently by locating its x and y intercepts. A third point, if desired, can be plotted to ensure against errors and to promote graphic accuracy by selecting points which are spaced sufficiently far apart.

EXAMPLE 5. Graph the function defined by $3x - 4y = 12$.

SOLUTION: For $x = 0$, $-4y = 12$ from which $y = -3$. For $y = 0$, $3x = 12$ from which $x = 4$. This is sufficient to determine the graph (see Figure 7.15). A third point $(8, 3)$ is plotted as a partial check of the intercepts.

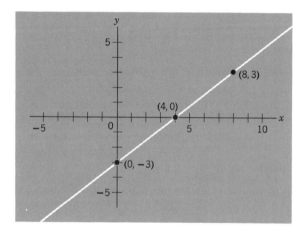

Figure 7.15

EXERCISE 7.4

The Linear Function

Graph each of the following functions by locating the y-intercept and then determining a second point by using the slope. Verify your result by checking whether a third point on the line satisfies the equation.

1. $y = x + 1$ $\qquad$ 2. $y = \frac{1}{2}x - 3$ $\qquad$ 3. $y = 2x - 2$

4. $y = -2x + 7$ $\qquad$ 5. $y = -x$ $\qquad$ 6. $y = -2$

Without graphing, determine the slope and the y-intercept of the line represented by each of the following functions.

7. $y = 3x - 5$ 8. $y = -2x - 1$ 9. $y = x + 9$

10. $y = \frac{1}{2}x - 4$ 11. $y = 7x$ 12. $y = -7$

Graph the straight line that satisfies the following conditions and determine its equation (Problems 13–20).

13. Intersects the y-axis at $(0, 4)$ with a slope of -1.
14. Passes through the point $(2, 1)$ with a slope of $\frac{1}{2}$.
15. Passes through the points $(7, 3)$ and $(1, -3)$.
16. Crosses the y-axis at $y = 2$ and is parallel to $y = 3x - 1$.
17. Passes through the origin and the point $(-2, -4)$.
18. Passes through the origin with a slope of -2.
19. Contains the points $(1, 5)$ and $(3, 7)$.
20. Passes horizontally through the point $(1, 4)$.
21. For a fixed value of m, the equation $y = mx + b$ determines a system, or family, of parallel lines. On a single graph, illustrate the family of lines $y = 2x + b$ for $b = -2, -1, 0, 1, 2, 3$.
22. For a fixed value of b, the equation $y = mx + b$ determines a family of lines passing through the point $(0, b)$. On a single graph, illustrate the family of lines $y = mx + 3$ for $m = -4, -2, 0, 2, 4, 6$.

Determine the equation of the linear function which satisfies each of the following conditions (Problems 23–26).

23.

x	-2	-1	0	1	2	3
y	0	3	6	9	12	15

24.

x	-2	-1	0	1	2	3
y	5	3	1	-1	-3	-5

25.

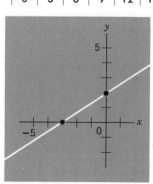

26.

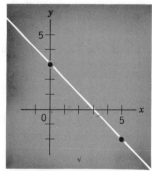

Rewrite each of the following equations in the form $y = mx + b$.

27. $3x + y = 9$ 28. $2x - y = 7$ 29. $x + 2y = 8$

30. $x - 2y = 6$ 31. $5x - 3y = 15$ 32. $2x + 7y = 21$

Graph the following linear functions by locating the x and y intercepts.

33. $x + 3y = 6$ 34. $2x - 3y = 24$ 35. $3x + y = 10$

36. $5x - 2y = 30$ 37. $x + 7y = 14$ 38. $3x - 4y = 18$

Graph each of the following sets of functions. What property or properties does each set exhibit?

39. $x + 2y = 5, 2x + 4y = 5, 4x + 8y = 5, -x - 2y = 5$

40. $3x - 2y = 6, 3x - 2y = 8, 6x - 4y = 24, -3x + 2y = 12$

41. $4x + 3y = 12, 8x + 6y = 24, 12x + 9y = 36, 16x + 12y = 48$

42. $2x - 3y = 9, 4x - 6y = 18, \frac{2}{3}x - y = 3, -2x + 3y = -9$

7.5 THE QUADRATIC FUNCTION $y = ax^2 + bx + c$

We have previously studied the quadratic equation $ax^2 + bx + c = 0, a \neq 0$, and noted that two and only two values of x will satisfy the equation for given values of a, b, and c. Consider now a relation defined by

$$y = ax^2 + bx + c, a \neq 0 \tag{1}$$

where the domain of x is the set of real numbers. Clearly, with each value of x is associated one and only one value of y.

Equation 1, therefore, represents a function. It is a member of an important set of functions known as polynomial functions, which are of the general form

$$y = ax^n + bx^{n-1} + cx^{n-2} + \ldots + k, a \neq 0, n \text{ a positive integer}$$

Polynomial functions of degree 1 reduce to the familiar linear function $y = ax + b$, and polynomial functions of degree 2 reduce to the form $y = ax^2 + bx + c$. They are known as quadratic functions and have important properties that are of interest in science and mathematics. Some of these properties are best introduced by examining the graphic characteristics of the function.

Graph of the Quadratic Function

Consider the quadratic function

$$y = x^2 - 4x - 5$$

To construct the graph of this function, it is convenient to make a table of ordered pairs as follows.

x	-2	-1	0	1	2	3	4	5	6
y	7	0	-5	-8	-9	-8	-5	0	7

The points represented by the ordered pairs are joined by a smooth curve, shown in Figure 7.16.

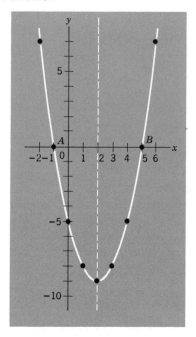

Figure 7.16

We make the following observations from the graph.

1. The curve, called a *parabola*, has a lowest, or *minimum* value of y at the point $(2, -9)$. This minimum point is called the *vertex* of the parabola.

2. The parabola is symmetric with respect to a line parallel to the y-axis and passing through the vertex. This line is called the *axis of symmetry*.

3. The parabola, for the given function, is said to open upward, or to be concave up.

4. The curve has two x-intercepts, at $A(-1, 0)$ and $B(5, 0)$. The x-intercepts of a function are also referred to as the *zeros of the function*. Thus, this function has two distinct zeros at $x = -1$ and $x = 5$.

In analytic geometry it is proved that the graph of every quadratic function is a parabola and, conversely, that every parabola with its axis parallel to the y-axis can be described by an equation of the form $y = ax^2 + bx + c$. The curve has many natural applications: the cables of a suspension bridge may form a parabola, the path of an unresisted projectile is a parabola, and many reflecting surfaces are designed to have parabolic cross-sections. Mathematically, the curve has the interesting property that all points on it are equally distant from a fixed point on its axis and a fixed line perpendicular to its axis. This property will be discussed in Section 7.6.

As a second example, and to provide additional detail on the graphic characteristics of the function, we consider the graph of the equation

$$y = -x^2 - 2x + 3$$

A suitable table of values is compiled as follows.

x	-4	-3	-2	-1	0	1	2	3
y	-5	0	3	$+4$	3	0	-5	-12

The graph is shown in Figure 7.17. We observe from the graph that for this
function the parabola has a highest, or *maximum*, value of y at the point $(-1, 4)$,
since the curve opens downward. The axis of symmetry is the vertical line
through the point $(-1, 4)$. The curve has two real zeros which are at the points
$(-3, 0)$ and $(1, 0)$.

It will be shown later that for the quadratic function $y = ax^2 + bx + c$:

1. If $a > 0$, there is a minimum point and the curve opens upward.
2. If $a < 0$, there is a maximum point and the curve opens downward.

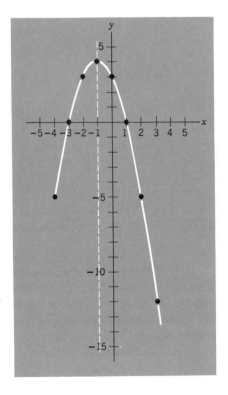

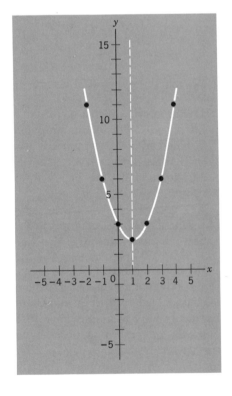

Figure 7.17   Figure 7.18

It should be noted that a quadratic function may have no real zeros. In Figure 7.18, which is the graph of $y = x^2 - 2x + 3$, it is clear that since the minimum point is (1, 2) and the curve opens upward, it will not intersect the x-axes and, therefore, will have no real zeros.

Maximum or Minimum Value of a Quadratic Function

We shall now prove that the quadratic function $y = ax^2 + bx + c$ has a maximum or minimum value at the point whose x-coordinate is $-\dfrac{b}{2a}$. To do this we shall complicate the form of the function, but the results will justify this procedure. We assume the reader will follow the algebraic process of each step.

$$y = ax^2 + bx + c \tag{1}$$

We factor out a,

$$y = a\left(x^2 + \frac{b}{a}x + \frac{c}{a}\right) \tag{2}$$

and add and subtract $\dfrac{b^2}{4a^2}$ to make a perfect square,

$$y = a\left(x^2 + \frac{b}{a}x + \frac{b^2}{4a^2} - \frac{b^2}{4a^2} + \frac{c}{a}\right) \tag{3}$$

We now combine the last two terms,

$$y = a\left(x^2 + \frac{b}{a}x + \frac{b^2}{4a^2} - \frac{b^2 - 4ac}{4a^2}\right) \tag{4}$$

and group the terms as the difference of two squares,

$$y = a\left[\left(x + \frac{b}{2a}\right)^2 - \left(\frac{\sqrt{b^2 - 4ac}}{2a}\right)^2\right] \tag{5}$$

We observe from Equation 5 that since the quantity $\left(x + \dfrac{b}{2a}\right)^2$ is either zero when $x = -\dfrac{b}{2a}$, or positive when $x \neq -\dfrac{b}{2a}$, the quantity in the brackets has the least value when $x = -\dfrac{b}{2a}$. Hence, when $a > 0$, y assumes its least value when $x = -\dfrac{b}{2a}$, and when $a < 0$, y assumes its greatest value when $x = -\dfrac{b}{2a}$. In either case, when $x = -\dfrac{b}{2a}$, $y = -\dfrac{b^2 - 4ac}{4a}$, which is either a maximum or minimum value of the function. Hence the coordinates of the maximum or minimum point of the parabola are

$$\left(-\frac{b}{2a}, -\frac{b^2 - 4ac}{4a}\right) \tag{6}$$

In practice, it is usually easier to determine the y-coordinate of the maximum or minimum point by first finding the x-value, $-\dfrac{b}{2a}$, and then substituting this value of x in the function. One more observation is worthy of note. Since a value of a greater than zero indicates that the curve has a minimum point, it follows that the parabola opens upward for $a > 0$. In a similar way we may show that the parabola opens downward when $a < 0$.

EXAMPLE 1. Find the coordinates of the maximum point of the curve $y = -3x^2 - 12x + 5$, and locate the axis of symmetry.

SOLUTION: The maximum point of the curve has the x-coordinate $-\dfrac{b}{2a} = \dfrac{12}{-6}$ $= -2$. For $x = -2$, $y = 17$. Hence the coordinates of the vertex are $(-2, 17)$. The axis of symmetry is the vertical line through the point $(-2, 17)$.

EXAMPLE 2. What is the minimum value of the expression $2x^2 - 20x + 17$?

SOLUTION: Consider the function $y = 2x^2 - 20x + 17$. The minimum point of this curve has the x-coordinate $\dfrac{20}{4} = 5$. For $x = 5$, $y = -33$. Therefore, the minimum value of the expression $2x^2 - 20x + 17$ for any value of x is -33.

EXAMPLE 3. Show that the graph of $y = -x^2 + x - 1$ has no real zeros.

SOLUTION: Since $a < 0$, the curve opens downward. The maximum point of the curve is $(\frac{1}{2}, -\frac{3}{4})$, which is below the x-axis. Therefore the curve cannot cross the x-axis, and the function has no real zeros.

Sketching the Quadratic Function

The foregoing discussion furnishes us with a rapid means of sketching the graph of the quadratic function, as follows.

1. Find and plot the y-intercept.
2. Find and plot the coordinates of the maximum or minimum point.

3. Draw the axis of symmetry of the curve.

4. Find and plot a point symmetrical to the y-intercept with respect to the axis of symmetry.

5. The three points thus determined are sufficient to sketch the curve. Additional points may be plotted, particularly in the neighborhood of the vertex and zeros, if necessary.

EXAMPLE 4. Sketch the graph of the quadratic function $y = x^2 - 5x + 4$.

SOLUTION:

1. The y-intercept is $(0, 4)$.
2. The minimum point is $(5/2, -9/4)$.
3. The axis of symmetry is the vertical line through the point $(5/2, -9/4)$.
4. The point symmetric to $(0, 4)$ is $(5, 4)$.
5. Although we have enough information to sketch the curve, the following additional points will refine the graph.

x	-1	0	1	2	3	4	5	6
y	10	4	0	-2	-2	0	4	10

The graph is illustrated in Figure 7.19.

Quadratic Inequalities

The graph of the quadratic function provides us with a procedure of unusual clarity for solving certain quadratic inequalities. For example, consider the

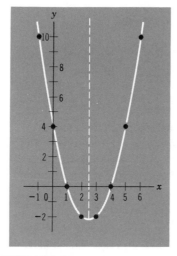

Figure 7.19

expression $x^2 - 5x + 4$ which is graphed in Figure 7.19. It is immediately apparent that

$$x^2 - 5x + 4 > 0 \qquad \text{for} \qquad x < 1 \text{ or } x > 4$$
$$x^2 - 5x + 4 < 0 \qquad \text{for} \qquad 1 < x < 4$$
$$x^2 - 5x + 4 = 0 \qquad \text{for} \qquad x = 1 \text{ or } x = 4$$

EXAMPLE 5.   Solve the inequality $-2x^2 - 15x + 27 > 0$.

SOLUTION: The graph of the corresponding quadratic function
$y = -2x^2 - 15x + 27$ is a parabola which is concave down. Its zeros are the solution set of the quadratic equation $-2x^2 - 15x + 27 = 0$, namely, $x = \dfrac{3}{2}, x = -9$.

Therefore, the solution set of the given inequality is $-9 < x < \dfrac{3}{2}$ (see Figure 7.20).

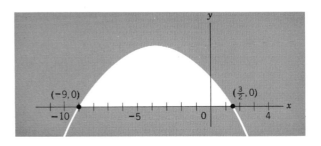

Figure 7.20

EXERCISE 7.5

The Quadratic Function $y = ax^2 + bx + c$

1. Given the quadratic function $y = 4x^2 + 8x - 5$:
   (a) Compile a table of ordered pairs for $x = -4, -3, -2, -1, 0, 1, 2$.
   (b) Plot the points listed in the table and draw the parabola.
   (c) Solve the equation $4x^2 + 8x - 5 = 0$. How are the roots of this equation
       related to the x-intercepts of the given function?
2. Given the quadratic function $y = -2x^2 + 15x - 7$:
   (a) Compile a table of ordered pairs for $x = -1, 0, 1, 2, 3, 4, 5, 6, 7, 8$.
   (b) Plot the points listed in the table and draw the parabola.
   (c) Solve the equation $-2x^2 + 15x - 7 = 0$. How are the roots of this
       equation related to the x-intercepts of the given function?

For each of the following parabolas, (a) determine the coordinates of the vertex, and (b) state whether the vertex is a minimum or a maximum point.

3. $y = x^2 - 6x + 5$ 4. $y = x^2 + 12x - 10$ 5. $y = -3x^2 - 6x - 1$
6. $y = -2x^2 + 24x + 3$ 7. $y = x^2 + x + 9$ 8. $y = x^2 + 7x - 8$
9. $y = -3x^2 - 2x + 2$ 10. $y = -5x^2 + 4x - 2$ 11. $y = \frac{1}{2}x^2 - 7x$

Sketch the graph of each of the following functions. For each function give: (a) the coordinates of the vertex, (b) the coordinates of the y-intercept, (c) the axis of symmetry, (d) the coordinates of the point symmetric to the y-intercept, and (e) the coordinates of the real zeros.

12. $y = x^2 - 8x$ 13. $y = x^2 - 25$ 14. $y = x^2 - 6x + 5$
15. $y = -x^2 - 4x + 12$ 16. $y = 4x^2 - 4x - 15$ 17. $y = 2x^2 - 3x - 9$
18. $y = -3x^2 - 11x + 4$ 19. $y = -x^2 - 8x - 16$ 20. $y = 2x^2 + 5x - 7$
21. $y = x^2 + x + 3$ 22. $y = -2x^2 - x - 1$ 23. $y = 2x^2 - 2x - 24$

For each of the following quadratic expressions, determine the values of x for which the expression is (a) positive, (b) negative, (c) zero, and (d) a minimum or a maximum value (Problems 24–32).

24. $x^2 - 3x + 2$ 25. $x^2 - 7x + 10$ 26. $2x^2 - 5x - 12$
27. $2x^2 - 7x + 5$ 28. $-x^2 + 6x + 16$ 29. $-x^2 - 4x + 21$
30. $4x^2 - 12x + 9$ 31. $-9x^2 + 30x - 25$ 32. $7x^2 - 35$

33. What is the minimum value of the expression $x(x + 3)$?
34. What is the maximum value of the expression $x(5 - x)$?
35. Separate 24 into two numbers whose product is a maximum. (*Suggestion:* Let x be one of the numbers, express the other number in terms of x, and write their product as a function of x.)
36. Find the area of the largest rectangle which has a perimeter of 50 feet.
37. The height of a ball thrown upward with an initial speed of 96 feet per second is given by the equation $h = 96t - 16t^2$, where t is measured in seconds and h is measured in feet. What is the greatest height to which the ball rises?
38. A camp site along a river is to be fenced. If 700 feet of fencing is available, and no fencing is needed along the river, what dimensions will provide a rectangular site of greatest area? See Figure 7.21.

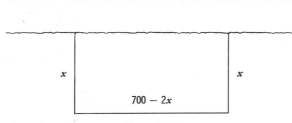

Figure 7.21

39. A helicopter service carries an average of 300 riders daily at a rate of $12 per ride. By lowering the fare $1, the average number of riders increases to 340. If we assume that each $1 decrease in fare will increase the number of riders by 40, what fare will provide the maximum gross revenue for the enterprise?

7.6 CONIC SECTIONS

The straight line and the parabola are among the most frequently studied plane figures in mathematics. Three additional geometric figures which are studied extensively are the circle, the ellipse, and the hyperbola. Each of these plane curves is called a *conic section* because it can be obtained by intersecting a plane and a right circular cone, as illustrated in Figure 7.22.

If the plane is passed through the vertex of the cone, then the intersection will result in a point, a line, or two intersecting lines, as illustrated in Figure 7.23. These possibilities are known as *degenerate cases* of conic sections.

The study of conic sections is treated extensively in more advanced mathematics courses; in this book we shall consider only the most elementary forms of their equations. The derivation of the equations is based on some rather interesting properties. Since these properties are concerned with distances measured between two points on the coordinate plane, we shall first develop a general formula for expressing such distances algebraically.

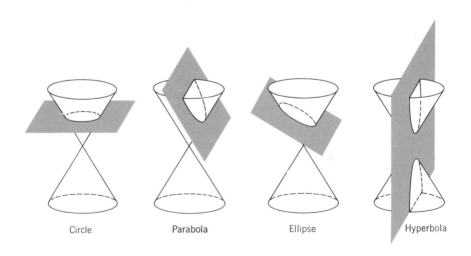

| Circle | Parabola | Ellipse | Hyperbola |

Figure 7.22

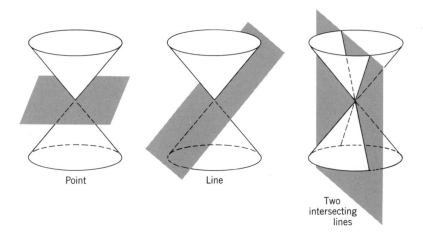

Figure 7.23

Distance Between Two Points

We noted in Problems 25–30 of Section 7.2 how the Pythagorean theorem can be used to find the distance between two fixed points. If the two points are $P_1(x_1, y_1)$ and $P_2 (x_2, y_2)$ then, by reference to Figure 7.24, we see that

$$d^2 = (x_2 - x_1)^2 + (y_2 - y_1)^2$$
$$d = \sqrt{(x_2 - x_1)^2 + (y_2 - y_1)^2}$$

EXAMPLE 1. Find the distance between $(-9, 3)$ and $(15, 10)$.

SOLUTION: It does not matter which point is considered P_1 or P_2, since the respective differences in the formula are to be squared. If P_1 is $(-9, 3)$ and P_2 is $(15, 10)$ then

$$d = \sqrt{(x_2 - x_1)^2 + (y_2 - y_1)^2}$$
$$d = \sqrt{24^2 + 7^2}$$
$$d = \sqrt{625} = 25$$

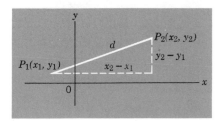

Figure 7.24

EXAMPLE 2.   Find the distance from the origin to the point (x, y).

SOLUTION: If P_1 is $(0, 0)$ and P_2 is (x, y), then

$$d = \sqrt{(x_2 - x_1)^2 + (y_2 - y_1)^2}$$
$$d = \sqrt{x^2 + y^2}$$

As indicated in Example 2, the use of the distance formula need not be limited to finding a numerical distance between two fixed points—it is also useful in developing an algebraic expression for the distance between a fixed and a variable point. It is this latter application that enables us to determine equations for certain conic sections. In each case we shall start with a definition of the curve based on a distance property, and then utilize the distance formula to determine its equation.

The Circle

DEFINITION 7.4   A *circle* is a subset of all points in the coordinate plane such that the distance between a fixed point and any point on the circle is a constant. The fixed point is called the *center* and the fixed distance is called the *radius*.

If we choose the center at the origin, and designate any variable point on the circle as $P(x, y)$, then the equation of the circle can be found by using Definition 7.4 and the distance formula. Using r as the fixed distance, as indicated in Figure 7.25, we have

$$d = \sqrt{(x - 0)^2 + (y - 0)^2} = r$$
$$\sqrt{x^2 + y^2} = r$$
$$x^2 + y^2 = r^2 \qquad (1)$$

Equation 1 is therefore the equation of a circle with radius r and center at the origin.

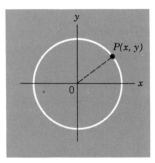

Figure 7.25

EXAMPLE 3. Discuss the graph of the equation $x^2 + y^2 = 25$.

SOLUTION: This is an equation of the form $x^2 + y^2 = r^2$, and therefore its graph is a circle with radius 5 and center at the origin (see Figure 7.26). Note that the graph does not represent a function since, except for $x = -5$ or $x = 5$, each permissible value of x is associated with two values of y. For example, for $x = 4$, we have the ordered pairs $(4, 3)$ and $(4, -3)$. We could, by solving for y, represent the equation $x^2 + y^2 = 25$ by the two equations

$$y = \sqrt{25 - x^2}$$
$$y = -\sqrt{25 - x^2}$$

The graphs of these two equations appear in Figures 7.27 and 7.28. Each of them represents a function, since one and only one value of y is associated with each value of x. The domain of these functions is $\{x \mid -5 \le x \le 5\}$. The range of the function illustrated in Figure 7.27 is $\{y \mid 0 \le y \le 5\}$, and that in Figure 7.28 is $\{y \mid -5 \le y \le 0\}$.

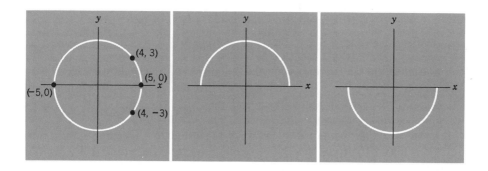

Figure 7.26 $x^2 + y^2 = 25$ **Figure 7.27** $y = \sqrt{25 - x^2}$ **Figure 7.28** $y = -\sqrt{25 - x^2}$

The Parabola

DEFINITION 7.5 A *parabola* is a subset of all points in the coordinate plane equidistant from a fixed point and a fixed line. The fixed point is called the *focus* and the fixed line is called the *directrix*.

Consider the parabola illustrated in Figure 7.29, that is, one with its focus at $(0, p)$ and directrix the horizontal line $y = -p$. We choose any point $P(x, y)$ on

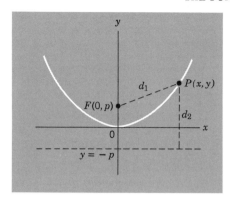

Figure 7.29

the parabola and specify that the distances d_1 and d_2 are equal. Then

$$d_1 = d_2$$
$$\sqrt{x^2 + (y - p)^2} = y + p$$
$$x^2 + (y - p)^2 = (y + p)^2$$
$$x^2 + y^2 - 2py + p^2 = y^2 + 2py + p^2$$
$$x^2 = 4py \tag{2}$$

Equation 2, therefore, represents the equation of a parabola with focus $(0, p)$ and directrix $y = -p$. This is consistent with our previous discussion of the parabola as the graph of a quadratic function, since the equation $x^2 = 4py$ can be expressed in the form $y = ax^2 + bx + c$.

Equations of parabolas with vertex at the origin but opening in the other directions may be derived in similar manner, and are illustrated in Figure 7.30.

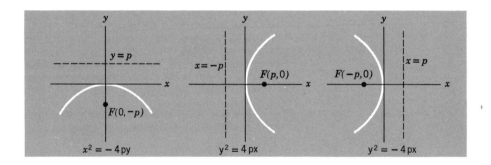

Figure 7.30

EXAMPLE 4. Discuss the graph of the equation $y^2 = 12x$.

SOLUTION: This is a parabola with vertex at $(0, 0)$ and opening to the right (see Figure 7.31). Since $4p = 12$, $p = 3$. Therefore the focus is at $(3, 0)$ and the directrix is the vertical line $x = -3$. When $x = 3$, $y = \pm 6$. Therefore the points $(3, 6)$ and $(3, -6)$ are points on the graph. As in the case of the circle, the graph of this parabola is not the graph of a function since for any given value of x there is more than one corresponding value of y.

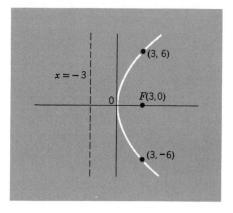

Figure 7.31

The Ellipse and the Hyperbola

DEFINITION 7.6   A subset of all points in the coordinate plane such that the *sum* of the distances to each of two fixed points is a constant is an *ellipse*. If the *difference* of the distances is a constant, the subset of points is a *hyperbola*. For both the ellipse and the hyperbola, the two fixed points are called *foci*, and each is called a *focus*.

The derivation of the ellipse, although lengthy, is straightforward, and is based on the distance formula and the simplification of radical equations. Most of the algebraic manipulation is left as an exercise for the student. The important steps in the derivation are as follows.

From Figure 7.32, if we choose the foci at $(-c, 0)$ and $(c, 0)$, and choose the constant sum of the distances to be $2a$, then

$$d_1 + d_2 = 2a$$
$$\sqrt{(x + c)^2 + y^2} + \sqrt{(x - c)^2 + y^2} = 2a$$

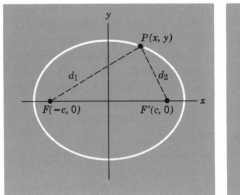

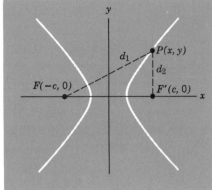

Figure 7.32   **Figure 7.33**

By using the methods for solving radical equations, and simplifying the results, this reduces to

$$(a^2 - c^2)x^2 + a^2y^2 = a^2(a^2 - c^2)$$

To simplify further, we let a $a^2 - c^2 = b^2$. Then

$$b^2x^2 + a^2y^2 = a^2b^2$$

$$\frac{x^2}{a^2} + \frac{y^2}{b^2} = 1 \tag{3}$$

Equation 3 represents an ellipse with foci at $(-c, 0)$ and $(c, 0)$ where $c^2 = a^2 - b^2$ and the sum of the distances from any point on the ellipse to the foci is the constant $2a$.

In a similar manner (see Figure 7.33), the equation of the hyperbola is based on the condition that $d_1 - d_2 = 2a$, resulting in

$$\frac{x^2}{a^2} - \frac{y^2}{b^2} = 1 \tag{4}$$

Equation 4 is the equation of a hyperbola with foci at $(-c, 0)$ and $(c, 0)$ where $c^2 = a^2 + b^2$ and the constant difference of distances from any point on the curve to the foci is $2a$.

EXAMPLE 5.   Discuss the graph of $\dfrac{x^2}{25} + \dfrac{y^2}{9} = 1$.

SOLUTION: Since this is an equation of the form $\dfrac{x^2}{a^2} + \dfrac{y^2}{b^2} = 1$, it represents an ellipse. The simplest way to sketch the curve is to find its intercepts. If we set

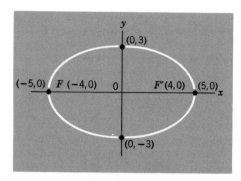

Figure 7.34

$x = 0$, then $y = \pm 3$, so that the y-intercepts are at $(0, 3)$ and $(0, -3)$. Similarly, the x-intercepts are at $(5, 0)$ and $(-5, 0)$ (see Figure 7.34). To locate the foci, we note that

$$c^2 = a^2 - b^2$$
$$c^2 = 25 - 9 = 16$$
$$c = \pm 4$$

Therefore, the foci are at $(-4, 0)$ and $(4, 0)$. The sum of the distances from any point on the curve to the foci is $2a = 10$.

EXAMPLE 6. Discuss the graph of $\dfrac{x^2}{9} - \dfrac{y^2}{9} = 1$.

SOLUTION: This is an equation of the form $\dfrac{x^2}{a^2} - \dfrac{y^2}{b^2} = 1$. Therefore the graph is a hyperbola. The x-intercepts, found by setting $y = 0$, are at $(-3, 0)$ and $(3, 0)$. There are no y-intercepts. The curve shows that there will be no permissible values of x in the interval $-3 < x < 3$. This is easily verified algebraically by solving the given equation for y. For $x = 5$ and $x = -5$, we obtain the ordered pairs $(5, 4)$, $(5, -4)$, $(-5, 4)$, and $(-5, -4)$ as indicated in Figure 7.35. The foci are located at $(\pm c, 0)$, where

$$c^2 = a^2 + b^2$$
$$c^2 = 9 + 9 = 18$$
$$c = \pm\sqrt{18} = \pm 3\sqrt{2}$$

Therefore, the foci are at $(-3\sqrt{2}, 0)$ and $(3\sqrt{2}, 0)$. The difference of the distances from any point on the curve to the foci is $2a = 6$.

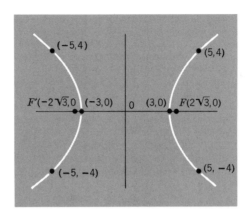

Figure 7.35

As in the case of the parabola, the ellipse and hyperbola may have its foci along the y-axis instead of the x-axis. Furthermore, the center of the conic curve may be at some point other than the origin, which complicates the equation. Finally, the axis of symmetry of the conic may not be parallel to either of the co-ordinate axes, which further complicates the equation of the curve. All of these considerations are appropriately deferred to the study of analytic geometry.

EXERCISE 7.6

Conic Sections

Find the distance between each pair of points (Problems 1–4).

1. $(6, 1)$ and $(10, 4)$
2. $(-9, -6)$ and $(3, 1)$
3. $(-3, 3)$ and $(3, -8)$
4. $(1, 1)$ and $(9, -2)$
5. For what value of x will $(x, 3)$ be equidistant from the origin and $(5, 5)$?
6. For what value of x will $(x, 4)$ be at a distance of 5 from $(1, 1)$?
7. What is the equation of a set of points equidistant from the origin and $(2, 3)$?
8. What is the equation of a set of points equidistant from $(0, 4)$ and $(3, 0)$?

Graph and identify each of the following equations.

9. $x^2 + y^2 = 4$
10. $x^2 + y^2 = 36$
11. $y^2 = 10 - x^2$
12. $x^2 = 1 - y^2$
13. $x^2 = 12y$
14. $x^2 = 9y$

15. $x^2 = -y$

16. $x^2 = -8y$

17. $y^2 = 4x$

18. $y^2 = -20x$

19. $\dfrac{x^2}{9} + \dfrac{y^2}{4} = 1$

20. $\dfrac{x^2}{4} + \dfrac{y^2}{1} = 1$

21. $\dfrac{x^2}{169} + \dfrac{y^2}{25} = 1$

22. $\dfrac{x^2}{100} + \dfrac{y^2}{36} = 1$

23. $\dfrac{x^2}{16} - \dfrac{y^2}{9} = 1$

24. $\dfrac{x^2}{4} - \dfrac{y^2}{1} = 1$

25. $\dfrac{x^2}{9} - \dfrac{y^2}{4} = 1$

26. $\dfrac{x^2}{64} - \dfrac{y^2}{36} = 1$

Solve each of the following equations for y, then (a) rewrite each equation as two separate equations each of which defines a function, and (b) state the domain and range of each function.

27. $x^2 + y^2 = 9$

28. $x^2 + y^2 = 25$

29. $y^2 = 16x$

30. $y^2 = -36x$

Write the equation of a curve such that every point on the curve is:

31. Eight units from the origin.

32. Three units from the origin.

33. Equidistant from $(0, 5)$ and the line $y = -5$.

34. Equidistant from $(0, -3)$ and the line $y = 3$.

chapter 8

systems of equations and inequalities

8.1 EQUATIONS OF FIRST DEGREE IN TWO VARIABLES

WE HAVE SEEN THAT SOME PROBLEMS INVOLVING SEVERAL unknowns may be solved by expressing all of the unknowns in terms of one of them. Thus, if the sum of two numbers is 15, we may let x equal one of the numbers, and then the other will equal $15 - x$. If the difference of these numbers is 7, then we may write the equation

$$x - (15 - x) = 7 \qquad (1)$$

Solving Equation 1, we find $x = 11$, the first number; and $15 - x = 4$ is the other.

In many cases, it is more convenient to use two or more symbols to represent the unknowns. In the above example, we may use x and y to represent the two numbers, so that we may write their relationship as

$$x + y = 15 \qquad (2)$$

Obviously many pairs of values of x and y will satisfy Equation 2, such as $x = 1$ and $y = 14$, $x = 4$ and $y = 11$, and so on. This becomes even more evident when we write Equation 2 as

$$y = 15 - x \qquad (3)$$

which represents a linear function for which the domain and range are the set of real numbers. When we express the second condition, that the difference of the numbers is 7, as

$$x - y = 7 \tag{4}$$

only one pair of numbers will satisfy both Equations 2 and 4, that is, $x = 11$ and $y = 4$, as before.

We shall first limit our discussion to equations with two variables, and state the following definition.

DEFINITION 8.1   A pair of equations of the form

$$ax + by = c$$
$$dx + ey = f$$

where x and y are variables and the other letters are constants, is called a system of linear equations in *two variables*.

Although a system of linear equations in two variables may consist of any number of equations, we have used the term "pair" of equations simply because we are concerned here only with two equations.

The pair of equations

$$3x + 4y = 25$$
$$2x + y = 10$$

is a system of linear equations in two variables.

Graphical Solution of Systems of Linear Equations in Two Variables

A pair of values that satisfy both equations of a system of equations is called a solution of the system. There may be no pair of values, one pair of values, or an unlimited number of pairs, which satisfy a given system of equations. This is evident from the following considerations. The graph of each linear equation is a straight line. These lines (Figure 8.1a) may have one point of intersection whose coordinates will then satisfy both equations; they may have (Figure 8.1b) no point of intersection, in which case there is no point whose coordinates satisfy both equations; or as in Figure 8.1c; they may be coincident, in which case the coordinates of every point satisfy both equations. Stated in terms of solutions, a linear system in two variables may have just one solution, no solution, or an unlimited number of solutions.

A system of equations with one and only one solution is called *consistent and independent*; a system with no solution is called *inconsistent*, and a system with an unlimited number of solutions is called *consistent and dependent*. At present, we shall determine the nature of a system of linear equations by drawing the graph of each equation and observing whether they intersect, are parallel, or are coincident. It should be kept in mind that a graphical solution of a system of

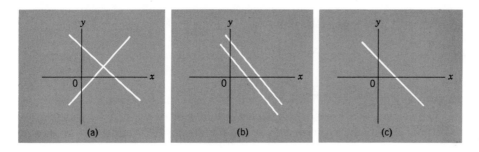

Figure 8.1

linear equations is at best an estimate, since it may be quite impossible to determine the exact point of intersection from a graph.

EXAMPLE 1.   Determine the nature of the system of linear equations

$$x + 2y = 8$$
$$x - 2y = 2$$

SOLUTION: The graph (Figure 8.2) indicates that the lines intersect in the point
$\left(5, \dfrac{3}{2}\right)$. The system is therefore consistent and independent. Substitution of
$x = 5$ and $y = \dfrac{3}{2}$ in both equations yields

$$5 + 2\left(\frac{3}{2}\right) = 8, \text{ or } 8 = 8$$
$$5 - 2\left(\frac{3}{2}\right) = 2, \text{ or } 2 = 2$$

so that $x = 5$, $y = 3/2$, is a solution, and the only solution of the system.

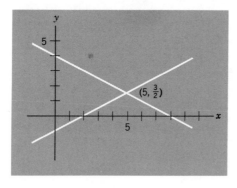

Figure 8.2

EXAMPLE 2.   Determine the nature of the system of linear equations

$$x + 3y = 4$$
$$2x + 6y = 8$$

SOLUTION: The graph (Figure 8.3) indicates that the lines coincide, and therefore the system is consistent and dependent. It can be verified by substitution that three of the solutions are $x = 1, y = 1; x = 7, y = -1;$ and $x = -5, y = 3.$

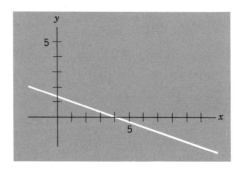

Figure 8.3

It should be observed that the nature of the system of Example 2 could have been anticipated without drawing the graph by observing that if the second equation is divided by 2, the equations are identical.

EXAMPLE 3.   Determine the nature of the system of linear equations

$$2x + y = 6$$
$$4x + 2y = 8$$

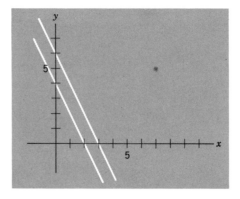

Figure 8.4

SOLUTION: The graph (Figure 8.4) indicates that the lines are parallel. The system is therefore inconsistent, and there is no solution. Here, as in Example 2, the nature of the system could have been anticipated by observing that the slope of each line is -2, but the y-intercepts are different, that is, 6 for the first equation and 4 for the second. The lines are therefore parallel and distinct.

EXERCISE 8.1

Equations of the First Degree in Two Variables

Determine graphically the nature of each of the following systems of linear equations. If the system has a single solution, estimate the value of x and y and check by substitution. If there is an unlimited number of solutions, give three of them and check by substitution.

1. $x - 2y = 2$	2. $x + y = 8$	3. $4x - 3y = 6$
$x + y = 5$	$x - y = 6$	$8x - 6y = 12$
4. $2x - 2y = 14$	5. $5x + 2y = 10$	6. $x + y = 13$
$x - y = 7$	$10x + 4y = 30$	$x - y = 13$
7. $x - y = -3$	8. $2x - 3y = 15$	9. $2x + 4y = 19$
$x + y = 11$	$x + y = 0$	$4x - 2y = 3$
10. $3x - y = 4$	11. $4x + 2y = 8$	12. $6x - 2y = 18$
$x + y = 6$	$2x + y = 3$	$3x - y = 6$
13. $2x + y = 13$	14. $7x - 9y = 13$	15. $3x + 3y = 17$
$2x - y = 11$	$x + y = -5$	$x - y = 1$
16. $3x - 3y = 3$		
$2x + y = 6$		

8.2   ALGEBRAIC SOLUTION OF SYSTEMS OF EQUATIONS IN TWO VARIABLES

As we have previously stated, it may not be possible to determine the exact point of intersection from a graph, in which case the solution can only be approximate. There are several methods for solving these systems algebraically, all of which depend upon combining the two equations in a manner that will eliminate one of the variables so that the resulting equation will be of the form $ax = b$, or $cy = d$. We shall indicate here only the techniques employed, leaving a discussion of the theoretical basis to more advanced courses such as college algebra or linear algebra.

Elimination by Addition

Consider the linear system

$$3x + 2y = 12 \tag{1}$$
$$2x + 3y = 13 \tag{2}$$

If we multiply the first equation by 3, and the second equation by -2, the coefficients of y will be numerically equal but opposite in sign. Thus we shall have

$$9x + 6y = 36 \tag{3}$$
$$-4x - 6y = -26 \tag{4}$$

We may add equations 3 and 4, by Axiom 3.4, obtaining the equation

$$5x = 10 \tag{5}$$

or

$$x = 2 \tag{6}$$

To find the corresponding value of y, we may repeat the procedure and eliminate x from the system, or we may substitute the value of x, that is, 2, in either of the two given equations. Thus, substituting $x = 2$ in Equation 1, we have

$$6 + 2y = 12 \tag{7}$$
$$y = 3 \tag{8}$$

Therefore, the solution of the given system is $x = 2$ and $y = 3$. To check our solution, we substitute $x = 2$ and $y = 3$ in both equations of the given system. For Equation 1

$$3(2) + 2(3) = 12$$
$$12 = 12$$

For Equation 2

$$2(2) + 3(3) = 13$$
$$13 = 13$$

We may summarize the procedure of elimination by addition as follows.

1. Multiply one or both equations by suitable constants so that the coefficients of one of the variables are equal in absolute value but opposite in signs.
2. Add the two equations thus obtained to get an equation in only one variable.
3. Solve the resulting equation.

4. Find the value of the other variable by repeating the procedure or by substituting the result of step 3 in either of the given equations.

5. Check by substitution in the original equations.

EXAMPLE 1. Solve the system

$$x + 6y = 4 \tag{1}$$
$$-2x + 3y = -3 \tag{2}$$

We need only multiply the first equation by 2 to eliminate the variable x.

$$2x + 12y = 8 \tag{3}$$
$$-2x + 3y = -3 \tag{4}$$

By addition

$$15y = 5 \tag{5}$$
$$y = \frac{1}{3} \tag{6}$$

To avoid the substitution of a fraction, we may next eliminate y by multiplying the second equation by -2

$$x + 6y = 4 \tag{7}$$
$$4x - 6y = 6 \tag{8}$$

By addition

$$5x = 10 \tag{9}$$
$$x = 2 \tag{10}$$

The solution is $x = 2$, $y = \frac{1}{3}$, which may be checked by substitution as usual.
Thus

$$2 + 6\left(\frac{1}{3}\right) = 4$$
$$2 + 2 = 4$$
$$4 = 4$$

and

$$-2(2) + 3\left(\frac{1}{3}\right) = -3$$
$$-3 = -3$$

Elimination by Substitution

While the method of elimination by addition is applicable to any system of linear equations, and while it is quite simple and direct, the method of *substitution* has a much wider application to systems which are not linear. We shall introduce the method of substitution as applied to systems of linear equations. Consider the system

$$4x + 3y = 26 \tag{1}$$
$$3x - y = 13 \tag{2}$$

To solve this system by substitution, we solve either equation for one unknown in terms of the other. Since the coefficient of y in the second equation is -1, we can avoid fractions by solving for y in that equation. Therefore, since

$$3x - y = 13 \tag{3}$$

solving for y,

$$y = 3x - 13 \tag{4}$$

Substituting this value of y in the first equation eliminates the variable y, and we have

$$4x + 3(3x - 13) = 26 \tag{5}$$
$$13x = 65 \tag{6}$$
$$x = 5 \tag{7}$$

Since the value of y in terms of x was previously found to be

$$y = 3x - 13$$

we have

$$y = 15 - 13 \tag{8}$$
$$y = 2 \tag{9}$$

Therefore, the solution is $x = 5$, $y = 2$. The check is performed by substituting $x = 5$ and $y = 2$ in both of the original equations. It should be observed that if we had solved for y in terms of x in the first equation, we would have had

$$y = \frac{26 - 4x}{3} \tag{10}$$

which yields a more complicated equation when this value of y is then substituted in the second equation.

We may summarize the process of elimination by substitution as follows.

1. Solve either equation for one variable in terms of the other (if possible, select a variable whose coefficient is $+1$ or -1 to avoid fractions).
2. Substitute the expression obtained in step 1 in the remaining equation.
3. Solve the resulting equation.
4. Find the value of the remaining unknown by substitution in the expression obtained in step 1.
5. Check by substitution in the original equations.

EXERCISE 8.2

Algebraic Solution of Systems of Equations in Two Variables

Solve by the method of elimination by addition.

1. $x + y = 13$
   $x - y = 3$

2. $3x - y = 0$
   $3x + y = 24$

3. $x + 7y = 21$
   $-x + y = 11$

4. $x - y = -3$
   $x + y = 11$

5. $x - y = 6$
   $x + y = 8$

6. $4x - y = 15$
   $3x - y = 9$

7. $2x + 4y = 1$
   $x - y = -4$

8. $4x - 5y = -20$
   $6x - y = 9$

9. $2x + y = 13$
   $3x + y = 21$

10. $3x + 4y = 7$
    $2x + 3y = 4$

11. $2x + 3y = -15$
    $3x - 5y = 63$

12. $3x + 4y = -27$
    $2x - 3y = -1$

13. $2x - 3y = 15$
    $x + y = 0$

14. $x + 2y = 11$
    $2x + y = 10$

15. $3x - 2y = 14$
    $2x + 3y = 8$

16. $2x - 5y + 43 = 0$
    $6x - y + 31 = 0$

17. $6x + 9y = 7$
    $3x - 6y = -14$

18. $2x - y = 5$
    $x - 3y = 5$

Solve by the method of elimination by substitution.

19. $x + y = 9$
    $y = 2x$

20. $y - 3x = 0$
    $3x + y = 24$

21. $x - y = 4$
    $2y = x$

22. $2x + 4y = 1$
    $x + y = 4$

23. $x + y = 15$
    $x = 4y$

24. $8x - 3y = 30$
    $y = x - 5$

25. $2x + 3y = 27$
    $y - x = 4$

26. $2x + y = 26$
    $3x + y = 21$

27. $y + 9 = 6x$
    $5y - 4x = 7$

28. $x + y = 1$
    $y = 2x - 11$

29. $6x - 5y = 10$
    $2y - 3 = x$

30. $9x - 2y = 17$
    $x + 3y = -11$

8.3 SYSTEMS OF ONE QUADRATIC AND ONE LINEAR EQUATION IN TWO VARIABLES

As we have seen, the graph of the quadratic function $y = ax^2 + bx + c$ is a parabola, and the graph of the linear function $y = mx + b$, or $ax + by = c$, is a straight line. The number of points which a straight line and a parabola may have in common is two, one, or none, as is evident from Figure 8.5. In the examples that follow we shall illustrate each of these three cases.

EXAMPLE 1. Solve the system of equations

$$y = x^2 - 6x + 9 \qquad (1)$$
$$y = x + 3 \qquad (2)$$

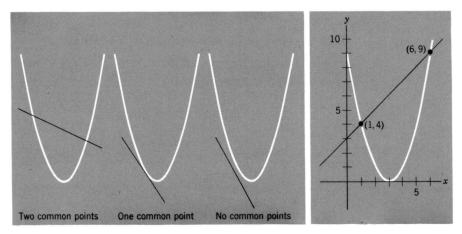

Figure 8.5   Figure 8.6

SOLUTION: Using the method of substitution, we substitute $x + 3$ for y in equation 1, so that

$$x + 3 = x^2 - 6x + 9 \tag{3}$$

Writing Equation 3 in the standard form of a quadratic equation,

$$x^2 - 7x + 6 = 0 \tag{4}$$

The roots of Equation 4 are $x = 1$ and $x = 6$. Since $y = x + 3$, the solution of the given system is

$$x = 1, y = 4$$

and

$$x = 6, y = 9$$

Figure 8.6, the graph of the system, indicates that our solution is probably correct. We may prove that the solution is correct by substituting each solution in both equations of the given system, as usual.

EXAMPLE 2. Solve the system

$$y = 3x^2 - 2x + 5 \tag{1}$$
$$y = 4x + 2 \tag{2}$$

SOLUTION: Substituting the value of y from Equation 2 in Equation 1,

$$4x + 2 = 3x^2 - 2x + 5 \tag{3}$$

Writing Equation 3 in standard form,

$$3x^2 - 6x + 3 = 0 \tag{4}$$

We may simplify Equation 4 by dividing both members by 3, so that

$$x^2 - 2x + 1 = 0 \tag{5}$$

Equation 5 has two equal roots, each equal to 1. For $x = 1$, from Equation 2 we have $y = 6$. Therefore the system has but one common solution:

$$x = 1, \qquad y = 6$$

Figure 8.7, the graph of the system, indicates that our solution is probably correct.

EXAMPLE 3.   Solve the system

$$y = -x^2 + 7x - 5 \tag{1}$$
$$y - 2x = 2 \tag{2}$$

SOLUTION: Solving Equation 2 for y, and substituting in Equation 1,

$$2x + 2 = -x^2 + 7x - 5 \tag{3}$$

Writing Equation 3 in standard form,

$$x^2 - 5x + 7 = 0 \tag{4}$$

Since the discriminant, $b^2 - 4ac$, of Equation 4 equals $25 - 28$, or -3, Equation 4 has no real roots, and therefore the system has no real solution. In terms of the graph, Figure 8.8 shows that the parabola and the straight line have no point in common.

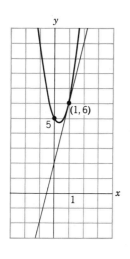

Figure 8.7

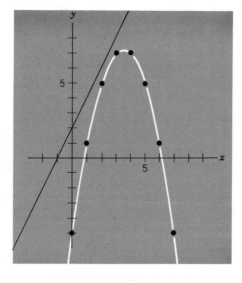

Figure 8.8

Equation of a Tangent to a Parabola

Example 2 illustrates the case where the straight line is tangent to the parabola, that is, the straight line and the parabola have but one point in common.[1] Let us consider the problem of determining the tangent to a parabola when the slope of the tangent is given.

EXAMPLE 4. Find the equation of the tangent to the parabola $y = x^2 - 6x + 9$, if the slope of the tangent equals 2.

SOLUTION: The equation

$$y = 2x + k \tag{1}$$

represents a family of parallel lines with slope 2, some of which intersect the parabola in two points, others which have no point of intersection with the parabola, and just one which intersects the parabola in only one point. The problem is to find the value of k so that the graph of Equation 1 intersects the parabola in just one point. If we solve the system

$$y = 2x + k \tag{1}$$
$$y = x^2 - 6x + 9 \tag{2}$$

by substitution, we get for the first step

$$2x + k = x^2 - 6x + 9$$

or

$$x^2 - 8x + 9 - k = 0 \tag{3}$$

The condition that Equation 3 has but one solution is that the discriminant, $b^2 - 4ac$ equals 0. Therefore

$$64 - 4(9 - k) = 0$$

or

$$k = -7$$

Substituting this value of k in Equation 1, we have $y = 2x - 7$ which is the equation of the tangent to the given parabola when the slope of the tangent is equal to 2. Figure 8.9 is the graph of the parabola and the tangent. The student may verify that the point of contact is $(4, 1)$.

Example 4 illustrates an important application of the discriminant of a quadratic equation. Thus we see that, although the quadratic formula was developed as a general procedure for solving quadratic equations, a considera-

---

[1] For a precise definition of the tangent to a curve, see M. Eulenberg and T. Sunko, *Inquiry Into College Mathematics*, Wiley, 1969, p. 224.

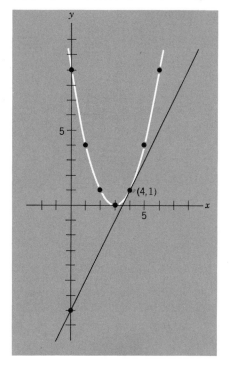

Figure 8.9

tion of some of its characteristics, such as the discriminant, has led to a significant application which is mathematically much more sophisticated than the mere solution of quadratic equations.

EXERCISE 8.3

Systems of One Quadratic and One Linear Equation in Two Variables

Solve each of the following systems. Check by drawing the graph of each system.

1. $y = x^2 - x - 6$
   $y = -2x$

2. $y = x^2 - 9x + 14$
   $y = x - 2$

3. $y = -x^2 + 4x$
   $y + 2x = 9$

4. $y = x^2 - x - 2$
   $x - y = 3$

5. $y = x^2 - 3x + 2$
   $x - y = 1$

6. $y = x^2 + 4x - 10$
   $y - 5 = 6x$

7. $y = x^2 + 4x - 7$
   $y = x + 3$

8. $y = x^2 - 5x + 3$
   $y = x - 6$

9. $y = x^2 - x - 16$
   $y = x - 8$

10. $y = x^2 + 2x - 7$
    $y = x - 1$

In Problems 11 to 16, find the equation of the tangent to the given parabola, given the slope m of the tangent as indicated. Draw the graph of the parabola and the tangent.

11. $y = x^2 - 4x + 6$, $m = 2$ 12. $y = 4x^2 + 10x$, $m = -6$

13. $y = x^2 - 6x + 4$, $m = 2$ 14. $y = 2x^2 - 5x + 3$, $m = 7$

15. $y = -x^2 + 4x - 4$, $m = 6$ 16. $y = x^2 - 6x + 4$, $m = -4$

8.4 ALGEBRAIC SOLUTION OF SYSTEMS OF LINEAR EQUATIONS IN THREE VARIABLES

An equation of the form

$$ax + by + cz = d \tag{1}$$

is called a linear equation in three variables. In this equation x, y, and z, are the variables, and the other letters are constants. Any solution of Equation 1 is a set of three numbers replacing x, y, and z, which satisfies the equation.

EXAMPLE 1. Find a solution of the equation

$$3x + 4y + 5z = 13 \tag{2}$$

SOLUTION: If we chose $x = 2$ and $y = 3$, by substitution

$$6 + 12 + 5z = 13$$
$$z = -1$$

Then one solution of Equation 2 is $x = 2$, $y = 3$, and $z = -1$.

Obviously, the number of solutions is unlimited, since any choice of values for two of the variables will determine the value of the third variable.

It is shown in analytic geometry that the totality of solutions of a linear equation in three variables, considered as points in a three-dimensional coordinate system, all lie in a plane. Suppose we have three such equations. The three planes determined by three linear equations in three variables may have various relative positions. They may coincide, they may be parallel, and therefore have no point in common, they may intersect in one line, in two lines, in three lines, or in one point. This last case may be envisioned by observing the point where two adjacent walls of a room intersect the ceiling. We shall be interested only in this last case, that is, where the three planes intersect in one point, and the equations have one and only one common solution.

Solution of Systems of Linear Equations in Three Variables

The methods of algebraically solving three equations in three variables are very similar to the methods of the previous section for solving systems of two equations. We choose two of the equations and eliminate one of the variables by addition. We then select another pair and eliminate the same variable. We now have two equations in two variables, which may be solved by elimination by addition or substitution. By substituting the values thus found in one of the original equations, the third variable may be found. Before choosing the variable to eliminate in the first step of the solution, a careful study of the three equations will often reveal a particular choice which will reduce the work of obtaining the solution.

EXAMPLE 2. Solve the system

$$2x - y + 4z = 1 \tag{1}$$
$$x - y + z = 0 \tag{2}$$
$$x + y + z = 1 \tag{3}$$

SOLUTION: We observe that by multiplying Equation 1 by -1, the variable y can be eliminated by adding Equations 1 and 2 and also by adding Equations 2 and 3. After multiplying Equation 1 by -1, as suggested, we may write the two pairs of equations

$$-2x + y - 4z = -1 \tag{4}$$
$$x - y + z = 0 \tag{2}$$
$$x + y + z = 1 \tag{3}$$

Eliminating y from both pairs of equations, we have

$$-x - 3z = -1 \tag{5}$$
$$2x + 2z = 1 \tag{6}$$

Solving Equations 5 and 6 by addition, we have

$$x = \frac{1}{4}$$

$$z = \frac{1}{4}$$

When these values of x and z are substituted in any of the three original equations, we find that $y = \frac{1}{2}$. The solution of the system is then $x = \frac{1}{4}$, $y = \frac{1}{2}$, and $z = \frac{1}{4}$. If these values are substituted in each of the equations 1, 2, and 3, the solution may be verified.

EXAMPLE 3. Solve the system

$$2x + 3y - 4z = -8 \tag{1}$$
$$x + y - 2z = -5 \tag{2}$$
$$7x - 2y + 5z = 4 \tag{3}$$

SOLUTION: Unlike Example 2, we cannot eliminate any variable from two pairs of equations by a single multiplication. However, both x and z may be eliminated from equations 1 and 2 by multiplying Equation 2 by -2. Then

$$2x + 3y - 4z = -8 \tag{1}$$
$$-2x - 2y + 4z = 10 \tag{4}$$

By addition, we have $y = 2$. Although we may now eliminate either x or z from another pair of equations, we can more conveniently substitute $y = 2$ in Equations 2 and 3 to get two equations in two variables. Thus, making the substitution $y = 2$ in Equations 2 and 3, we have

$$x - 2z = -7 \tag{5}$$
$$7x + 5z = 8 \tag{6}$$

Solving Equations 5 and 6, we have $z = 3$ and $x = -1$. The solution of the system is then $x = -1$, $y = 2$, and $z = 3$. The solution should be checked by substituting these values in each of the original equations.

EXERCISE 8.4

Algebraic Solution of Systems of Linear Equations in Three Variables

Solve the following systems of linear equations.

1. $2x - 3y + z = 5$
   $3x + y - z = 3$
   $x + 2y + z = 8$

2. $x - y + 4z = 9$
   $2x + y - 2z = 8$
   $4x + 2y - z = 19$

3. $x + y - z = 5$
   $x - 2y + 4z = 10$
   $3x + y - 3z = 5$

4. $2x + 3y - 7z = -5$
   $5x + 4y + 2z = 39$
   $9x - 11y + 3z = 32$

5. $x - 2y + z = -3$
   $2x + y + z = 5$
   $2x + 3y + 3z = 1$

6. $x + 2y + 3z = 11$
   $2x - y + 2z = 8$
   $3x + 3y - z = 17$

7. $x - 7y + 9z = -17$
   $5x - 9y + 11z = -25$
   $7x + 2y - 5z = 0$

8. $2x - 3y + 2z = 5$
   $3x - y - z = -6$
   $3x - y - 3z = 10$

9. $x + 4y + z = 12$
   $3x - 4y + 4z = 7$
   $2x + 2y + 3z = 15$

10. $2x - y + z = 8$
    $2x + 2y - z = -1$
    $3x + y + 2z = 11$

11. $2x - y + 3z = 19$
    $4x - 3y - 2z = 7$
    $3x + 3y - 2z = -2$

12. $3x + 5y + 2z = 0$
    $12x - 15y + 4z = 12$
    $6x + 20y - 4z = -8$

8.5 DETERMINANTS

In Chapter 5 we developed a formula for solving quadratic equations by considering the general quadratic equation $ax^2 + bx + c = 0$, rather than a particular equation such as $2x^2 - 2x - 5 = 0$, thus leading to the general solution for all quadratic equations. In much the same manner we shall now consider a generalized system of linear equations in two variables and obtain a formula for the solution of any system of linear equations in two variables. The general system of two linear equations in two variables may be written as:

$$a_1 x + b_1 y = c_1 \tag{1}$$
$$a_2 x + b_2 y = c_2 \tag{2}$$

We can eliminate the variable y by multiplying Equation 1 by b_2, and Equation 2 by $-b_1$, adding these equations as in Section 8.2, and solving for x. The steps in this procedure are as follows. Multiplying by b_2 and $-b_1$, as stated above,

$$a_1 b_2 x + b_1 b_2 y = b_2 c_1 \tag{3}$$
$$-a_2 b_1 x - b_1 b_2 y = -b_1 c_2 \tag{4}$$

The sum of Equations 3 and 4 is

$$a_1 b_2 x - a_2 b_1 x = b_2\, c_1 - b_1 c_2 \tag{5}$$

Factoring the left-hand member of Equation 5, we have

$$x(a_1 b_2 - a_2 b_1) = b_2 c_1 - b_1 c_2 \tag{6}$$

Dividing both members of Equation 6 by the coefficient of x, we have

$$x = \frac{b_2 c_1 - b_1 c_2}{a_1 b_2 - a_2 b_1} \tag{7}$$

We can eliminate the variable x, and thus solve for y, by a similar procedure, multiplying equation 1 by a_2 and Equation 2 by $-a_1$, and then following the steps as given above. The result will be

$$y = \frac{a_1 c_2 - a_2 c_1}{a_1 b_2 - a_2 b_1} \tag{8}$$

Clearly, Equations 7 and 8 express the solution of any system of linear equations in two variables, provided, of course, that a solution exists. To illustrate this, consider the following example.

EXAMPLE 1. Solve the system

$$3x + 2y = 12$$
$$4x - 3y = -1$$

SOLUTION: Comparing the given equations with Equations 1 and 2, we have

$$a_1 = 3, b_1 = 2, c_1 = 12, a_2 = 4, b_2 = -3$$

and

$$c_2 = -1$$

Substituting these values in Equations 7 and 8, we have

$$x = \frac{(-3)(12) - (2)(-1)}{(3)(-3) - (4)(2)} = \frac{-34}{-17} = 2$$

$$y = \frac{(3)(-1) - (4)(12)}{(3)(-3) - (4)(2)} = \frac{-51}{-17} = 3$$

As usual, the correctness of the solution may be verified by substituting the values $x = 2$ and $y = 3$ in both of the original equations.

Determinants of Order Two

Equations 7 and 8 may be expressed in a more elegant manner by the use of *determinants*, a notation developed as early as 1683 in connection with the solution of systems of linear equations. As has often been the case with mathematical ideas developed for specific purposes, the study of determinants and their properties now forms an important branch of mathematics apart from their original role in the solution of equations. In this discussion we shall limit ourselves to the use of determinants in solving systems of linear equations; some of the properties of determinants will be developed in the exercises.

DEFINITION 8.2   The symbol

$$\begin{vmatrix} a_1 & b_1 \\ a_2 & b_2 \end{vmatrix}$$

is called a *determinant of second order*, and its value is defined by the equation

$$\begin{vmatrix} a_1 & b_1 \\ a_2 & b_2 \end{vmatrix} = a_1b_2 - a_2b_1$$

The numbers a_1, a_2, b_1, b_2 are called the *elements* of the determinant, and the value $a_1b_2 - a_2b_1$ is called the *expanded* form of the determinant. The elements a_1, a_2, and b_1, b_2, form the *columns* of the determinant, and the elements a_1, b_1, and a_2, b_2, form the *rows* of the determinant.

EXAMPLE 2.   Evaluate, or expand, the determinant

$$\begin{vmatrix} 2 & 3 \\ 3 & -1 \end{vmatrix}$$

SOLUTION: From the definition of a second-order determinant, we have

$$\begin{vmatrix} 2 & 3 \\ 3 & -1 \end{vmatrix} = (2)(-1) - (3)(3) = -2 - 9 = -11$$

EXAMPLE 3. Evaluate the determinant

$$\begin{vmatrix} 3 & 5 \\ -2 & 3 \end{vmatrix}$$

SOLUTION:

$$\begin{vmatrix} 3 & 5 \\ -2 & 3 \end{vmatrix} = (3)(3) - (-2)(5) = 9 + 10 = 19$$

EXERCISE 8.5

Determinants of Order Two

Evaluate the following determinants. $(i = \sqrt{-1})$

1. $\begin{vmatrix} 2 & 3 \\ 1 & 5 \end{vmatrix}$ 2. $\begin{vmatrix} 1 & 2 \\ 4 & -5 \end{vmatrix}$ 3. $\begin{vmatrix} 5 & 3 \\ -2 & -7 \end{vmatrix}$ 4. $\begin{vmatrix} 9 & -2 \\ 7 & -5 \end{vmatrix}$

5. $\begin{vmatrix} 0 & 3 \\ 2 & 4 \end{vmatrix}$ 6. $\begin{vmatrix} 1 & -2 \\ 0 & 3 \end{vmatrix}$ 7. $\begin{vmatrix} 0 & 3 \\ 0 & -2 \end{vmatrix}$ 8. $\begin{vmatrix} a & b \\ -b & a \end{vmatrix}$

9. $\begin{vmatrix} a & b \\ b & a \end{vmatrix}$ 10. $\begin{vmatrix} 2 & i \\ i & 3 \end{vmatrix}$ 11. $\begin{vmatrix} 2i & 3i \\ 3i & -6i \end{vmatrix}$ 12. $\begin{vmatrix} 2 & -i \\ i & 1 \end{vmatrix}$

13. $\begin{vmatrix} 2 & 2 \\ 3 & 3 \end{vmatrix}$ 14. $\begin{vmatrix} 3 & 4 \\ 3 & 4 \end{vmatrix}$ 15. $\begin{vmatrix} 2 & 3 \\ 2 & 3 \end{vmatrix}$ 16. $\begin{vmatrix} a & b \\ a & b \end{vmatrix}$

17. Generalize the results of Problems 13 to 16 by completing the statement: The value of a second order determinant is zero if the elements of . . . .

18. In the determinant

$$\begin{vmatrix} a_1 & b_1 \\ a_2 & b_2 \end{vmatrix}$$

will its value equal zero if (a) a_1 and $b_1 = 0$? (b) a_1 and $b_2 = 0$? (c) a_1 and $a_2 = 0$?

19. From the results of Problem 18, complete the statement: the value of a second order determinant is zero if both elements of. . . . .

20. Evaluate each of the following pairs of determinants.

(a) $\begin{vmatrix} 1 & 3 \\ 2 & 4 \end{vmatrix}$ and $\begin{vmatrix} -1 & 3 \\ -2 & 4 \end{vmatrix}$ (b) $\begin{vmatrix} 1 & -3 \\ 3 & 5 \end{vmatrix}$ and $\begin{vmatrix} -1 & 3 \\ 3 & 5 \end{vmatrix}$

21. From the results of Problem 20, complete the following statement: The value of a second order determinant is changed in sign if the elements of.........

22. By expanding the determinants

$$\begin{vmatrix} ma & b \\ mc & d \end{vmatrix} \quad \text{and} \quad \begin{vmatrix} ma & mb \\ c & d \end{vmatrix}$$

Show that

$$\begin{vmatrix} ma & b \\ mc & d \end{vmatrix} = m \begin{vmatrix} a & b \\ c & d \end{vmatrix}$$

and that

$$\begin{vmatrix} ma & mb \\ c & d \end{vmatrix} = m \begin{vmatrix} a & b \\ c & d \end{vmatrix}$$

23. From the results of Problem 22, complete the statement: If the elements of a row or of a column of a second order determinant are multiplied by any number, ...

24. Verify the results of Problems 22 and 23 by expanding each pair of determinants, and then comparing their values.

(a) $\begin{vmatrix} 2 & 3 \\ 1 & 2 \end{vmatrix}$ and $\begin{vmatrix} 6 & 9 \\ 1 & 2 \end{vmatrix}$ (b) $\begin{vmatrix} 3 & -4 \\ 2 & 1 \end{vmatrix}$ and $\begin{vmatrix} 3 & 8 \\ 2 & -2 \end{vmatrix}$

Solve the following systems of linear equations using Equations 7 and 8 of this section, as in example 1.

25. $2x + 3y = 12$
   $3x - 2y = 5$

26. $4x + 5y = 12$
   $2x + 3y = 8$

27. $6x + 5y = -1$
   $2x - 3y = 1$

28. $2x + 3y = 2$
   $4x - 3y = 1$

29. $3x + 2y = 7a$
   $2x - 3y = -4a$

30. $4x + 3y = 15$
   $2x + y = 5$

31. $4x - 3y = 0$
   $3x - 4y = -7$

32. $3x + 2y = 7$
   $2x - 3y = 5$

8.6 SOLUTION OF SYSTEMS OF LINEAR EQUATIONS IN TWO VARIABLES BY DETERMINANTS

In Section 8.5 we developed the equations, or formulas, for solving the general system of linear equations in two variables

$$a_1x + b_1y = c_1 \tag{1}$$

$$a_2x + b_2y = c_2 \tag{2}$$

For convenience, we restate these equations

$$x = \frac{b_2 c_1 - b_1 c_2}{a_1 b_2 - a_2 b_1} \qquad (3)$$

$$y = \frac{a_1 c_2 - a_2 c_1}{a_1 b_2 - a_2 b_1} \qquad (4)$$

The form of Equations 3 and 4 suggests that the right-hand member of each may be expressed as the quotient of two determinants of second order, and this is indeed the case. If we write

$$x = \frac{\begin{vmatrix} c_1 & b_1 \\ c_2 & b_2 \end{vmatrix}}{\begin{vmatrix} a_1 & b_1 \\ a_2 & b_2 \end{vmatrix}} \qquad (5)$$

$$y = \frac{\begin{vmatrix} a_1 & c_1 \\ a_2 & c_2 \end{vmatrix}}{\begin{vmatrix} a_1 & b_1 \\ a_2 & b_2 \end{vmatrix}} \qquad (6)$$

it is easily verified that the expanded forms of the determinants are equivalent to the right-hand members of Equations 3 and 4.

If we now designate the denominator of each solution, Equations 5 and 6, as D, and the numerators as D_x and D_y, respectively, so that

$$x = \frac{D_x}{D} \qquad (7)$$

$$y = \frac{D_y}{D} \qquad (8)$$

we may state the steps in setting up the solutions for x and y in determinant form.

For a system of linear equations written in the form of Equations 1 and 2, the elements of the determinant of the denominator of the solution for both x and y are the coefficients of the variables in the same order as they appear in the equations, that is

$$D = \begin{vmatrix} a_1 & b_1 \\ a_2 & b_2 \end{vmatrix}$$

The elements of the determinant D_x in the solution for x differ from the elements of D in that a_1 and a_2 are replaced by the constants c_1 and c_2, that is,

$$D_x = \begin{vmatrix} c_1 & b_1 \\ c_2 & b_2 \end{vmatrix}$$

The elements of the determinant D_y in the solution for y differ from the elements of D in that b_1 and b_2 are replaced by the constants c_1 and c_2, that is,

$$D_y = \begin{vmatrix} a_1 & c_1 \\ a_2 & c_2 \end{vmatrix}$$

These last two steps are easily remembered if we note that the solution for x replaces the coefficients of x by the constant terms, and the solution for y replaces the coefficients of y by the constant terms.

It is of utmost importance that the system of equations be written in the form of Equations 1 and 2 before setting up the solution in determinant form.

EXAMPLE 1.   Solve the system

$$2x + 3y = 4$$
$$3x - 2y = -2$$

SOLUTION: Since the equations are in the form of Equations 1 and 2, we have

$$x = \frac{\begin{vmatrix} 4 & 3 \\ -2 & -2 \end{vmatrix}}{\begin{vmatrix} 2 & 3 \\ 3 & -2 \end{vmatrix}} = \frac{-8 + 6}{-4 - 9} = \frac{2}{13}$$

$$y = \frac{\begin{vmatrix} 2 & 4 \\ 3 & -2 \end{vmatrix}}{\begin{vmatrix} 2 & 3 \\ 3 & -2 \end{vmatrix}} = \frac{-4 - 12}{-4 - 9} = \frac{16}{13}$$

As in the solution of all equations, the results should be checked by substitution.

EXAMPLE 2.   Solve the system

$$2x + 3y - 6 = 0$$
$$2y = 3x$$

SOLUTION: We must first rewrite both equations in the form of equations 1 and 2.

$$2x + 3y = 6$$
$$3x - 2y = 0$$

We may then write the solutions as

$$x = \frac{\begin{vmatrix} 6 & 3 \\ 0 & -2 \end{vmatrix}}{\begin{vmatrix} 2 & 3 \\ 3 & -2 \end{vmatrix}} = \frac{-12}{-4-9} = \frac{12}{13}$$

$$y = \frac{\begin{vmatrix} 2 & 6 \\ 3 & 0 \end{vmatrix}}{\begin{vmatrix} 2 & 3 \\ 3 & -2 \end{vmatrix}} = \frac{-18}{-13} = \frac{18}{13}$$

Substitution of these values of x and y in the *original equations* will verify that they are correct.

EXERCISE 8.6

Solution of Systems of Linear Equations in Two Variables by Determinants

For each of the following systems of linear equations, write (a) D, (b) D_z, and (c) D_y. Remember that the equations must be in the form of Equations 1 and 2, as in Example 2 of the discussion.

1. $x + 2y = 7$
   $2x - y = 3$

2. $3x - y = -7$
   $2x + y = 3$

3. $x + y - 1 = 0$
   $2x - y + 3 = 0$

4. $x = 2y - 7$
   $2x = 3y + 2$

5. $2y + x = 13$
   $2y - x = 4$

6. $x = 3y$
   $3x = 2y + 2$

Solve the following linear systems of equations by determinants. Check each solution by substitution in the original equations.

7. $5x - 2y = 4$
   $2x + 3y = 13$

8. $5y + 2x = 11$
   $2y - 3x = -7$

9. $x + y = 0$
   $2x - 3y = 15$

10. $x + 2y - 9 = 0$
    $2x - y - 3 = 0$

11. $4x + 5y = 7$
    $3x + 4y = 5$

12. $3x + y = 2$
    $2x - y = 1$

13. $x - y = 3$
    $-x + 2y = 3$

14. $y - x = -7$
    $2x - 2y = 7$

15. $4x + 2y = 5$
    $3x - y = 0$

For Problems 16 and 17, (a) show that $D = 0$, but $D_x \neq 0$, and $D_y \neq 0$; (b) draw the graphs of each pair of equations; (c) does the system of equations have a solution? (d) what may be inferred if for a system of linear equations in two variables, $D = 0$, but $D_x \neq 0$, and $D_y \neq 0$?

16. $2x + y = 8$
$\ 2x + y = -10$

17. $x + y = 7$
$\ 2x + 2y = -15$

For Problems 18, 19, and 20 (a) show that $D \neq 0$, but either $D_x = 0$, or $D_y = 0$; (b) solve each equation for x and y; (c) what may be inferred if for a system of linear equations in two variables, $D \neq 0$, but $D_x = 0$, or $D_y = 0$, or $D_x = D_y = 0$?

18. $3x + 2y = 6$
$\ 2x + y = 3$

19. $2x + 3y = 8$
$\ 3x - y = 12$

20. $x = 3y$
$\ 3x + 4y = 0$

For Problems 21 and 22, (a) show that $D = 0$, $D_x = 0$, and $D_y = 0$; (b) draw the graph of each pair of equations; (c) how many solutions do the systems have? (d) what may be inferred if for a system of linear equations in two variables, D, D_x, and D_y all are equal to zero?

21. $x + y = 7$
$\ 2x + 2y = 14$

22. $3x - y = 7$
$\ 6x - 2y = 14$

23. From the results of Problems 16 to 22, show how the nature of a system of linear equations, discussed in Section 8.1, may be determined without drawing the graphs or solving the equations.

8.7 SOLUTION OF SYSTEMS OF LINEAR EQUATIONS IN THREE VARIABLES BY DETERMINANTS

Having defined and applied second order determinants to the solution of a system of two linear equations in two variables, the question naturally arises, does a system of three linear equations in three variables have a solution in terms of determinants? It is of interest that not only can the method of determinants be applied to the solution of a system of linear equations in three variables, but it can be generalized to solve any system of n linear equations in n variables, where n is an integer greater than or equal to 2. However, we shall limit our discussion to systems of linear equations in three variables, since the study of any system of higher order would require a more general definition of determinants and a consideration of their properties which are beyond the intended scope of this book.[1]

DEFINITION 8.3   The symbol

$$\begin{vmatrix} a_1 & b_1 & c_1 \\ a_2 & b_2 & c_2 \\ a_3 & b_3 & c_3 \end{vmatrix}$$

[1] For a more complete treatment of determinants, see Adele Leonhardy, *College Algebra*, Second Edition, Wiley. New York, 1968, pp. 289–292.

is called a determinant of third order, and is defined by the equation

$$\begin{vmatrix} a_1 & b_1 & c_1 \\ a_2 & b_2 & c_2 \\ a_3 & b_3 & c_3 \end{vmatrix} = a_1b_2c_3 + a_3b_1c_2 + a_2b_3c_1 - a_3b_2c_1 - a_1b_3c_2 - a_2b_1c_3 \qquad (1)$$

A careful reader will notice that the expansion of both second- and third-order determinants consists of all possible products of the elements of the determinant in such a way that each product contains precisely one element from each row and each column. The expansion of a fourth-order determinant, that is, one with four columns and four rows, has 24 terms, the expansion of a fifth-order determinant has 120 terms, and the expansion of a sixth-order determinant has 720 terms. It is for this reason that determinants of higher order than three require more general definitions, and the development of certain properties, to make their evaluation possible in a practical sense.

Evaluation of Third-Order Determinants

There are several methods of writing the expansion of a third-order determinant without memorizing the six products of Equation 1. We shall first give a method that has the advantage of simplicity, although it can be applied only to third-order determinants. The method is as follows.

1. Rewrite the first two columns to the right of the determinant.
2. Referring to Equation 2 below, the first three terms of the expansion are the products of the elements along the three diagonals marked $+$. The last three terms of the expansion are the products of the elements along the three diagonals marked $-$, the negative sign indicating that these products are to be multiplied by -1.

$$\begin{vmatrix} a_1 & b_1 & c_1 \\ a_2 & b_2 & c_2 \\ a_3 & b_3 & c_3 \end{vmatrix} \begin{matrix} a_1 & b_1 \\ a_2 & b_2 \\ a_3 & b_3 \end{matrix} = a_1b_2c_3 + b_1c_2a_3 + c_1a_2b_3 - a_3b_2c_1 - b_3c_2a_1 - c_3a_2b_1 \qquad (2)$$

Comparison of Equations 1 and 2 will show that they are equivalent, although some of the terms differ in the order in which the elements are written.

EXAMPLE 1.   Evaluate the third order determinant

$$\begin{vmatrix} -2 & -4 & 1 \\ 4 & 1 & 2 \\ 3 & -2 & 1 \end{vmatrix}$$

SOLUTION: Rewriting the first two columns of the determinant, and lightly sketching in the diagonals with their proper sign, we have

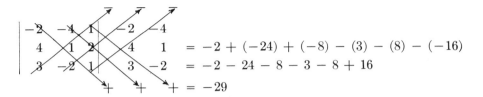

$$= -2 + (-24) + (-8) - (3) - (8) - (-16)$$
$$= -2 - 24 - 8 - 3 - 8 + 16$$
$$= -29$$

A second method of evaluating a third-order determinant is called *expansion by minors.* This method has the advantage of being applicable to determinants of higher order, and on the basis of certain general properties of determinants, reducing the amount of arithmetic involved. We shall discuss this method only in its application to third-order determinants.

We first rewrite Equation 1 in an equivalent form

$$\begin{vmatrix} a_1 & b_1 & c_1 \\ a_2 & b_2 & c_2 \\ a_3 & b_3 & c_3 \end{vmatrix} = a_1b_2c_3 - a_1b_3c_2 - a_2b_1c_3 + a_2b_3c_1 + a_3b_1c_2 - a_3b_2c_1 \qquad (3)$$

We may factor each pair of terms in the right-hand member of Equation 3, so that

$$\begin{vmatrix} a_1 & b_1 & c_1 \\ a_2 & b_2 & c_2 \\ a_3 & b_3 & c_3 \end{vmatrix} = a_1(b_2c_3 - b_3c_2) - a_2(b_1c_3 - b_3c_1) + a_3(b_1c_2 - b_2c_1) \qquad (4)$$

Equation 4 may now be written in terms of second order determinants

$$\begin{vmatrix} a_1 & b_1 & c_1 \\ a_2 & b_2 & c_2 \\ a_3 & b_3 & c_3 \end{vmatrix} = a_1 \begin{vmatrix} b_2 & c_2 \\ b_3 & c_3 \end{vmatrix} - a_2 \begin{vmatrix} b_1 & c_1 \\ b_3 & c_3 \end{vmatrix} + a_3 \begin{vmatrix} b_1 & c_1 \\ b_2 & c_2 \end{vmatrix} \qquad (5)$$

Each of the three second-order determinants in the expansion given by Equation 5 is called a *minor* of an element of the first column, that is, the elements a_1, a_2, and a_3, respectively. Although it is possible to expand a determinant by using minors of the elements of any row or column, we shall use only elements of the first column.

The following representation shows that the minor associated with a given element is obtained by deleting the row and the column containing that element, then writing the four remaining elements in their natural order as a second order determinant. Thus, the minors associated with the elements of the first column are, respectively,

$$\begin{vmatrix} a_1 & b_1 & c_1 \\ a_2 & b_2 & c_2 \\ a_3 & b_3 & c_3 \end{vmatrix} \longrightarrow \begin{vmatrix} b_2 & c_2 \\ b_3 & c_3 \end{vmatrix} \tag{6}$$

$$\begin{vmatrix} a_1 & b_1 & c_1 \\ a_2 & b_2 & c_2 \\ a_3 & b_3 & c_3 \end{vmatrix} \longrightarrow \begin{vmatrix} b_1 & c_1 \\ b_3 & c_3 \end{vmatrix} \tag{7}$$

$$\begin{vmatrix} a_1 & b_1 & c_1 \\ a_2 & b_2 & c_2 \\ a_3 & b_3 & c_3 \end{vmatrix} \longrightarrow \begin{vmatrix} b_1 & c_1 \\ b_2 & c_2 \end{vmatrix} \tag{8}$$

Multiplying each of these minors by the elements a_1, $-a_2$, and a_3, respectively, and combining, gives the expansion of Equation 5.

In expanding a determinant by minors, the student should delete rows and columns mentally, to avoid errors which might result from undue marking up of the original determinant.

EXAMPLE 2.
$$\begin{vmatrix} 2 & -2 & 1 \\ -3 & 1 & -2 \\ 2 & 3 & 3 \end{vmatrix} = 2\begin{vmatrix} 1 & -2 \\ 3 & 3 \end{vmatrix} - (-3)\begin{vmatrix} -2 & 1 \\ 3 & 3 \end{vmatrix} + 2\begin{vmatrix} -2 & 1 \\ 1 & -2 \end{vmatrix}$$
$$= 2(9) + 3(-9) + 2(3) = -3$$

Solution of Systems of Linear Equations in Three Variables by Determinants

If the symbols D, D_x, D_y, and D_z, are the determinants defined as in Section 8.5, then the solution of a system of linear equations in three variables is

$$x = \frac{D_x}{D}, \qquad y = \frac{D_y}{D}, \qquad z = \frac{D_z}{D} \tag{9}$$

Although it is possible to show, using the method of Section 8.4 on a general system of linear equations in three variables, that Equations 9 are solutions, the work is quite laborious, though not difficult, and we shall not present it here.

EXAMPLE 3. Solve by determinants

$$\begin{aligned} 2x - y - z &= -3 \\ x + y + z &= 6 \\ x - 2y + 3z &= 6 \end{aligned}$$

SOLUTION: From Equations 9 we have

$$x = \frac{\begin{vmatrix} -3 & -1 & -1 \\ 6 & 1 & 1 \\ 6 & -2 & 3 \end{vmatrix}}{\begin{vmatrix} 2 & -1 & -1 \\ 1 & 1 & 1 \\ 1 & -2 & 3 \end{vmatrix}} = \frac{15}{15} = 1$$

$$y = \frac{\begin{vmatrix} 2 & -3 & -1 \\ 1 & 6 & 1 \\ 1 & 6 & 3 \end{vmatrix}}{\begin{vmatrix} 2 & -1 & -1 \\ 1 & 1 & 1 \\ 1 & -2 & 3 \end{vmatrix}} = \frac{30}{15} = 2$$

$$z = \frac{\begin{vmatrix} 2 & -1 & -3 \\ 1 & 1 & 6 \\ 1 & -2 & 6 \end{vmatrix}}{\begin{vmatrix} 2 & -1 & -1 \\ 1 & 1 & 1 \\ 1 & -2 & 3 \end{vmatrix}} = \frac{45}{15} = 3$$

If 1, 2, and 3, are substituted for x, y, and z, respectively, in each of the three equations, it will be found that they satisfy each equation, and therefore $x = 1$, $y = 2$, and $z = 3$, is the correct solution of the given system of equations.

EXERCISE 8.7

Solution of Systems of Linear Equations in Three Variables by Determinants

Evaluate each of the following determinants by rewriting the first two columns, as in Example 1.

1. $\begin{vmatrix} 1 & -1 & 1 \\ 1 & 2 & -1 \\ 1 & 2 & 3 \end{vmatrix}$

2. $\begin{vmatrix} 2 & 1 & 4 \\ -1 & 3 & -2 \\ 4 & 2 & 5 \end{vmatrix}$

3. $\begin{vmatrix} 7 & 0 & 1 \\ 2 & -1 & 6 \\ 9 & 4 & 0 \end{vmatrix}$

4. $\begin{vmatrix} 12 & 8 & 6 \\ 1 & -4 & 5 \\ 6 & 4 & 3 \end{vmatrix}$

5. $\begin{vmatrix} 1 & 2 & -1 \\ 2 & -1 & 3 \\ -3 & -4 & 5 \end{vmatrix}$

Evaluate each of the following determinants by the method of minors.

6. $\begin{vmatrix} 1 & 1 & 1 \\ 2 & 0 & 1 \\ 1 & -1 & 2 \end{vmatrix}$

7. $\begin{vmatrix} 1 & 0 & 2 \\ 2 & 1 & 0 \\ -1 & 0 & 2 \end{vmatrix}$

8. $\begin{vmatrix} 1 & 2 & -1 \\ 1 & 3 & 4 \\ 4 & 1 & 5 \end{vmatrix}$

9. $\begin{vmatrix} 1 & 2 & 5 \\ 0 & 5 & 4 \\ 0 & 0 & 6 \end{vmatrix}$

10. $\begin{vmatrix} 4 & 2 & -8 \\ 9 & 0 & 8 \\ 2 & 1 & -1 \end{vmatrix}$

Solve each of the following systems of equations by determinants. Check each solution by substitution in the original equations.

11. $x + 2y + 3z = 4$
$\quad x + y + z = 1$
$\quad x + 3y + 7z = 13$

12. $2x - 3y + z = 6$
$\quad x + 4y - 3z = -17$
$\quad 3x + y + z = -8$

13. $5x - 2y - z = -30$
$\quad x + y - 7z = 13$
$\quad x + 3y + z = -13$

14. $3x + y - 2z = 1$
$\quad 2x - 3y + z = -1$
$\quad 4x - 2y + 3z = 14$

15. $x + 2y - 7z = -5$
$\quad 3x - 5y + 7z = 19$
$\quad 5x - 8y - 11z = -13$

16. $3x - y + 4z = 11$
$\quad 2x + y - z = 7$
$\quad x + 2y - 3z = 4$

8.8 APPLICATIONS OF SYSTEMS OF LINEAR EQUATIONS

Verbal problems involving two or more unknowns, as are many of those given in Section 3.5, are often more easily solved by using two or more variables to express the equations symbolizing the relationships, and many problems can only be solved in this manner. Our first example is a very simple one that indicates the general method.

EXAMPLE 1. Find two numbers such that twice the first added to the second equals 19, and three times the first is 21 more than the second.

SOLUTION: Let $x =$ the first number and $y =$ the second number. The equations are

$$2x + y = 19 \text{ (twice the first added to the second equals 19)}$$
$$3x = y + 21 \text{ (three times the first is 21 more than the second)}$$

The solution of this system is

$$x = 8, \text{ the first number}$$
$$y = 3, \text{ the second number}$$

To check the solution, we must show that the two numbers, 8 and 3, satisfy the conditions of the original problem. Thus twice 8 added to 3 equals 19, and 3 times 8, or 24, is 21 more than 3.

EXAMPLE 2.   As we have seen in Section 7.5, the graph of the quadratic function $y = ax^2 + bx + c$ is a parabola. Find the equation of a parabola passing through the points $(-1, 11)$, $(1, 3)$, and $(2, 5)$, by determining the values of a, b, and c from the given data.

SOLUTION: Since the coordinates of the three given points must satisfy the equation of the parabola, we write (for convenience) the quadratic function as

$$ax^2 + bx + c = y$$

and substitute the coordinates of each of the three points for x and y. Thus

substituting $(-1, 11)$ for x and y, we have $a - b + c = 11$
substituting $(1, 3)$ for x and y, we have $a + b + c = 3$
substituting $(2, 5)$ for x and y, we have $4a + 2b + c = 5$

The solution of this system is

$$a = 2$$
$$b = -4$$
$$c = 5$$

Therefore the equation of the parabola is

$$y = 2x^2 - 4x + 5$$

It is easy to verify that the coordinates of each of the three given points satisfy the equation.

EXAMPLE 3.   Two trackmen are running on a circular race track 300 feet in circumference. Running in opposite directions, they meet every 10 seconds. Running in the same direction, the faster passes the slower every 50 seconds. Find their rates in feet per second.

SOLUTION: Let x = rate of the faster runner and y = rate of the slower runner. Using the formula

$$\text{distance} = \text{rate} \times \text{time}$$

the equations are

$$10x + 10y = 300$$

since in opposite directions they must cover a total of 300 feet each time they meet, and

$$50x - 50y = 300$$

since the faster runner must gain 300 feet each time he overtakes the slower runner. These equations may be simplified, so that we have

$$x + y = 30$$
$$x - y = 6$$

The solution of this system is

$$x = 18$$
$$y = 12$$

The rates are therefore 18 feet per second for the faster runner and 12 feet per second for the slower runner.

To check the solution, we note that in 10 seconds the runners travel a total of 180 feet + 120 feet, or 300 feet, the length of the track. When they run in the same direction, in 50 seconds the faster travels 900 feet and the slower travels 600 feet, so that the faster runner runs 300 feet more than the slower, and therefore catches up with him every 50 seconds.

EXERCISE 8.8

Applications of Systems of Linear Equations

In Problems 1 and 2, write the equation of a plane passing through the given points. The equation of these planes may be written as $Ax + By + Cz = 1$.

1. Determine the equation of a plane passing through the points $(2, 1, 3)$, $(2, 2, 4)$, and $(-2, 2, 8)$.
2. Determine the equation of a plane passing through the points $(2, -1, 1)$, $(-2, 1, 1)$, and $(2, 1, -2)$.
3. Determine the equation of a parabola passing through the points $(0, -1)$, $(1, 1)$, and $(2, 5)$.
4. Determine the equation of a parabola passing through the points $(1, 2)$, $(2, 9)$, and $(-2, 17)$.
5. A steamer goes downstream (with the current) 70 miles in 5 hours. The return trip takes 7 hours. Find the rate of the steamer in still water and the rate of the current.

6. A boat can go downstream (with the current) a distance of 42 miles in 3 hours. In 2 hours it can go 16 miles upstream. Find the rate of the boat in still water and the rate of the current.

7. Two persons, 15 miles apart, will meet in 2 hours if they walk toward each other, and the faster will overtake the slower in 6 hours if they walk in the same direction. Find their rates of walking in miles per hour.

In Problems 8 and 9, find the equations of the circle passing through the given points. The equation of a circle is $x^2 + y^2 + cx + dy + e = 0$.

8. Find the equation of a circle passing through the points $(1, 1)$, $(-2, 3)$, and $(3, 4)$.

9. Find the equation of a circle passing through the points $(4, -1)$, $(2, 2)$, and $(1, 2)$.

10. Two rubber cords, 30 inches long and 24 inches long, respectively, hang side by side on a horizontal support. Each ounce of weight hung on the longer cord stretches it 2 inches, while the other cord stretches 3 inches for each ounce of weight added. Find the weight to be added to stretch the cords to the same length, and what the length will be.

11. Two springs are 15 inches and 21 inches long, respectively. The first stretches 0.2 inches for each pound of force applied and the second stretches 0.5 inches for each pound of force. What force will stretch them to the same length, and what will the length be? Discuss the meaning of your solution.

12. Two freight trains are 720 feet long and 600 feet long, respectively. When they move in opposite directions it takes 25 seconds to pass each other; when they move in the same direction the faster train passes the slower train in 3 minutes and 45 seconds. What are the rates of the trains in miles per hour? *Suggestion:* First convert the feet to miles and minutes and seconds to hours before solving the equation.

8.9 LINEAR INEQUALITIES IN TWO VARIABLES

Figure 8.10 is the graph of the linear function $y = \frac{1}{2}x$. Each of the points A, B, C, and D, satisfy the equation, since they all lie on the graph. The points A', B', C', and D' have the same abscissas as A, B, C, D, respectively, but their ordinates are greater, since they lie above the line. Since all of the points above the line $y = \frac{1}{2}x$ have ordinates which are greater than the ordinates of the corresponding points on the line, for all points above the line,

$$y > \tfrac{1}{2}x$$

In the same manner, all points below the line $y = \frac{1}{2}x$ satisfy the inequality

$$y < \tfrac{1}{2}x$$

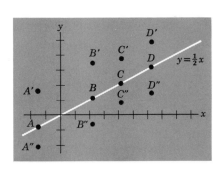

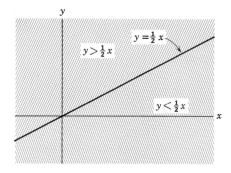

Figure 8.10   **Figure 8.11**

The line $y = \frac{1}{2}x$ therefore divides the xy-plane into two parts, shown in Figure 8.11. For the part of the plane above the line, $y > \frac{1}{2}x$, and for the part of the plane below the line, $y < \frac{1}{2}x$.

Graph of an Inequality in Two Variables

Expressions such as $y > 3x$, and $2y + 3x > 12$, are called inequalities in two variables. Since the solutions of such inequalities consist of all points in a particular region of the xy-plane, it is customary to indicate the region by shading it in some manner, as in Examples 1 and 2 which follow. The theorems concerning inequalities, Section 3.3, also apply to inequalities in two variables.

EXAMPLE 1.   Solve the inequality $2x - y > 4$ for y in terms of x, and draw its graph.

SOLUTION:
$$2x - y > 4$$
$$-y > -2x + 4$$
$$y < 2x - 4$$

Therefore whenever $y < 2x - 4$, the inequality is satisfied. To graph the inequality, we first draw the graph of $y = 2x - 4$ as a dotted line, to indicate that the points on this line do not satisfy the given inequality. We then shade the area below the line, since all points below the line satisfy the given inequality. Figure 8.12 is a graph of this inequality. As a partial check, we note that when the coordinates of the point $(3, -2)$, which is in the shaded area, are substituted in the given inequality,

$$6 - (-2) > 4$$

or

$$6 + 2 > 4$$

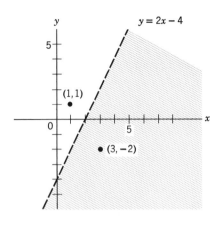

Figure 8.12

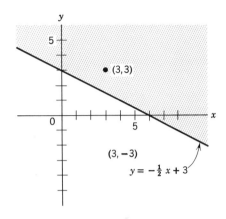

Figure 8.13

so that the point $(3, -2)$ satisfies the inequality. When the point $(1, 1)$, which is not in the shaded area, is substituted in the inequality

$$2 - 1 > 3$$
$$1 \not> 3$$

so that the point $(1, 1)$ does not satisfy the inequality.

EXAMPLE 2.   Solve the inequality $x + 2y \geq 6$ for y in terms of x and draw its graph.

SOLUTION:
$$x + 2y \geq 6$$
$$2y \geq -x + 6$$
$$y \geq -\tfrac{1}{2}x + 3$$

Since $x + 2y$ is "greater than or equal" to 6, we draw the graph of $x + 2y = 6$ as a solid line to indicate that the points on the line also satisfy the inequality. Figure 8.13 is a graph of this inequality. As a partial check, the student may verify the fact that the point $(3, 3)$ in the shaded region satisfies the inequality $x + 2y \geq 6$, and that the point $(3, -3)$ below the line does not satisfy the given inequality. The graph consists of all points on or above the line $x + 2y = 6$.

Systems of Linear Inequalities in Two Variables

Consider the system of linear inequalities in two variables

$$y - x < 4 \tag{1}$$
$$y + x > 6 \tag{2}$$

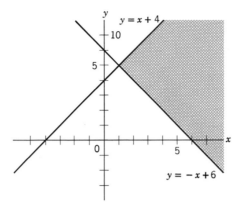

Figure 8.14

Solving each inequality for y, we have the equivalent system,

$$y < \quad x + 4 \tag{3}$$
$$y > -x + 6 \tag{4}$$

Since all points below the line $y = x + 4$ satisfy the first inequality (3), and all points above the line $y = -x + 6$ satisfy the second inequality (4), the doubly shaded area (Figure 8.14) satisfies both inequalities. As a partial check, the point (4, 4) in this area satisfies both inequalities 1 and 2, since

$$4 - 4 < 4$$
$$4 + 4 > 6$$

If we add a third inequality, $y > 3x - 6$, so that our system now is

$$y < \quad x + 4 \tag{5}$$
$$y > -x + 6 \tag{6}$$
$$y > \quad 3x - 6 \tag{7}$$

the graph of this system (Figure 8.15) consists of all points within the triangular region bounded by the lines, but not on the lines, $y = x + 4$, $y = -x + 6$, and $y = 3x - 6$. As a partial check, the point (3, 5), within this region, satisfies each of the three inequalities.

The Vertices of a Polygon

If the inequalities 5, 6, and 7 are rewritten as

$$y \leq \quad x + 4 \tag{8}$$
$$y \geq -x + 6 \tag{9}$$
$$y \geq \quad 3x - 6 \tag{10}$$

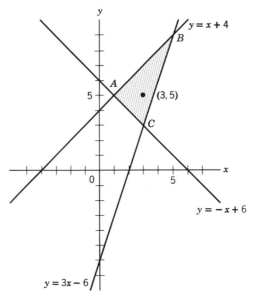

Figure 8.15

then the graph will include the boundary of the triangle in Figure 8.15 as well as the interior points. The vertices of the triangle, points A, B, and C, may then be found by solving the three systems of linear equations obtained from 8, 9, and 10,

$$\begin{cases} y = \quad x + 4 \\ y = -x + 6 \end{cases} \tag{11}$$

$$\begin{cases} y = \quad x + 4 \\ y = 3x - 6 \end{cases} \tag{12}$$

$$\begin{cases} y = -x + 6 \\ y = \quad 3x - 6 \end{cases} \tag{13}$$

The solutions of 11, 12, and 13 are the pairs $(1, 5)$, $(5, 9)$, and $(3, 3)$, respectively, which are the coordinates of the vertices A, B, and C of the triangle in Figure 8.15.

Polygons of more than three sides, and the interior points, may constitute the region satisfying a system of four or more inequalities.

EXAMPLE 3. Draw the graph of the given system of inequalities, and determine the coordinates of the vertices of the polygon which forms the boundary.

$$y \leq \quad 3x - 3 \tag{1}$$
$$3y \leq 24 - 2x \tag{2}$$
$$2y \geq \quad 3x - 10 \tag{3}$$
$$y \geq -x + 5 \tag{4}$$

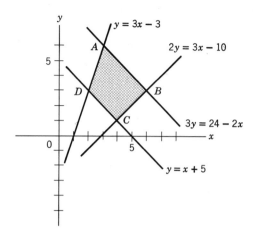

Figure 8.16

SOLUTION: The graph of the given system of inequalities (Figure 8.16) consists of the shaded area and the four lines which form the boundary, that is, the polygon $ABCD$. The vertex A is found by solving the system obtained by writing Equations 1 and 2 as

$$y = 3x - 3 \tag{5}$$
$$3y = 24 - 2x \tag{6}$$

Solving the system of equations 5 and 6, we have

$$x = 3, \quad y = 6$$

The coordinates of the vertex A are therefore $(3, 6)$. In a similar manner, the coordinates of B, C, and D are found to be $(6, 4)$, $(4, 1)$, and $(2, 3)$, respectively.

EXERCISE 8.9

Linear Inequalities in Two Variables

Solve each of the following inequalities for y in terms of x. Draw the graph and indicate by shading the part of the xy-plane for which the inequality is true.

1. $3x - 2y + 6 > 0$
2. $y + 2 < x$
3. $2x - 3y \leq 6$
4. $y - x \geq 6$
5. $x + y > 6$
6. $y + 8 > 2x$
7. $y - 2 \leq 2x$
8. $x - y - 4 \leq 0$
9. $y + 3x - 6 \geq 0$
10. $3x + 2y > 12$
11. $y + x < 2x$
12. $2y - 3x \leq 6$

13. Describe the part of the xy-plane where the inequality $x > y - 2$ is satisfied. Note that x is solved in terms of y.

14. Describe the part of the xy-plane where the inequality $x < y - 2$ is satisfied. Note that x is solved in terms of y.

Draw the graph of each of the following systems of inequalities, shading the part of the xy-plane for which the inequality is true.

15. $2x + 3y > 6$ 16. $3x - 2y \geq 6$ 17. $3x + y \leq 6$
$\quad\ 3x - 2y < 6$ $\quad\ 2x -\ y \leq 4$ $\quad\ x + y \geq 0$

18. $y > 0$ 19. $2x - y < 4$ 20. $x - 3y < 6$
$\quad\ y < 3x$ $\quad\ x + y > 2$ $\quad\ x +\ \ y > 2$

Draw the graphs of each of the following systems of inequalities. Determine the vertices of the polygons determined by each system.

21. $x \geq 0$ 22. $x + y \leq 8$ 23. $5x + 3y \geq 15$
$\quad\ x \leq 6$ $\quad\ 5y - 3x \leq 0$ $\quad\ y \leq 5$
$\quad\ y \geq 0$ $\quad\ y \geq 0$ $\quad\ x + y \leq 8$
$\quad\ x + y \leq 8$ $\quad\ y \geq 0$

24. $x \geq 1$ 25. $\ \ y -\ \ x \leq\ \ 1$
$\quad\ y \geq 0$ $\quad\ 7y + 2x \geq 34$
$\quad\ y \leq 6$ $\quad\ y + 2x \leq 22$
$\quad\ 2x + y \leq 10$

8.10 LINEAR PROGRAMMING

An important application of linear inequalities is called *linear programming*, a mathematical procedure for determining the most efficient operations relative to such considerations as profit, costs in business, military operations, use of machinery and materials, and other similar activities. In every area of application, problems that lend themselves to linear programming techniques always contain the following elements.

1. There is a variable to be optimized as a *maximum* profit, or a *minimum* time, or a *least* cost, or a *greatest* yield, and so on.

2. The variable is expressible as a linear function.

3. There are restrictions on the domain of the variable, called *constraints*, which are expressible as linear inequalities.

The following example illustrates a business situation that can be solved by linear programming.

EXAMPLE 1. A wholesale outlet has room in its radio and television section for not more than 150 radio and television sets. A radio set weighs 50 pounds and a television set weighs 100 pounds, and the floor is limited by the city inspector to a total weight of 10,000 pounds. The profit on a radio set is $50, and the profit on a television set is $75. In order to realize a maximum profit, how many of each shall be stocked? We shall assume, of course, that radio sets and television sets sell equally well.

SOLUTION: Let x = the number of radio sets and y = the number of television sets. Because of the limitation on weight, we have the first constraint

$$50x + 100y \leq 10{,}000 \tag{1}$$

Since at most 150 sets can be stocked, the second constraint is

$$x + y \leq 150 \tag{2}$$

Since the number of sets of either kind cannot be less than zero, we have two more constraints

$$x \geq 0 \tag{3}$$
$$y \geq 0 \tag{4}$$

The graph of this system (noting that inequality 1 can be reduced to $x + 2y \leq 200$) is shown in Figure 8.17. It is clear that only points such as P_1 which lie within or on the boundary of the polygon will satisfy the given constraints, as discussed in Section 8.8, and are therefore called *feasible points*. We now consider the profit equation

$$50x + 75y = P \tag{5}$$

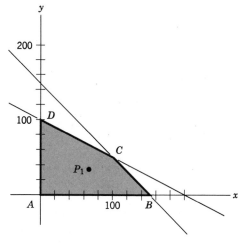

Figure 8.17

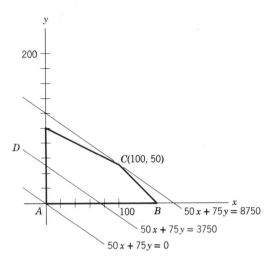

Figure 8.18

For all values of P, Equation 5 represents a system of parallel lines, as shown in Figure 8.18. We note further that as P increases, the lines move to the right. Of particular significance is the fact that the maximum *profit* occurs at the vertex C, since no feasible points exist beyond this point. The coordinates of point C are found by solving the system of equations, derived from the first two constraints

$$\begin{aligned} x + y &= 150 \\ x + 2y &= 200 \end{aligned} \tag{6}$$

The solution of Equations 6 is

$$x = 100, \text{ the number of radio sets}$$
$$y = 50, \text{ the number of television sets}$$

Thus the maximum profit is

$$P = 100(50) + 50(75) = \$8750$$

Observing that the minimum profit occurs at the vertex A, we state without proof the following principle of linear programming.

> The maximum or minimum value of the variable under consideration always occurs at a vertex of the polygon defined by the given constraints.

The particular vertex at which a maximum or minimum value occurs is usually determined, as in the following example, by tabulating the value of the variable at each vertex, since it may be difficult to determine graphically the particular vertex which yields a maximum or minimum value.

EXAMPLE 2. A metal stamping company makes two kinds of metal book ends, requiring the following time schedule:

	Stamping and Forming	Painting	Packing
Model A	5 minutes	2 minutes	1 minute
Model B	6 minutes	1 minute	2 minutes

The stamping and forming department must work at least 35 hours per week. The painting and packing is done at an outside paint shop that cannot give more than 16 hours for painting and 10 hours for packing. Previous sales indicate that Model A sells at least three times as well as Model B. The cost of producing Model A is 30 cents and Model B 20 cents. How many of each model should be made to minimize the cost of producing both models?

SOLUTION: Let x = the number of Model A book ends. Let y = the number of Model B books ends. The constraints are then

$$\frac{1}{12} x + \frac{1}{10} y \geq 35 \tag{1}$$

$$\frac{1}{30} x + \frac{1}{60} y \leq 16 \tag{2}$$

$$\frac{1}{60} x + \frac{1}{30} y \leq 10 \tag{3}$$

$$x \geq 3y \tag{4}$$

Neither x nor y can be negative, so we also have

$$y \geq 0 \tag{5}$$

(From Equation 4, Equation 5 also implies that $x \geq 0$.) The cost equation is

$$0.30x + 0.20y = C \tag{6}$$

The graph of the inequalities 1 to 5 determines the polygon of Figure 8.19. The graph of the cost equation is shown for $C = 30$, and while it is clear geometrically that the first vertex it will intersect is A, at which point the minimum cost should

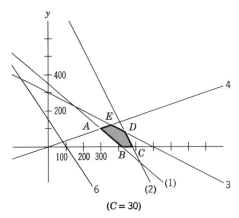

$(C = 30)$

Figure 8.19

occur, we shall tabulate the cost at each of the vertices. The coordinates of each vertex may be determined as in Section 8.8.

Vertex	x	y	Cost = 0.30 x + 0.20 y
A	300	100	$110
B	420	0	126
C	480	0	144
D	440	80	148
E	360	120	132

Thus we see that the least cost, occurring at vertex A, is obtained by making 300 Model A book ends, and 100 Model B book ends. We also note that the greatest cost occurs at vertex D, which is the last point that the cost line intersects.

EXERCISE 8.10

Linear Programming

A problem in linear programming is subject to the following constraints: $y \geq 0$, $x + 2y \leq 14$, $3x + 2y \leq 30$, $7x + 3y \geq 21$. Find the point or points at which h is maximized, and the maximum value of h in each of the following cases (Problems 1–4).

1. $h = x + y$ 2. $h = 2x + y$ 3. $h = x + 3y$ 4. $h = x + 2y$

5. A supermarket has a one-day special sale on two brands of coffee. The profit on brand A is 40 cents per can, and the profit on brand B is 60 cents a can. The store manager estimates that brand B will sell not more than twice as many cans as brand A. There is room on the shelves for not more than 600 cans in all. How many cans of each brand should be stocked for maximum profit?

6. A builder of homes in a high-priced area is restricted to building not more than 60 homes. The profit on the Colonial model is $6000, and the profit on the Deluxe model is $8000. The size of the lots limits the number of Colonial models to 50, and the number of Deluxe models to 40. To maintain the high property value, the builders agreed to build not less than one of the Deluxe models for every two of the less pretentious Colonial models. How many of each model should be built for maximum profit to the builder?

7. Two formulas of balanced foods are available for feeding animals. The composition of the formulas is as follows.

	Carbohydrates (Grams per Unit)	Proteins (Grams per Unit)	Fats (Grams per Unit)
Formula 1	15	20	1
Formula 2	30	10	5

It is estimated that each animal should receive daily not more than 180 grams of carbohydrates and a minimum of 120 grams of proteins and 15 grams of fats. If formula 2 costs three times as much per unit as formula 1, what combination of the two formulas will meet (or exceed) the minimum requirements at least cost?

8. In Problem 7, if the ratio of the costs of formula 1 to formula 2 is 3 to 1, what combination of the two formulas will satisfy the minimum requirements at least cost?

9. A manufacturer of electric alarm systems makes two types of bells, a model A and a model B. The time for processing is as follows.

	Department A (Fabricating)	Department B (Assembly)	Department C (Finishing)
Model A	20 minutes	30 minutes	12 minutes
Model B	30 minutes	15 minutes	12 minutes

Departments A and B cannot work more than 40 hours per week, and Department C must work at least 10 hours per week. The profit on Model A is $27.50 and the profit on model B is $25.00. How many bells of each model should be manufactured each week in order to realize a maximum profit, and what is the maximum profit?

chapter 9

sequences, progressions, and the binomial theorem

9.1 SEQUENCES

A SEQUENCE OF NUMBERS IS A SET OF NUMBERS THAT
are ordered. That is, there is a first number, a second number, a third number,
and so on. Each of the numbers of a sequence of numbers is called a term or
member of the sequence.

Some sequences have terms that are not numbers. The terms can and frequently are algebraic expressions.

Intelligence tests frequently use sequences by indicating a number of terms
and then asking for additional terms. For example, if you are told the first four
terms of a sequence are 1, 4, 9, and 16, you can readily see the terms are the
squares of the integers and that the next two terms are 25 and 36.

Another way of specifying a sequence is to utilize a function. If we require
that the domain of the function is the set of positive integers or a subset thereof,
the function would then determine a sequence. For example, if

$$F(x) = 2x - 1 \text{ and } x = \{1, 2, 3, 4, 5, 6\}$$
$$F(1) = 2 - 1 = 1$$

$$F(2) = 4 - 1 = 3$$
$$F(3) = 6 - 1 = 5$$
$$F(4) = 8 - 1 = 7$$
$$F(5) = 10 - 1 = 9$$
$$F(6) = 12 - 1 = 11$$

The ordered values of $F(x)$, namely 1, 3, 5, 7, 9, and 11, are the terms of this sequence.

This sequence has a finite number of terms (six) because of the restriction on the domain. If, however, the domain were changed to the set of positive integers, then the sequence would have an infinite number of terms and is called an infinite sequence.

Factorial Notation

In writing the function that determines the terms of a sequence there is a need for a notation to indicate the product of all the integers from 1 to another positive integer. To simplify the writing of such a product we utilize the factorial symbol. The symbol used is the exclamation mark (!), but in mathematics this symbol is read as "factorial."

$$3! \text{ (read 3 factorial)} = (1)(2)(3) = 6$$
$$5! \text{ (read 5 factorial)} = (1)(2)(3)(4)(5) = 120$$

If n is a positive integer, then $n! = (1)(2)(3) \ldots (n - 1)(n)$

EXAMPLE 1. Find the first six terms of the sequence determined by the function $g(x)$, where $x = 1, 2, 3, 4, 5, 6$.

$$g(x) = \frac{x^2}{x!}, \, x \text{ a positive integer}$$

$$g(1) = \frac{1}{1!} = 1$$

$$g(2) = \frac{4}{2!} = \frac{4}{2} = 2$$

$$g(3) = \frac{9}{3!} = \frac{9}{6} = \frac{3}{2}$$

$$g(4) = \frac{16}{4!} = \frac{16}{24} = \frac{2}{3}$$

$$g(5) = \frac{25}{5!} = \frac{25}{120} = \frac{5}{24}$$

$$g(6) = \frac{36}{6!} = \frac{36}{720} = \frac{1}{20}$$

If we consider simplifying the function $g(x) = \dfrac{x^2}{x!}$ before we evaluate, we would write

$$g(x) = \frac{x^2}{(1)(2) \ldots (x-1)x}$$

Upon dividing the numerator and denominator by x, we would obtain

$$g(x) = \frac{x}{1(2) \ldots (x-1)}$$

$$= \frac{x}{(x-1)!}.$$

If we use this form of $g(x)$ and find $g(2)$, $g(3)$, $g(4)$, $g(5)$, $g(6)$, we could obtain the same results as we did before with a little less effort. However, when we try to evaluate $g(1)$, we encounter a denominator of $0!$. Since we have already determined $g(1)$ to be 1 by using the original form of $g(x)$, $\dfrac{1}{0!}$ should be equal to one. The symbol $0!$ arises rather frequently and in all cases we find our results are consistent if we define it to be one. That is, $0! = 1$.

With this extension to the definition of factorial, we have:

$$0! = 1$$
$$1! = 1$$
$$2! = (1)(2)$$
$$x! = (1)(2) \ldots (x) \qquad x \text{ an integer}$$

EXAMPLE 2. Find the value of $\dfrac{7!}{5!}$.

$$\frac{7!}{5!} = \frac{\cancel{1}(\cancel{2})(\cancel{3})(\cancel{4})(\cancel{5})(6)(7)}{\cancel{1}(\cancel{2})(\cancel{3})(\cancel{4})(\cancel{5})}$$

$$= 6(7)$$

$$= 42$$

EXAMPLE 3. Find the value of $\dfrac{5!\,6!}{4!\,7!}$.

$5! = (4!)(5)$ and $7! = (6!)(7)$. Substituting the values of 5! and 7! we have

$\dfrac{5!\,6!}{4!\,7!} = \dfrac{(4!)(5)(6!)}{(4!)(6!)(7)}$. Dividing out the common factors 4! and 6!

$$= \frac{5}{7}.$$

EXERCISE 9.1

Sequences

In Problems 1–10 determine the next two terms of the sequences.

1. 2, 6, 10, 14, 18
2. 2, 4, 8, 16, 32
3. 2, 3, 5, 8, 12
4. 1, 2, 1, 4, 1, 6
5. 6, 4, 2, 0, −2
6. 24, 24, 12, 4, 1
7. −1, 4, 9, 14
8. 24, 21, 18, 15, 12
9. 2, 6, 18, 54, 162
10. 48, 24, 12, 6, 3

In Problems 11–26 find the first four terms of the sequence determined by the function given. The domain is the set of positive integers.

11. $F(x) = 3x + 1$
12. $F(x) = x^2 - x$
13. $F(x) = x^2 - 2$
14. $F(x) = \dfrac{12}{x}$
15. $F(x) = \dfrac{2x - 3}{5}$
16. $F(x) = \dfrac{1}{x^2}$
17. $F(x) = \dfrac{2x + 1}{x^2}$
18. $F(x) = 2^{x-1}$
19. $F(x) = 3^x + 1$
20. $F(x) = 3(2^x)$
21. $F(x) = \dfrac{81}{3^x - 1}$
22. $F(x) = \dfrac{64}{2^x}$
23. $F(x) = x + \dfrac{2^x}{x}$

24. $F(x) = x^x$

25. $F(x) = (2x)^{x-1}$

26. $F(x) = 3x^{x-1}$

In Problems 27–40 simplify the following expressions.

27. $\dfrac{7!}{4!}$

28. $\dfrac{4!\,8!}{5!\,9!}$

29. $\dfrac{4!}{0!}$

30. $\dfrac{3!\,0!}{1!\,4!}$

31. $\dfrac{1! + 0!}{2!}$

32. $\dfrac{1}{3!} + \dfrac{1}{4!}$

33. $\dfrac{1}{3!} + \dfrac{5}{5!}$

34. $\dfrac{5! + 6!}{4!}$

35. $\dfrac{n!}{(n-1)!}$

36. $\dfrac{(n-3)!}{(n-1)!}$

37. $\dfrac{(n+1)!}{(n-1)!}$

38. $\dfrac{(n+1)!}{3!\,n!}$

39. $\dfrac{(n+1)!}{n^2 + n}$

40. $\dfrac{(n+1)!}{n^3 - n}$

9.2 ARITHMETIC PROGRESSIONS

If the difference of successive terms of a sequence is a constant, then the terms are said to be terms of an arithmetic progression. Examples of arithmetic progressions are as follows:

$$2, 4, 6, 8, \ldots \qquad \text{common difference} = 2$$
$$1, 5, 9, 13, \ldots \qquad \text{common difference} = 4$$
$$\frac{1}{12}, \frac{1}{6}, \frac{1}{4}, \frac{1}{3} \ldots \qquad \text{common difference} = \frac{1}{12}$$
$$7, -1, -9, -17, \ldots \qquad \text{common difference} = -8$$

The terms of a general arithmetic progression can be written in algebraic form. If we let a = 1st term and d = common difference, then the terms of a general arithmetic progression are:

$$\text{1st term} = a$$
$$\text{2nd term} = a + d$$
$$\text{3rd term} = a + 2d$$

$$\text{4th term} = a + 3d$$

$$\cdot \qquad\qquad \cdot$$
$$\cdot \qquad\qquad \cdot$$
$$\cdot \qquad\qquad \cdot$$

$$n\text{th term} = a + (n-1)d$$

We shall use the symbol "l" to represent the nth term so that

$$l = a + (n-1)d$$

EXAMPLE 1. If the first term of an arithmetic progression is 4 and the common difference is 3, find the first 5 terms and the 32nd term. $a = 4$ and $d = 3$

$$\text{1st term} = a = 4$$
$$\text{2nd term} = a + d = 4 + 3 = 7$$
$$\text{3rd term} = a + 2d = 4 + 2(3) = 10$$
$$\text{4th term} = a + 3d = 4 + 3(3) = 13$$
$$\text{5th term} = a + 4d = 4 + 4(3) = 16$$
$$\text{32nd term} = a + (32-1)\,d = 4 + 31(3) = 97$$

EXAMPLE 2. If the 6th term of an arithmetic progression is 8 and the 11th term is -2, what is the 1st term? What is the common difference?

11th term: $a + (11-1)\,d = -2$

6th term: $a + (6-1)\,d = 8$. Simplifying the above equations we obtain:

$$a + 10d = -2 \qquad\qquad\qquad\qquad (1)$$
$$a + 5d = 8 \qquad\qquad\qquad\qquad (2)$$
$$5d = -10 \qquad \text{Subtracting (2) from (1)}$$
$$d = -2 \qquad \text{Substituting in (1)}$$
$$a + 10(-2) = -2$$
$$a = 18$$

The first term is 18 and the common difference is -2.

THEOREM 9.1. If the function that generates a sequence is a linear function, and the domain is a set of consecutive positive integers, then the sequence generated is an arithmetic progression.

PROOF: The general linear function is $F(x) = Ax + B$

$$F(1) = A + B$$
$$F(2) = 2A + B$$
$$F(3) = 3A + B.$$

We can see that for the values of $x = 1, 2,$ and 3 the difference of the consecutive terms of the sequence is A. The *nth* term is

$$F(n) = An + B$$

and its successor is

$$F(n + 1) = A(n + 1) + B$$

The difference

$$F(n + 1) - F(n) = [An + A + B] - [An + B] = A$$

Since the difference between the *nth* term and its successor is a constant, the sequence generated is an arithmetic progression.

EXAMPLE 3. Determine the first four terms and 12th term of the arithmetic progression generated by $F(x) = 2x + 3$.

$$\text{1st term} = F(1) = 2(1) + 3 = 5$$
$$\text{2nd term} = F(2) = 2(2) + 3 = 7$$
$$\text{3rd term} = F(3) = 2(3) + 3 = 9$$
$$\text{4th term} = F(4) = 2(4) + 3 = 11$$
$$\text{12th term} = F(12) = 2(12) + 3 = 27$$

Note: For this progression $a = 5$ and $d = 2$. The coefficient of x in the linear function will always be the common difference for the arithmetic progression.

EXAMPLE 4. If an arithmetic progression is generated by the linear function $F(x) = -3x + 14$, what is the first term? What is the 15th term? What is the common difference?

$$\text{1st term} = F(1) = -3 + 14 = 11$$
$$\text{15th term} = F(15) = -3(15) + 14 = -31$$
$$d = -3, \text{ the coefficient of the linear term}$$

Sum of an Arithmetic Progression. If we let S_n denote the sum of the first n terms of a sequence, then for an arithmetic progression

$$S_n = a + (a + d) + (a + 2d) + \ldots + (l - d) - l \qquad (1)$$

If the terms of the right member are written in reverse order, then

$$S_n = l + (l - d) + (l - 2d) + \ldots + (a + d) + a \qquad (2)$$

Adding Equations 1 and 2 we obtain

$$2S_n = (a + l) + (a + l) + (a + l) \ldots + (a + l) + (a + l) \qquad (3)$$

All of the n terms in the right member are $a + l$ so Equation 3 can be written

$$2S_n = n(a + l).$$

Hence

$$S_n = \frac{n}{2}(a + l)$$

EXAMPLE 5. Find the sum of the first 25 even integers.

$$a = 2, n = 25, d = 2$$
$$l = a + (n - 1)d$$
$$= 2 + (25 - 1)2$$
$$= 50$$
$$S_{25} = \frac{25}{2}(2 + 50)$$
$$= 25(26)$$
$$= 650$$

EXAMPLE 6. Find the sum of the first 20 terms of the arithmetic progression $-9, -3, 3, \ldots$

$$a = -9, d = 6, n = 20$$
$$l = -9 + (19)(6)$$
$$= -9 + 114$$
$$= 105$$
$$S_{20} = \frac{20}{2}(-9 + 105)$$
$$= 10(96)$$
$$= 960$$

Arithmetic Means. If two numbers are given and a number of terms are to be inserted between them so that the entire set forms an arithmetic progression, the terms inserted are called arithmetic means. If only one term is inserted, then it is called the arithmetic mean of the two numbers.

EXAMPLE 7. Insert 4 arithmetic means between 1 and 36.

$$a = 1, l = 36, \text{ and } n = 6 \text{ since there will be six terms}$$
$$l = a + (n - 1)d$$
$$36 = 1 + 5d$$
$$5d = 35$$
$$d = 7$$

The arithmetic means are: 8, 15, 22, and 29. The arithmetic progression is 1, 8, 15, 22, 29, 36.

EXAMPLE 8. Insert 3 arithmetic means between 5 and 15.

$$a = 5, l = 15, n = 5$$
$$l = a + (n - 1)d$$
$$15 = 5 + 4d$$
$$10 = 4d$$
$$d = \frac{5}{2}$$

The arithmetic means are $\frac{15}{2}$, 10, and $\frac{25}{2}$ and the arithmetic progression is 5, $\frac{15}{2}$, 10, $\frac{25}{2}$, 15.

EXERCISE 9.2

Arithmetic Progressions

In Problems 1–20 some of the sequences are arithmetic progressions, others are not arithmetic progressions. Determine whether the given sequence is an arithmetic progression. If the sequence is an arithmetic progression, find the 10th term and the 21st term.

1. 4, 7, 10, 13, . . .

2. 1, 2, 4, 7, . . .

3. 1, 3, 9, 27, . . .

4. $\frac{1}{2}$, 3, $\frac{11}{2}$, 8, . . .

5. $-2, 0, 2, 4, \ldots$

6. $-19, -16, -13, -10, \ldots$

7. 29, 32, 35, 38, . . .

8. 31, 32, 34, 37, . . .

9. 25, 26, 28, 31, . . .

10. $-4, 2, -1, \frac{1}{2}$

11. $-17, -10, -3, 4, \ldots$

12. $-24, -19, -14, -9, \ldots$

13. $-1, \frac{1}{3}, \frac{5}{3}, 3, \ldots$

14. $\frac{1}{12}, \frac{1}{4}, \frac{5}{12}, \frac{7}{12}$

15. $-5, 1, 7, 13, \ldots$

16. $7, 3, -1, -5, \ldots$

17. $7, 4\frac{1}{3}, 1\frac{2}{3}, -1, \ldots$

18. $9, 8, 6, 3, \ldots$

19. $\frac{1}{2}, \frac{1}{3}, \frac{1}{4}, \frac{1}{5}, \ldots$

20. $6, 4\frac{1}{5}, 2\frac{2}{5}, \frac{3}{5}, \ldots$

In Problems 21–30 the domain of the functions is the set of positive integers. Determine the first four terms of the sequence and state whether or not the sequence is an arithmetic progression.

21. $F(x) = 2x - 5$

22. $F(x) = 3x + 1$

23. $F(x) = \frac{1}{3}x + 2$

24. $F(x) = \frac{1}{2}x^2 - 3$

25. $G(x) = \dfrac{x^2 + 2x}{x}$

26. $G(x) = \dfrac{2x^2 - 3x}{x}$

27. $G(x) = \dfrac{x^2 + 2x}{2}$

28. $G(x) = \dfrac{x^2 - 1}{x + 1}$

29. $H(x) = \dfrac{x^3 + 1}{x^2 - x + 1}$

30. $H(x) = \dfrac{x^2 + 1}{x + 1}$

In Problems 31–40 find the sum of the first 40 terms of the arithmetic progression.

31. $4, 8, 12, 16, \ldots$

32. $1, 6, 11, 16, \ldots$

33. $17, 14, 11, 8, \ldots$

34. $-6, -4, -2, 0, \ldots$

35. $\frac{1}{24}, \frac{1}{12}, \frac{1}{8}, \frac{1}{6}, \ldots$

36. $\frac{5}{6}, \frac{3}{4}, \frac{2}{3}, \frac{7}{12}, \ldots$

37. $8, 3, -2, -7, \ldots$

38. $1.6, 1.9, 2.2, 2.5, \ldots$

39. $2\pi, 3\pi, 4\pi, 5\pi, \ldots$

40. $40, 38, 36, 34, \ldots$

41. Insert three arithmetic means between 4 and 20.

42. Insert four arithmetic means between -2 and 13.

43. Insert four arithmetic means between 3 and 12.

44. Insert three arithmetic means between 2 and 9.

45. By using literal symbols, m and n, show that their arithmetic mean is also their average value.

46. Find the sum of all of the positive integers less than 200 which end in 7.

47. Find the sum of all of the positive integers less than 200 which are exactly divisible by 7.

48. Find the sum of all of the positive integers less than 200 which are exactly divisible by 2 or by 3 but not divisible by both 2 and 3.

49. Show that the sum of the first n odd integers is n^2.

50. Show that the sum of the first n even integers is $n^2 + n$.

9.3 EXPONENTIAL FUNCTIONS

A function of the form $y = a \cdot b^x$ where a and b are constants and $b > 0$ is an exponential function. Examples of exponential functions are: $y = 3 \cdot 2^x$, $y = \dfrac{1}{3} \cdot 16^x$, and $y = 12 \cdot \left(\dfrac{1}{2}\right)^x$. The last example can also be written in another form. Using the laws of exponents $y = 12(\frac{1}{2})^x$ can also be written as:

$$y = 12 \cdot \frac{1^x}{2^x}$$

since $1^x = 1$, then

$$y = 12 \cdot \frac{1}{2^x}$$

which can be written as

$$y = 12 \cdot 2^{-x}$$

Exponential functions can be readily evaluated for x an integer. However, difficulties arise when evaluating the function for rational nonintegral values of x or irrational values of x. However, this difficulty will be resolved in the next chapter with the treatment of logarithms and their applications.

It is sufficient for our purpose to consider several examples of exponential functions and to study the nature of their graphs.

EXAMPLE 1. Graph the function $y = 2^x$.

$$y = f(x) = 2^x$$

$$f(0) = 2^0 = 1 \qquad\qquad f(-1) = 2^{-1} = \frac{1}{2}$$

$$f(1) = 2^1 = 2 \qquad\qquad f(-2) = 2^{-2} = \frac{1}{4}$$

$$f(2) = 2^2 = 4 \qquad\qquad f(-3) = 2^{-3} = \frac{1}{8}$$

$$f(3) = 2^3 = 8 \qquad\qquad f(-4) = 2^{-4} = \frac{1}{16}$$

$$f(4) = 2^4 = 16$$

When these points are plotted and a smooth curve is drawn through them, we have the graph of the exponential function $y = 2^x$ (Figure 9.1).

Notice that the curve passes through $(0, 1)$ and that as you move from $x = -4$ to $x = 0$ the change in y is small; but as you follow the curve to the right of the y-axis the change in y for unit change in x gets much larger.

EXAMPLE 2.   Graph $y = 4^x$.

The table of values for the integers -3 to 3 can be determined to be:

x	-3	-2	-1	0	1	2	3
y	$\dfrac{1}{64}$	$\dfrac{1}{16}$	$\dfrac{1}{4}$	1	4	16	64

Figure 9.2 is the graph of $y = 4^x$ although it is not practical to plot the points corresponding to $x = -3$ or $x = 3$ on this coordinate system.

When this curve is compared to the graph of $y = 2^x$ (Figure 9.1), we see that the general shape is the same. Both curves pass through the point $(0,1)$, that is, both have a y-intercept of 1. If we consider the curves to the left of the y-axes, we see that the curve of Figure 9.2 approaches the x-axis faster than the curve of Figure 9.1.

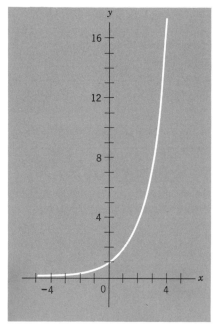

Figure 9.1

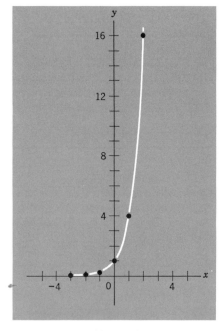

Figure 9.2

EXAMPLE 3. Graph the function $y = 4^{-x}$. Evaluating the function for integers from -3 to 3, we have

$$f(-3) = 4^{-[-3]} = 4^3 = 64$$
$$f(-2) = 4^{-[-2]} = 4^2 = 16$$
$$f(-1) = 4^{-[-1]} = 4^1 = 4$$
$$f(0) = 4^0 = 1$$
$$f(1) = 4^{-1} = \frac{1}{4}$$
$$f(2) = 4^{-2} = \frac{1}{4^2} = \frac{1}{16}$$
$$f(3) = 4^{-3} = \frac{1}{4^3} = \frac{1}{64}$$

x	-3	-2	-1	0	1	2	3
y	64	16	4	1	$\frac{1}{4}$	$\frac{1}{16}$	$\frac{1}{64}$

Figure 9.3 is the graph of $y = 4^{-x}$.

The graph of $y = 4^x$ of the Figure 9.2 and the graph of $y = 4^{-x}$ of Figure 9.3 are mirror images of each other.

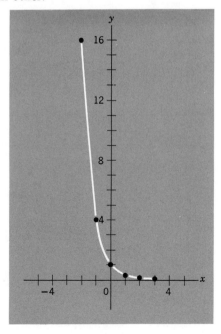

Figure 9.3

EXAMPLE 4.   Graph the function $y = 3 \cdot 2^x$.

In Example 1 we determined the values of 2^x for x an integer and $-4 \leq x \leq 4$. The values of y for this function then must be three times the corresponding values of y of Example 1.

x	−4	−3	−2	−1	0	1	2	3	4
y	$\dfrac{3}{16}$	$\dfrac{3}{8}$	$\dfrac{3}{4}$	$\dfrac{3}{2}$	3	6	12	24	48

The graph of this function is shown in Figure 9.4.

From these four examples we can see some of the features of the graph of $y = ab^x$, $a > 0$, and $b > 0$. The y-intercept of the function is a. If $a > 1$, the curve will approach the x-axis to the left of the y-axis and the y value increases as the x value increases. The graph will be in quadrants 1 and II.

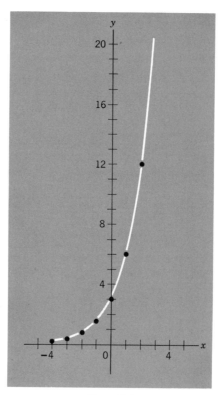

Figure 9.4

EXERCISE 9.3

Exponential Functions

Make a table of values for each of the following functions. Use $x = -4, -3 \ldots$
2, 3, 4. Use a separate coordinate system for each problem. Plot the points of the
table (It may not be convenient to plot them all.) and draw the graph.

1. $y = 3^x$

2. $y = 3^{-x}$

3. $y = 2^{-x}$

4. $y = \left(\dfrac{1}{3}\right)^x$

5. $y = 2(3^x)$

6. $y = \dfrac{1}{2}(3^x)$

7. $y = \left(\dfrac{3}{2}\right)^x$

8. $y = \left(\dfrac{2}{3}\right)^x$

9. $y = 3\left(\dfrac{1}{2}\right)^x$

10. $y = 2\left(\dfrac{1}{3}\right)^x$

11. $y = -2^x$

12. $y = -3^x$

13. The paragraph after Example 4 discusses $y = a \cdot b^x$, $b > 0$, and $a > 0$. In
    a similar fashion discuss the exponential function $y = a \cdot b^x$, $b > 0$, and
    $a < 0$.

9.4   GEOMETRIC PROGRESSIONS

In Section 9.2 we considered sequences in which successive elements or terms
had a common difference. These were called arithmetic progressions. If instead
of comparing successive terms by difference we compare them by their ratio
and we find all such ratios are equal, then the sequence is a geometric progression.

Some geometric progressions are:

$$1, 2, 4, 8, \ldots$$
$$3, 12, 48, 192, \ldots$$
$$32, 16, 8, 4, \ldots$$
$$1, -3, 9, -27 \ldots$$

The common ratios are 2, 4, $\dfrac{1}{2}$, and -3, respectively.

Geometric progressions can be generated by exponential functions if the
domain of the function is restricted to the set of non-negative integers. This can

readily be shown by considering the exponential function $y = ab^x$ and replacing b by r, then

$$f(0) = ar^0 = a$$
$$f(1) = ar^1 = ar$$
$$f(2) = ar^2$$
$$f(3) = ar^3$$

The terms in the right column are the first four terms of a geometric progression.

EXAMPLE 1.   Find the next three terms of the geometric progression 1, 2, 4, 8, ... The common ratio is 2 so the 5th term is $8 \times 2 = 16$. The 6th term is $16 \times 2 = 32$. The 7th term is $32 \times 2 = 64$. The first seven terms of the geometric progression are:

$$1, 2, 4, 8, 16, 32, 64$$

EXAMPLE 2.   Find the next three terms of the geometric progression 27, -9, 3, -1, ... The common ratio obtained by dividing any term by the term preceding it is $-\frac{1}{3}$. The 5th term is $(-1)\left(-\frac{1}{3}\right) = \frac{1}{3}$, the 6th term is $\left(\frac{1}{3}\right)\left(-\frac{1}{3}\right) = -\frac{1}{9}$, and the 7th term is $\left(-\frac{1}{9}\right)\left(-\frac{1}{3}\right) = \frac{1}{27}$.

EXAMPLE 3.   Find the first four terms of the geometric progression generated by the exponential function $f(x) = 12\left(\frac{3}{2}\right)^x$ if the domain of the function is the set of nonnegative integers (0, 1, 2, 3, . . .).

$$f(0) = 12\left(\frac{3}{2}\right)^0 = 12(1) = 12$$

$$f(1) = 12\left(\frac{3}{2}\right) = 18$$

$$f(2) = 12\left(\frac{3}{2}\right)^2 = 12\left(\frac{9}{4}\right) = 27$$

$$f(3) = 12\left(\frac{3}{2}\right)^3 = 12\left(\frac{27}{8}\right) = \frac{81}{2}$$

The first four terms are 12, 18, 27, and $\frac{81}{2}$.

If we let a represent the first term of a geometric progression, r the common ratio and l the nth term, the first n terms of a geometric progression are:

$$a, ar, ar^2, ar^3, \ldots, l = ar^{n-1}$$

The exponent of r in any term of a geometric progression is one less than the number of the term.

EXAMPLE 4. Find the 10th term of the geometric progression $3, 6, 12, 24, \ldots$.

$$a = 3 \quad \text{and} \quad r = 2$$

If we let l represent the 10th term

$$\begin{aligned}
l &= 3(2)^{10-1} \\
&= 3(2)^9 \\
&= 3(512) \\
&= 1536
\end{aligned}$$

EXAMPLE 5. If the 8th term of a geometric progression is 16 and the common ratio is -3, what is the 12th term?

$$\begin{aligned}
\text{the 8th term} &= 16 = ar^7 \\
\text{the 12th term} &= ar^{11} \\
&= (ar^7)r^4 \\
&= (16)(-3)^4 \\
&= (16)(81) \\
&= 1296
\end{aligned}$$

S_n: The Sum of the First n Terms of a Geometric Progression

$$S_n = a + ar + ar^2 + \ldots + ar^{n-1} \tag{1}$$

If we multiply both members of Equation 1 by r, we obtain

$$rS_n = ar + ar^2 + ar^3 + \ldots + ar^{n-1} + ar^n \tag{2}$$

For convenience let us rewrite Equations 1 and 2 and then subtract Equation 2 from Equation 1 to obtain Equation 3.

$$S_n = a + ar + ar^2 + \ldots + ar^{n-1} \tag{1}$$
$$rS_n = \quad\ \ ar + ar^2 + \ldots + ar^{n-1} + ar^n \tag{2}$$
$$S_n - rS_n = a \qquad\qquad\qquad\qquad\quad\ - ar^n \tag{3}$$

By factoring the left member of (3) we obtain $(1 - r)S_n = a - ar^n$. Solving for S_n by dividing both members by $1 - r$ we have

$$S_n = \frac{a - ar^n}{1 - r}$$

$$= \frac{a(1 - r^n)}{1 - r}$$

EXAMPLE 6.   First the sum of the first ten terms of the geometric progression: 15, 30, 60, 120 . . . .

$$a = 15, r = 2, \text{ and } n = 10$$
$$S_{10} = \frac{15(1 - 2^{10})}{1 - 2}$$
$$= \frac{15(1 - 1024)}{-1}$$
$$= 15(1023)$$
$$= 15{,}345$$

EXAMPLE 7.   Find the sum of the first eight terms of the geometric progression: $4, \dfrac{-4}{3}, \dfrac{4}{9}, \dfrac{-4}{27}$.

$$a = 4, r = \frac{-1}{3}, \text{ and } n = 8$$

$$S_8 = \frac{4\left[1 - \left(-\dfrac{1}{3}\right)^8\right]}{1 - \dfrac{1}{3}}$$

$$= \frac{4\left(1 - \dfrac{1}{6561}\right)}{\dfrac{2}{3}}$$

$$= 4\left(\frac{3}{2}\right)\left(\frac{6560}{6561}\right)$$

$$= 6\left(\frac{6560}{6561}\right) = \frac{13{,}120}{2187}$$

The problem of finding the sum of a finite number of terms of a geometric progression can be a tedious task because of the necessity of finding the value of r^n. However, under some circumstances the problem of finding the sum of an infinite number of terms of a geometric progression may be a simple one. Consider the sum of a geometric progression with an infinite number of terms and the absolute value of the ratio r less than one.

$$S_n = a + ar + ar^2 + ar^3 + \ldots + ar^{n-1} + \ldots$$

The sum of the first n terms of a geometric progression

$$S_n = \frac{a(1 - r^n)}{1 - r}$$

can be written as

$$S_n = \frac{a}{1 - r} - \frac{ar^n}{1 - r} \tag{4}$$

When $|r| < 1$, $|r^n|$ decreases as n increases and by making n larger and larger we can make $|r^n|$ and consequently $|ar^n|$, differ from zero by as little as we please. Therefore, the second term of S_n of Equation 4 will approach zero as the number of terms increases beyond all bound.

This is indicated symbolically as

$$\lim_{n \to \infty} S_n = \frac{a}{1 - r}, \; |r| < 1 \tag{5}$$

$\lim_{n \to \infty} S_n$ can be read as "the limit of the sum as n increases beyond all bound."
This limiting value of S_n is called the sum of the infinite geometric progression.

EXAMPLE 8. Find the sum of the infinite geometric progression: $2, 1, \dfrac{1}{2}, \dfrac{1}{4}, \ldots$

Since we are dealing with an infinite geometric progression and $|r| < 1$ we can use formula (5) to find the sum.

$$a = 2, r = \frac{1}{2}$$

$$\lim_{n \to \infty} S_n = \frac{2}{1 - \dfrac{1}{2}}$$

$$= \frac{2}{\dfrac{1}{2}} = 4$$

This result can also be attained by considering Figure 9.5.

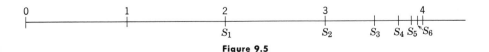

Figure 9.5

From the figure we can see the values of the sums are: $S_1 = 2$, $S_2 = 3$, $S_3 = 3\frac{1}{2}$, and $S_4 = 3\frac{3}{4}$. To find the position on the number scale for each of the successive sums, we move from the present position to the right one-half of the distance from the present position to the position of 4. It will not take many such steps after S_6 until we are so close to 4 that we will not be able to divide the line segment remaining in half.

Repeating decimals can be converted to fractional form by considering the repeating decimal as the sum of terms of an infinite geometric progression.

EXAMPLE 9.   Convert the repeating decimal .477477 . . . to a fraction.

$$.477477 \ldots = .477 + .000477 + .000000477 + \ldots$$
$$a = .477 \text{ and } r = .001$$
$$\lim_{n \to \infty} S_n = \frac{.477}{1 - .001}$$
$$= \frac{477}{999} = \frac{53}{111}$$

$\frac{53}{111}$ is the fractional equivalent of the repeating decimal .477477 . . . .

The reader should contrast this method with the method for determining the rational form of repeating decimals of Section 3.5.

EXERCISE 9.4

Geometric Progressions

In Problems 1–16 determine whether the given sequence forms a geometric progression. If the sequence is a geometric progression, find the next three terms and also the nth term.

1. 64, 32, 16, 8, . . .

2. 3, 6, 12, 24, . . .

3. $1, \frac{1}{3}, \frac{1}{9}, \frac{1}{27}, \ldots$

4. $\frac{-1}{4}, \frac{-1}{2}, 1, 2, \ldots$

5. 1, 2, 4, 7, . . .

6. $12, 8, \frac{16}{3}, \frac{32}{9}, \ldots$

7. 16, 24, 36, 54, . . .

8. $4, -2, 1, \frac{-1}{2}, \ldots$

9. $1000, 100, 10, 1, \ldots$

10. $2, 4, 12, 48, \ldots$

11. $27, -9, 3, -1, \ldots$

12. $216, 36, 6, 1, \ldots$

13. $12, 6, 3, 1, \ldots$

14. $4, \dfrac{4}{3}, \dfrac{4}{9}, \dfrac{4}{27}, \ldots$

15. $\dfrac{1}{24}, \dfrac{-1}{12}, \dfrac{1}{6}, \dfrac{-1}{3}, \ldots$

16. $-40, 20, -10, 5, \ldots$

In problems 17–26 use the given exponential function with the nonnegative real numbers for the domain to determine the first four terms of a geometric progression.

17. $F(x) = 2(2^x)$

18. $F(x) = 16(2^x)$

19. $F(x) = 2(-3)^x$

20. $F(x) = -2\left(\dfrac{1}{3}\right)^x$

21. $F(x) = 48\left(\dfrac{1}{2}\right)^x$

22. $F(x) = -2(-3)^x$

23. $F(x) = 32\left(-\dfrac{1}{2}\right)^x$

24. $F(x) = 7(10)^x$

25. $F(x) = 8\left(\dfrac{1}{10}\right)^x$

26. $F(x) = -8(-2)^x$

In Problems 27–36 you are given the first term and the common ratio of geometric progressions. Find the sum of the first eight terms of each progression.

27. $a = 8, r = 2$

28. $a = 12, r = 3$

29. $a = 1, r = \dfrac{1}{2}$

30. $a = 27, r = \dfrac{1}{3}$

31. $a = 9, r = \dfrac{-1}{3}$

32. $a = 16, r = \dfrac{-1}{2}$

33. $a = 64, r = \dfrac{3}{2}$

34. $a = 81, r = \dfrac{2}{3}$

35. $a = -4, r = -\dfrac{1}{2}$

36. $a = -32, r = -\dfrac{1}{2}$

In Problems 37–44 find the sum of the infinite geometric progressions.

37. $12, 6, 3, \dfrac{3}{2}, \ldots$

38. $24, 8, \dfrac{8}{3}, \dfrac{8}{9}, \ldots$

39. $3, -1, \dfrac{1}{3}, -\dfrac{1}{9}, \ldots$

40. $8, -4, 2, -1, \ldots$

41. $36, 24, 16, \dfrac{32}{3}, \ldots$

42. $.8, .08, .008, .0008, \ldots$

43. $.34, .0034, .000034, .00000034, \ldots$

44. $64, -48, 36, -27, \ldots$

In Problems 45–50 find the fraction form of each of the repeating decimals.

45. 0.3232 . . .   46. 0.4545 . . .

47. 0.127127 . . .   48. 0.324324 . . .

49. 2.313131 . . .   50. 1.474747 . . .

51. If a ball, dropped from a height of 20 ft, bounces back to a height of 10 ft and continues to rebound one half of the previous height, how far will it travel before it comes to rest?

52. If 1000 tons of ore are removed from a mine the first year, 250 tons the second year, and if in every year the yield is 25% of the preceding year, what is the total amount of ore that could be removed?

53. If a square is drawn by joining the midpoints of the sides of a square with sides 16 in. long, and a third square is drawn inside of the second square in the same way, and if this process is repeated indefinitely, approximately what is the sum of the perimeters?

54. If the midpoint procedure of Problem 53 is used to draw a set of quadrilaterals inside of a rectangle 10 × 24 in., find the approximate length of the sum of the perimeters.

9.5 THE BINOMIAL THEOREM

The theorem that enables us to write the sequence of terms which are obtained when a binomial is raised to a power is called the binomial theorem.

The following expansions of binomials raised to powers can readily be verified.

$$
\begin{aligned}
(a + x)^0 &= 1 \\
(a + x)^1 &= a + x \\
(a + x)^2 &= a^2 + 2ax + x^2 \\
(a + x)^3 &= a^3 + 3a^2x + 3ax^2 + x^3 \\
(a + x)^4 &= a^4 + 4a^3x + 6a^2x^2 + 4ax^3 + x^4 \\
(a + x)^5 &= a^5 + 5a^4x + 10a^3x^2 + 10a^2x^3 + 5ax^4 + x^5
\end{aligned}
$$

The above expansions are sufficient for us to make some general observations about the expansion of a power of a binomial. If n is the exponent of $(a + x)$ then:

1. The number of terms is $n + 1$.
2. The first term is a^n and the last term is x^n.
3. The second term is $na^{n-1}x$.
4. The exponent of a decreases by one and the exponent of x increases by one as we go from one term to the next.

5. The coefficient of the first term is 1, the coefficient of the second term is n, the coefficient of the third term is $\dfrac{n(n-1)}{2!}$, and the coefficient of the fourth term is $\dfrac{n(n-1)(n-2)}{3!}$.

The student should verify that each of the above statements is true of the expansions listed.

It can be proved, although it is beyond the scope of this text, that the expansion of the nth power of a binomial can be written as:

$$(a+x)^n = a^n + na^{n-1}x + \frac{n(n-1)}{2!}a^{n-2}x^2 + \frac{n(n-1)(n-2)}{3!}a^{n-3}x^3$$

$$+ \ldots + \frac{n(n-1)(n-2)\ldots(n-r+2)}{(r-1)!}a^{n-r+1}x^{r-1}$$

$$+ \ldots + nax^{n-1} + x^n$$

The term in the second line of the expansion is the rth term or general term of the binomial theorem. We use the rth term if we are interested in finding one term of a binomial expansion.

Before we consider examples that will necessitate the use of the binomial theorem, let us consider a method of determining the coefficients of the expansions for small values of n. This method was determined by the famous French mathematician, Blaise Pascal, and it is called Pascal's triangle.

First, write ones on two sides of a triangle as in Figure 9.6.

$$
\begin{array}{lccccccccccc}
n = 0 & & & & & & 1 & & & & & \\
n = 1 & & & & & 1 & & 1 & & & & \\
n = 2 & & & & 1 & & 2 & & 1 & & & \\
n = 3 & & & 1 & & 3 & & 3 & & 1 & & \\
n = 4 & & 1 & & 4 & & 6 & & 4 & & 1 & \\
n = 5 & 1 & & 5 & & 10 & & 10 & & 5 & & 1 \\
\end{array}
$$

Figure 9.6

These are the coefficients of a^n and b^n. For $n = 0$ there is only one term, for $n = 1$ there are two terms; therefore, these two rows are complete. The missing coefficient in the row for $n = 2$ is obtained by adding the numbers diagonally above it as shown in Figure 9.5. This process can be continued to get as many sets of coefficients as are desired.

EXAMPLE 1. Expand $(a + b)^5$.

SOLUTION: From Pascal's triangle, the coefficients of this expansion will be 1, 5, 10, 10, 5, 1. Therefore,

$$(a + b)^5 = a^5 + 5a^4b + 10a^3b^2 + 10a^2b^3 + 5ab^4 + b^5$$

EXAMPLE 2. Expand $(x + 2y)^5$.

SOLUTION: Using the general binomial expansion of Example 1, we have

$$(x + 2y)^5 = x^5 + 5x^4(2y) + 10x^3(2y)^2 + 10x^2(2y)^3 + 5x(2y)^4 + (2y)^5$$
$$= x^5 + 10x^4y + 40x^3y^2 + 80x^2y^3 + 80xy^4 + 32y^5$$

EXAMPLE 3. Expand $(2z - 3y)^4$.

$$(2z - 3y)^4 = (2z)^4 + 4(2z)^3(-3y) + 6(2z)^2 (-3y)^2 + 4(2z)(-3y)^3 + (-3y)^4$$
$$= 16z^4 + 4(8z^3)(-3y) + 6(4z^2)(9y^2) + 4(2z)(-27y^3) + 81y^4$$
$$= 16z^4 - 96z^3y + 216z^2y^2 - 216zy^3 + 81y^4$$

EXAMPLE 4. Find the 7th term of the expansion of $(p + q)^{10}$.

Since only the 7th term is to be determined we use the rth term of the binomial expansion. That is,

$$\frac{n(n - 1) \ldots (n - r + 2)}{(r - 1)!} a^{n-r+1}x^{r-1}$$

and use

$$r = 7, n = 10, a = p, \text{ and } x = q$$
$$\frac{10(9)(8) \ldots (5)}{6!} p^{10-7+1}q^{7-1}$$

When simplified

$$\frac{10(9)(8)(7)(6)(5)}{6(5)(4)(3)(2)}^{\,3} p^4q^6 = 210p^4q^6$$

is the 7th term of the expansion.

EXAMPLE 5. Find the 5th term of the expansion of $(3y - 4w)^8$. By substituting $a = 3y$, $x = -4w$, $n = 8$, and $r = 5$ in the formula for the rth term we obtain

$$\frac{8(7)(6)(5)}{4!}(3y)^4(-4w)^4 = \frac{\overset{2}{\cancel{8}}(7)(\cancel{6})(5)}{\cancel{4}(\cancel{3})(\cancel{2})}(81y^4)(256w^4)$$

$$= 70(81y^4)(256w^4)$$

$$= 1{,}451{,}520y^4w^4$$

EXERCISE 9.5

The Binomial Theorem

In Problems 1–20 complete the expansions and simplify the terms.

1. $(2b + x)^3$
2. $(a + 2y)^3$
3. $(3y - z)^4$
4. $(a - 3y)^4$
5. $(3b - 2y)^5$
6. $(2y - z)^5$
7. $(a - 2y)^5$
8. $(3x - y)^5$
9. $(a + 3y)^6$
10. $(2x + y)^6$
11. $(x - 2y)^6$
12. $(2x - 3y)^6$
13. $(a + x)^8$
14. $(a - y)^8$
15. $\left(\dfrac{b}{2} - y\right)^4$
16. $\left(b - \dfrac{y}{2}\right)^4$
17. $(y + \sqrt{y})^4$
18. $(z - \sqrt{z})^4$
19. $(y - 2\sqrt{y})^4$
20. $(2z + \sqrt{z})^4$

In Problems 21–30 find the indicated term of the expansion of the given binomial. Use the formula for the rth term—do not make the complete expansion.

21. Sixth term of $(2x + 3y)^7$
22. Fourth term of $(2x - 3y)^8$
23. Fifth term of $(a + x)^{10}$
24. Sixth term of $(4a - b)^7$
25. Third term of $(a + 3y)^{12}$
26. Third term of $(a - 4y)^8$
27. Tenth term of $(3a - y)^{10}$
28. Ninth term of $(2x + y)^{11}$
29. Ninth term of $(3a + y)^{12}$
30. Tenth term of $(2x - y)^{12}$

chapter 10

Logarithms

10.1 THE MEANING OF A LOGARITHM

AN IMPORTANT APPLICATION OF EXPONENTS DEALS WITH the simplification of computations that involve multiplication, division, powers, and roots. Exponents used for this purpose are called *logarithms*. Although, today, electronic computers and calculators have decreased our dependence on logarithmic computation, there are still many situations in which such computation is our only resource. Aside from their use for numerical calculations, logarithms play an important role in the theory and applications of higher mathematics.

Exponents as Irrational Numbers

It is instructive to review the generalization of the concept of exponents which leads to their use for computation. Initially, the definition of exponent was restricted to the set of natural numbers. Operating within this set, an exponent was defined as a symbol denoting the number of times a given quantity is to be used as a factor. Thus

$$x^m = x \cdot x \cdot x \cdots \text{ (a product of } m \text{ factors, } m \text{ a natural number)} \qquad (1)$$

The first generalization of the concept of an exponent was made to extend the domain of m to the set of integers, that is, to admit the use of negative integers and zero. In order to satisfy the properties defined as the *laws of exponents* (Section 4.1), the following interpretation of negative and zero exponents was shown to be necessary.

$$x^0 = 1 \qquad (x \neq 0) \qquad (2)$$

$$x^{-n} = \frac{1}{x^n} \qquad (x \neq 0) \qquad (3)$$

A subsequent extension was made to include the set of all rational numbers. Again, to maintain the consistency of the laws of exponents, it was necessary to assign certain definitions to rational exponents:

$$x^{1/q} = \sqrt[q]{x} \quad * \tag{4}$$

$$x^{p/q} = \sqrt[q]{x^p} = (\sqrt[q]{x})^p \quad * \tag{5}$$

Although it is beyond the scope of this book, it can be shown that the domain of an exponent can be further extended to include irrational numbers. Actually, this final extension is quite necessary to the study of logarithms since most logarithms are irrational numbers. The existence of irrational exponents is also implied when we draw the graph of the exponential function $y = a^x$ as a continuous curve. In effect, the function is defined for all real values of x, thus embracing irrational values for the exponent.

It should be noted that the initial definition of exponents as denoting repeated multiplication is no longer adequate when the domain is extended to the set of real numbers. For example, it is meaningless to speak of a fractional or irrational number of factors. However, the exponent symbol is defined for all real numbers in such a way as to satisfy the stated laws of exponents, and in this form the definitions are not only logically admissible but are very useful as well.

It is appropriate to mention here that, from a mathematician's point of view, the primary aim of such generalization is not its usefulness although this may be a welcome by-product. Fundamentally the mathematician is seeking to maintain the consistency of a logical structure while following a compelling curiosity concerning the effects of the generalization of a concept.

Definitions of a Logarithm

Using the extended concept that an exponent may be any real number, we can now express every positive number N in the form of an exponential quantity b^x. When this is done, the exponent x is called the logarithm of N to the base b. In symbols, the following relations are written. If

$$N = b^x \tag{6}$$

then

$$\log_b N = x \tag{7}$$

Statement 7 is read "The logarithm (or log, for short) of N to the base b is x."

For example, the number 343 can be written as 7^3. Therefore the logarithm of 343 to the base 7 is 3. Notice that a logarithm is an exponent and that the statements

$$343 = 7^3 \tag{8}$$

$$\log_7 343 = 3 \tag{9}$$

---

* We must exclude the case where x is negative and q is even.

express the same relationship in two ways. The first is called an *exponential form* and the second a *logarithmic form* of the relationship.

Below are written several exponential statements followed by their corresponding logarithmic forms and the verbal statement of the logarithmic relation.

(a) $8^2 = 64$ $\log_8 64 = 2$ The logarithm of 64 to the base 8 is 2.

(b) $3^0 = 1$ $\log_3 1 = 0$ The logarithm of 1 to the base 3 is 0.

(c) $10^{-1} = \dfrac{1}{10}$ $\log_{10} \dfrac{1}{10} = -1$ The logarithm of $\dfrac{1}{10}$ to the base 10 is -1.

(d) $49^{1/2} = 7$ $\log_{49} 7 = \dfrac{1}{2}$ The logarithm of 7 to the base 49 is $\dfrac{1}{2}$.

(e) $27^{2/3} = 9$ $\log_{27} 9 = \dfrac{2}{3}$ The logarithm of 9 to the base 27 is $\dfrac{2}{3}$.

As a result of these considerations, the following formal definition of a logarithm should now have meaning for the student.

DEFINITION 10.1.   The logarithm of a positive real number N to a given positive base b ($b \neq 1$) is the exponent x to which the base must be raised to equal the number.

The examples that follow illustrate methods of determining the value of N, b, or x in this relation.

EXAMPLE 1.   Find the value of x if $\log_4 64 = x$.

SOLUTION: The equivalent exponential form is $4^x = 64$. Therefore $x = 3$.

EXAMPLE 2.   Find the value of N if $\log_8 N = \dfrac{2}{3}$.

SOLUTION: The equivalent exponential form is $8^{2/3} = N$. Therefore $N = (\sqrt[3]{8})^2 = 4$.

EXAMPLE 3.   What is the value of b in the relation $\log_b \dfrac{1}{25} = -2$?

SOLUTION: The equivalent exponential form is $b^{-2} = \dfrac{1}{25}$. Then $1/b^2 = 1/25$ and $b = \pm 5$. Since the base b must be a positive number, $b = 5$.

EXERCISE 10.1

The Meaning of a Logarithm

Express each of the following in logarithmic form:

1. $11^2 = 121$
2. $10^2 = 100$
3. $2^5 = 32$

4. $27^{1/3} = 3$
5. $9^{1/2} = 3$
6. $2^{-3} = \dfrac{1}{8}$

7. $9^0 = 1$
8. $16^{1/4} = 2$
9. $5^3 = 125$

10. $9^{3/2} = 27$
11. $3^{-2} = \dfrac{1}{9}$
12. $256^{3/4} = 64$

Express each of the following in exponential form:

13. $\log_6 36 = 2$
14. $\log_2 8 = 3$
15. $\log_{49} 7 = \frac{1}{2}$

16. $\log_{27} 3 = \dfrac{1}{3}$
17. $\log_3 \dfrac{1}{9} = -2$
18. $\log_{10} 0.1 = -1$

19. $\log_3 1 = 0$
20. $\log_{81} 27 = \frac{3}{4}$
21. $\log_2 16 = 4$

Find the value of each of the given logarithms:

22. $\log_2 8$
23. $\log_3 343$
24. $\log_{10} 1000$

25. $\log_{10} 1$
26. $\log_5 \dfrac{1}{5}$
27. $\log_6 6$

28. $\log_{25} 125$
29. $\log_8 (8^5)$
30. $\log_7 \sqrt{7}$

Determine the value of N, b, or x, as required, in each of the following:

31. $\log_b 25 = 2$
32. $\log_3 N = -2$
33. $\log_4 64 = x$

34. $\log_2 N = 1$
35. $\log_{81} 9 = x$
36. $\log_b 64 = \dfrac{6}{5}$

37. $\log_b \dfrac{1}{3} = -1$
38. $\log_{10} N = -3$
39. $\log_8 N = \dfrac{2}{3}$

Find the value of each logarithm. How is the logarithm in part c related to the logarithms in parts a and b (Problems 40–47)?

40. (a) $\log_2 2$ (b) $\log_2 8$ (c) $\log_2 (2 \cdot 8)$

41. (a) $\log_3 81$ (b) $\log_3 9$ (c) $\log_3 (81 \cdot 9)$

42. (a) $\log_5 5^2$ (b) $\log_5 5^3$ (c) $\log_5 (5^2 \cdot 5^3)$

43. (a) $\log_{10} 100$ (b) $\log_{10} \dfrac{1}{1000}$ (c) $\log_{10} \left(\dfrac{100 \cdot 1}{1000} \right)$

44. (a) $\log_3 27$ (b) $\log_3 3$ (c) $\log_3 (27 \div 3)$

45. (a) $\log_2 128$ (b) $\log_2 8$ (c) $\log_2 (128 \div 8)$

46. (a) $\log_7 7^5$ (b) $\log_7 7^2$ (c) $\log_7 (7^5 \div 7^2)$

47. (a) $\log_{10} 100$ (b) $\log_{10} 0.1$ (c) $\log_{10} (100 \div 0.1)$
48. Find the value of (a) $\log_3 1$, (b) $\log_8 1$, (c) $\log_b 1$.
49. Find the value of (a) $\log_4 4$, (b) $\log_{10} 10$, (c) $\log_b b$.
50. Can the logarithm of a positive number be negative? If so give an example. If not, explain why.
51. Using a positive base, can a negative number have a logarithm in the set of real numbers? If so, give an example. If not, explain why.

10.2 THE LOGARITHMIC FUNCTION

The concept of logarithms introduces a new function, defined as follows.

DEFINITION 10.2.   If b is any positive number other than 1, then the function $\{(x,y) \mid y = \log_b x, x > 0\}$ is a logarithmic function with base b.

We note that the domain of this function is the set of positive real numbers. The range of such a function is best introduced by an examination of its graph. Since b is a positive number other than 1, it is clearly possible that $b > 1$ or that $0 < b < 1$. We consider first the case where $b > 1$, for example, the function represented by the equation

$$y = \log_2 x, x > 0$$

The graph of this function is illustrated in Figure 10.1.

If $b > 1$, the graph has the general shape shown in Figure 10.1. Notice that the region to the left of the y-axis is excluded, which is the graphic equivalent of the constraint that $x > 0$. There is no y-intercept, and the x-intercept is 1.

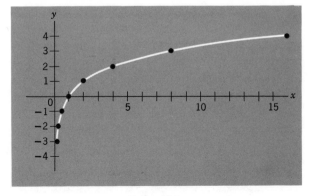

Figure 10.1

Table of Values for $y = \log_2 x$

x	(log. form)	(exp. form)	y
1	$y = \log_2 1$	$2^y = 1$	0
2	$y = \log_2 2$	$2^y = 2$	1
4	$y = \log_2 4$	$2^y = 4$	2
8	$y = \log_2 8$	$2^y = 8$	3
16	$y = \log_2 16$	$2^y = 16$	4
$\dfrac{1}{2}$	$y = \log_2 \dfrac{1}{2}$	$2^y = \dfrac{1}{2}$	-1
$\dfrac{1}{4}$	$y = \log_2 \dfrac{1}{4}$	$2^y = \dfrac{1}{4}$	-2
$\dfrac{1}{8}$	$y = \log_2 \dfrac{1}{8}$	$2^y = \dfrac{1}{8}$	-3

The range of the function is the set of all real numbers. Finally, it is of mathematical significance that y increases as x increases, but the increase is most rapid for small values of x and diminishes as x becomes larger.

Although we shall be concerned mainly with logarithms having a base greater than 1, it is useful to also examine the logarithmic function for values of b between 0 and 1. Figure 10.2 illustrates, for example, the function

$$y = \log_{\frac{1}{3}} x, \, x > 0$$

From Figure 10.2, we note that when the value of b is less than 1 the domain and range of the function do not change. Also, as for $b > 1$, there is no y-intercept and the x-intercept is 1. However, the function now is a decreasing one, that is, as x increases, y decreases. As before these changes are more marked for values of x near zero, and are dampened as x increases.

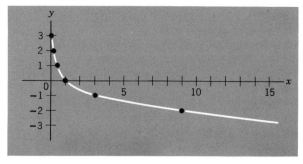

Figure 10.2

Table of Values for $y = \log_{\frac{1}{3}} x$

x	(log. form)	(exp. form)	y
1	$y = \log_{\frac{1}{3}} 1$	$\left(\dfrac{1}{3}\right)^{y} = 1$	0
3	$y = \log_{\frac{1}{3}} 3$	$\left(\dfrac{1}{3}\right)^{y} = 3$	-1
9	$y = \log_{\frac{1}{3}} 9$	$\left(\dfrac{1}{3}\right)^{y} = 9$	-2
$\dfrac{1}{3}$	$y = \log_{\frac{1}{3}} \dfrac{1}{3}$	$\left(\dfrac{1}{3}\right)^{y} = \dfrac{1}{3}$	1
$\dfrac{1}{9}$	$y = \log_{\frac{1}{3}} \dfrac{1}{9}$	$\left(\dfrac{1}{3}\right)^{y} = \dfrac{1}{9}$	2
$\dfrac{1}{27}$	$y = \log_{\frac{1}{3}} \dfrac{1}{27}$	$\left(\dfrac{1}{3}\right)^{y} = \dfrac{1}{27}$	3

EXERCISE 10.2

The Logarithmic Function

1. Sketch the graphs of (a) $y = \log_2 x$, (b) $y = \log_3 x$, and (c) $y = \log_4 x$ on the same set of axes. Formulate a conjecture based on these graphs.
2. Sketch the graphs of (a) $y = \log_2 x$, (b) $y = 2 \log_2 x$, and (c) $y = 3 \log_2 x$ on the same set of axes. Formulate a conjecture based on these graphs.
3. Sketch the graphs of (a) $y = \log_3 x$ and (b) $y = 3^x$ on the same set of axes. Is there any similarity between the graphs?
4. Sketch the graphs of (a) $y = \log_3 x$ and (b) $y = \log_{1/3} x$ on the same set of axes. Is there any similarity between the graphs?
5. Graph the function $f = \{(x,y) \,|\, y = \log_{10} x, \, x > 0\}$. (a) What is the range of f for $1 \leq x \leq 10$? (b) What is the range of f for $10 \leq x \leq 100$?
6. Graph the function $f = \{(x,y) \,|\, y = \log_{10} x, \, x > 0\}$ and $g = \{(x,y) \,|\, y = -\log_{10} x, \, x > 0\}$ on the same set of axes. How are the two graphs related?

10.3 PROPERTIES OF LOGARITHMS

By definition, logarithms are exponents. Therefore the laws that govern operations with exponents determine analogous laws that apply to operations with logarithms. In particular, the following laws of exponents.

$$b^x \cdot b^y = b^{x+y} \tag{1}$$

$$\frac{b^x}{b^y} = b^{x-y} \; (b \neq 0) \tag{2}$$

$$(b^x)^y = b^{xy} \tag{3}$$

lead to properties of logarithms that are of sufficient importance to warrant development and proof.

Logarithm of a Product

A numerical example may suggest that a simple relation exists between the logarithm of a product and the logarithms of its factors. Thus

$$\log_2 8 = 3$$
$$\log_2 32 = 5$$
$$\log_2 8 \cdot 32 = \log_2 256 = 8$$

In this case, the logarithm of the product equals the sum of the logarithms of its factors. Of course, this one example, or many such examples, does not prove that this relation is always true. To establish it for all admissible values of the variables, we shall prove Theorem 10.1.

THEOREM 10.1. $\log_b MN = \log_b M + \log_b N$ (4)

PROOF: Let $x = \log_b M$ and $y = \log_b N$

In exponential form, $M = b^x$ and $N = b^y$

Multiplying M by N, $MN = b^x \cdot b^y = b^{x+y}$

In logarithmic form, $\log_b MN = x + y$

Therefore, by substitution, $\log_b MN = \log_b M + \log_b N$

Logarithm of a Quotient

Note the relation of the logarithms in the following:

$$\log_3 2187 = 7$$
$$\log_3 9 = 2$$
$$\log_3 \frac{2187}{9} = \log_3 243 = 5$$

It is evident that in this instance, the logarithm of the quotient is equal to the logarithm of the numerator minus the logarithm of the denominator. We now prove the following theorem for all admissible values of the variables.

THEOREM 10.2. $\log_b M/N = \log_b M - \log_b N$ (5)

PROOF: Let $x = \log_b M$ and $y = \log_b N$

In exponential form, $M = b^x$ and $N = b^y$

Dividing M by N, $\dfrac{M}{N} = \dfrac{b^x}{b^y} = b^{x-y}$

In logarithmic form, $\log_b M/N = x - y$

Therefore, by substitution, $\log_b M/N = \log_b M - \log_b N$

Logarithm of a Power

Consider the following statements:

$$\log_2 64 = 6$$
$$\log_2 \sqrt[3]{64} = \log_2 64^{1/3} = \log_2 4 = 2$$

Thus the logarithm of the $\frac{1}{3}$ power of 64 is equal to $\frac{1}{3}$ of the logarithm of 64. In general, for all values of n in the set of real numbers we prove the following theorem.

THEOREM 10.3. $\log_b M^n = n \log_b M$ (6)

PROOF: Let $x = \log_b M$

In exponential form, $M = b^x$

Raising to the nth power, $M^n = (b^x)^n = b^{nx}$

In logarithmic form, $\log_b M^n = nx$

Therefore, by substitution, $\log_b M^n = n \log_b M$

Laws of Logarithms

The relations 4, 5, and 6, known as laws of logarithms, are used extensively in the application of logarithms to problems of computation. Their usefulness will be increased if the student learns to express them in words as well as in their symbolic form.

Law 1. The logarithm of a product is equal to the sum of the logarithms of its factors. That is, $\log_n MN = \log_b M + \log_b N$.

Law 2. The logarithm of a quotient is equal to the logarithm of its numerator minus the logarithm of its denominator. That is, $\log_b \dfrac{M}{N} = \log_b M - \log_b N$.

Law 3. The logarithm of a power of a number is equal to the exponent times the logarithm of the number. That is, $\log_b M^n = n \log_b M$.

EXAMPLE 1. Given $\log_{10} 2 = 0.3010$, find $\log_{10} 32$.

SOLUTION: $\log_{10} 32 = \log_{10} 2^5$
$$= 5 \log_{10} 2 \text{ (by Law 3)}$$
$$= 5(0.3010) = 1.5050$$

EXAMPLE 2. Given $\log_{10} 2 = 0.3010$ and $\log_{10} 3 = 0.4771$, find $\log_{10} \sqrt{6}$.

SOLUTION: $\log_{10} \sqrt{6} = \log_{10} (2 \cdot 3)^{1/2}$

$\qquad\qquad\qquad = \tfrac{1}{2} \log_{10} (2 \cdot 3)$ (by Law 3)

$\qquad\qquad\qquad = \tfrac{1}{2}(\log_{10} 2 + \log_{10} 3)$ (by Law 1)

$\qquad\qquad\qquad = \tfrac{1}{2}(0.3010 + 0.4771) = 0.3890$

EXAMPLE 3. If $\log_4 7 = n$, find $\log_4 \dfrac{1}{7}$.

SOLUTION: $\log_4 \dfrac{1}{7} = \log_4 1 - \log_4 7$ (by Law 2)

$\qquad\qquad\qquad = 0 - n = -n$

EXAMPLE 4. Express $\log_{10} \pi + 3 \log_{10} r$ as a single logarithm.

SOLUTION: $\log_{10} \pi + 3 \log_{10} r = \log_{10} \pi + \log_{10} r^3$ $\qquad$ (by Law 3)

$\qquad\qquad\qquad\qquad\qquad = \log_{10} \pi r^3$ $\qquad\qquad\qquad$ (by Law 1)

EXERCISE 10.3

Properties of Logarithms

If $m = \log_3 x$ and $n = \log_3 y$, express each of the following in terms of m and n.

1. $\log_3 x^2$	2. $\log_3 \dfrac{x}{y}$	3. $\log_3 \dfrac{y}{x}$
4. $\log_3 xy$	5. $\log_3 \sqrt[3]{y}$	6. $\log_3 x^3 y$
7. $\log_3 \sqrt{x/y}$	8. $\log_3 x^{1/4} y^3$	9. $\log_3 \dfrac{\sqrt{x}}{y^2}$
10. $\log_3 \sqrt{xy}$	11. $\log_3 \dfrac{1}{x}$	12. $\log_3 \dfrac{1}{xy}$

If $\log_{10} 2 = 0.3010$, $\log_{10} 3 = 0.4771$, and $\log_{10} 5 = 0.6990$, find the logarithms of each of the following quantities to the base 10. Express each result to four decimal places.

13. 15	14. $\sqrt[3]{5}$	15. 8	16. $\dfrac{9}{2}$
17. 6^7	18. 18	19. $\dfrac{25}{2}$	20. $\sqrt{15}$
21. $\sqrt{75}$	22. $\dfrac{5}{4}$	23. $\sqrt[4]{10}$	24. $12^{1/2}$

If $\log_{10} 27.8 = 1.4440$ and $\log_{10} 5.07 = 0.7050$, find the following logarithms to four decimal places:

25. $\log_{10} \sqrt{5.07}$ 26. $\log_{10} (27.8)^4$ 27. $\log_{10} \dfrac{27.8}{5.07}$

28. $\log_{10} (27.8)(5.07)$ 29. $\log_{10} \dfrac{5.07^2}{\sqrt{27.8}}$ 30. $\log_{10} 5.07 \sqrt{27.8}$

Express each of the given expressions as a single logarithm whose coefficient is 1.

31. $3 \log_2 x$ 32. $\log_2 a - \log_2 b$

33. $5 \log_{10} p + 3 \log_{10} q$ 34. $\log_b x - \log_b y + \log_b z$

35. $\frac{1}{2} \log_3 R - 2 \log_3 S$ 36. $\log_n 4 - \log_n 3 + \log_n \pi + 3 \log_n r$

Express $\log x$ in terms of $\log a$ and $\log b$. (All logarithms are to the same base.)

37. $x = ab$ 38. $x = ab^2$ 39. $x = a^2b^3$

40. $x = \dfrac{a}{b}$ 41. $x = \dfrac{b}{a}$ 42. $x = \sqrt{\dfrac{a}{b}}$

43. $x = \dfrac{\sqrt{a}}{b}$ 44. $x = \left(\dfrac{b}{a}\right)^3$ 45. $x = \dfrac{\sqrt{a}}{\sqrt[3]{b}}$

46. $x = (ab)^3$ 47. $x = a^2 \sqrt{b}$ 48. $x = (\sqrt{ab})^5$

In each of the following, express $\log y$ as an algebraic sum of logarithms, as illustrated in Problem 49. (All logarithms are to the same base.)

49. $y = \pi r^2 h$ Therefore $\log y = \log \pi + 2 \log r + \log h$

50. $y = \frac{1}{2}gt^2$ 51. $y = prt$ 52. $y = 4\pi r^2$

53. $y = p(1.07)^n$ 54. $y = \sqrt{\dfrac{h}{16}}$ 55. $y = \dfrac{KT}{p}$

10.4 COMMON LOGARITHMS

Logarithms are said to be in the same system if they have the same base. Two systems of logarithms are in general use. In one of these, the base is an irrational number, e, whose value is approximately 2.718. In the other, the base is the number 10. Logarithms to the base e, called *natural logarithms*, have certain advantages in the theory and solution of problems in advanced mathematics. Logarithms to the base 10, called *common logarithms*, are convenient for simplifying ordinary numerical computations.

Our study will be confined to the system of common logarithms. Since the base 10 will be used so frequently, hereafter, if no reference is made to the base of a logarithm, the base 10 will be understood. Thus the logarithm of N means the common logarithm of N, and

$$\log N \text{ means } \log_{10} N$$

The Two Parts of a Logarithm

The logarithm of 10,000 is 4 since $10^4 = 10,000$. Similarly, the logarithms of all other integral powers of 10 are integers. For example,

$$\log 1000 = 3 \qquad\qquad \log 0.1 = -1$$
$$\log 100 = 2 \qquad\qquad \log 0.01 = -2$$
$$\log 10 = 1 \qquad\qquad \log 0.001 = -3$$
$$\log 1 = 0 \qquad\qquad \log 0.0001 = -4$$

This listing suggests that the logarithm of a number between 100 and 1000 will be greater than 2 and less than 3, the logarithm of a number between 10 and 100 will be greater than 1 and less than 2, and so on. Therefore, the logarithm of the number 695, for example, will be 2, followed by a decimal fraction. In general, a logarithm will consist of two parts—an integer and a decimal fraction. The integral part of the logarithm is called its *characteristic*, and the decimal part is called its *mantissa*.

Let us assume that the logarithm of the number 695 is 2.842. Then 2 is the characteristic of this logarithm, and 0.842 is the mantissa. If we now list the logarithms of 695 times an integral power of 10, an important property of characteristics and mantissas can be observed. Thus

$\log 695 = 2.842$

$\log 69.5 = \log (0.1 \cdot 695) = \log 0.1 + \log 695 = -1 + 2.842 = 1.842$

$\log 6.95 = \log (0.01 \cdot 695) = \log 0.01 + \log 695 = -2 + 2.1842 = 0.842$

$\log 0.695 = \log (0.001 \cdot 695) = \log 0.001 + \log 695 = -3 + 2.842 = 0.842 - 1$

$\log 0.0695 = \log (0.0001 \cdot 695) = \log 0.0001 + \log 695 = -4 + 2.842$
$\qquad\qquad = 0.842 - 2$

It can be seen that if we choose to keep the decimal part of the logarithm positive, the mantissa is constant for the given sequence of significant figures. In other words, the value of the mantissa is not affected by the position of the decimal point in the sequence 695. Furthermore, the characteristic of the logarithm changes in a regular pattern according to the position of the decimal point in the sequence. This is an illustration of the important property that the sequence of significant digits in a given number may be used to determine the mantissa of its logarithm while the position of the decimal point in the sequence may be used to determine the characteristic of the logarithm.

Note, further, the convention introduced here for writing a logarithm so that the mantissa is always positive. When the characteristic is positive, it is combined with the mantissa to form a single number, as

$$\log 69.5 = 1.842$$

but when the characteristic is negative, it is written after the mantissa to form a binomial expression, as

$$\log 0.0695 = 0.842 - 2$$

Determining the Characteristic of a Logarithm

It will be recalled (Section 4.3) that every number N can be written in scientific notation in the form

$$N = k \cdot 10^c$$

where c is an integer and $1 \leq k < 10$. It follows that

$$\log N = \log (k \cdot 10^c)$$
$$= \log k + c \log 10$$
$$= \log k + c$$

Since $1 \leq k < 10$ and c is an integer, $\log k$ represents the mantissa of $\log N$ and c represents its characteristic. This fact may be utilized to determine the characteristic of the logarithm of a given number as follows:

Write the number in scientific notation. The characteristic of its logarithm is numerically equal to the power of 10.

This relation is illustrated in Table 10.1.

TABLE 10.1

Number N	N Expressed in Scientific Notation	Characteristic of log N	Logarithm
6950	6.95×10^3	3	3.842
69.5	6.95×10^1	1	1.842
6.95	6.95×10^0	0	0.842
0.0695	6.95×10^{-2}	-2	$0.842 - 2$
0.000695	6.95×10^{-4}	-4	$0.842 - 4$

Determining the Mantissa of a Logarithm

Earlier, we made the assumption

$$\log 695 = 2.842$$

The mantissa of this logarithm can be computed to any required number of significant digits by methods used in advanced mathematics. Since such computations are difficult and tedious, the results are usually tabulated for convenient reference. A table of mantissas approximated to four decimal places is given in Table II (Appendix). This table gives directly the mantissa of the logarithm of any number which has no more than three significant figures. In Section 10.6, we shall learn how this table may be extended with reasonable accuracy to obtain the logarithm of any number with four significant figures.

To find the mantissa of the logarithm of 695 in Table II, locate the first two significant figures in the column headed by N. The third significant figure is found as a column heading across the top of the table. The required mantissa is found in the row beginning with 69 and in the column headed by 5. This entry is 8420 and represents the mantissa correct to four decimal places. Since virtually all entries in the table are approximate numbers, the property that a given logarithm is approximate is assumed without further notation. Therefore we write

$$\log 695 = 2.8420$$

EXAMPLE 1.   Find the logarithm of 30,700.

SOLUTION: $30{,}700 = 3.07 \times 10^4$. The characteristic is 4. To find the mantissa, locate the entry in Table II which is in the row beginning with 30, and in the column headed by 7. It is 4871. Therefore $\log 30{,}700 = 4.4871$.

EXAMPLE 2.   What is the value of log 0.0148?

SOLUTION: $0.0148 = 1.48 \times 10^{-2}$. The characteristic is -2. The mantissa of the sequence of digits 148 is found in Table II to be 1703. Therefore, $\log 0.0148 = 0.1703 - 2$.

Antilogarithms

If $\log N = x$, then N is said to be the *antilogarithm* (or antilog) of x. That is, N is the number corresponding to a given logarithm x. For example, if

$$\log 261 = 2.4166$$

then

$$\text{antilog } 2.4166 = 261$$

Since the value of a logarithm is found by using a table of logarithms, an antilogarithm is determined by using the same table in reverse order.

It should be remembered that a table of logarithms lists only the mantissas of the logarithms. Therefore to find the antilogarithm of 2.4166 we locate the mantissa 4166 in the body of the table, and note that it corresponds to the sequence of significant digits 261. Since the characteristic is 2, the required number is

$$2.61 \times 10^2 = 261$$

EXAMPLE 3. Find the antilogarithm of 1.4349 to three significant figures.

SOLUTION: The mantissa 4349 does not appear in Table II. However, it falls between the two listed mantissas:

4346, whose antilogarithm is 272

and

4362, whose antilogarithm is 273

Since the given mantissa is closer in value to the mantissa 4346, the three figure sequence of digits in the antilogarithm is 272. Using the characteristic 1, we have $2.72 \times 10^1 = 27.2$.

EXAMPLE 4. Find N if $\log N = 0.7917 - 3$.

SOLUTION: Using Table II, the mantissa 7917 is found in the row which begins with 61 and in the column headed by 9. Therefore the antilogarithm is 619. Since the characteristic is -3, we have

$$N = 6.19 \times 10^{-3} = 0.00619$$

EXERCISE 10.4

Common Logarithms

Find the characteristic of the logarithm of each of the following numbers by writing each in scientific notation.

1. 73,200	2. 2.06	3. 51.3
4. 0.919	5. 2730	6. 0.00153
7. 39	8. 0.0202	9. 8
10. 219,000	11. 0.0005	12. 2,300
13. 0.0237	14. 60,500	15. 0.00777

Given the sequence of significant figures 874, place the decimal point correctly in this sequence if the characteristic of its logarithm is:

16. 2	17. 4	18. 0
19. -1	20. 1	21. -3

Use Table II to find the logarithm of each of the following numbers. Be sure to indicate both the characteristic and the mantissa.

22. 147	23. 0.525	24. 36,000
25. 20.7	26. 0.301	27. 0.009
28. 6	29. 2.03	30. 3,470
31. 0.076	32. 93,000,000	33. 30,700
34. 2.93	35. 37.5	36. 0.0000341
37. 100,000	38. 1.92×10^6	39. 3.08×10^{-7}

Use Table II to find the antilogarithm of each of the following logarithms correct to three significant figures.

40. 0.5366	41. 0.6920	42. 1.7694
43. 3.6785	44. $0.4330 - 2$	45. $0.1903 - 1$
46. 2.9020	47. 3.0000	48. $0.6180 - 3$
49. $0.7159 - 1$	50. 0.6044	51. $0.3000 - 5$
52. 4.3270	53. $0.8182 - 3$	54. $0.0505 - 6$

Given $\log x = 2.2900$ and $\log y = 1.7101$, find the antilogarithm of:

55. $\log x + \log y$	56. $2 \log x$	57. $3 \log y$
58. $\log x - \log y$	59. $\frac{1}{2} \log x$	60. $\frac{1}{4} \log x$
61. $\frac{1}{2} \log y$	62. $\frac{1}{4} \log y$	63. $2 \log x + \log y$
64. $\log x + 2 \log y$	65. $3 \log x - \frac{1}{2} \log y$	66. $\log (x^3)$

10.5 LOGARITHMIC COMPUTATIONS

In applying logarithms to the computation of products, quotients, powers, and roots, just two steps are generally involved:

1. The logarithm of the entire expression is obtained by applying the three laws of logarithms (Section 10.3).
2. The antilogarithm then determines the value of the given expression.

Although the theory of such logarithmic computation is simple, there are certain details of procedure that merit careful illustration. In particular, the requirements of maintaining a positive mantissa and an integral characteristic give rise to a device which is frequently useful in computing quotients or products. Furthermore, some systematic method of outlining the details of the entire computation is strongly recommended as an aid to speed and accuracy. These considerations are illustrated in the examples that follow.

Multiplication

The determination of a product by means of logarithms is based on the property that the logarithm of a product is equal to the sum of the logarithms of its factors.

EXAMPLE 1. Compute the value of N if $N = 36.9 \times 0.875 \times 4.26$.

SOLUTION: By Theorem 10.1, $\log N = \log 36.9 + \log 0.875 + \log 4.26$

$$\log 36.9 \ \ = 1.5670$$
$$\log 0.875 = 0.9420 - 1$$
$$\log 4.26 \ \ = 0.6294$$
$$\log N \quad \ \ = 3.1384 - 1 = 2.1384$$
$$N = \text{antilog } 2.1384 = 1.37 \times 10^2$$
$$N = 137$$

Division

As previously noted, the logarithm of a quotient is equal to the logarithm of its numerator minus the logarithm of its denominator.

If the mantissa and characteristic are each smaller in the denominator than in the numerator, the subtraction is performed easily; if this is not the case it becomes necessary, or at least highly desirable, to rewrite one of the logarithms in an equivalent form.

EXAMPLE 2. Evaluate $\dfrac{0.237}{58.1}$.

SOLUTION: Let $Q = (0.237) \div (58.1)$

Then $\log Q = \log 0.237 - \log 58.1$ (by Theorem 10.2)

$$\log 0.237 = 0.3747 - 1$$
$$\log 58.1 \ \ = 1.7642$$

This subtraction is an awkward one to perform if we are to maintain a positive mantissa, but it is greatly simplified if 2 is added to and subtracted from the first logarithm. We then have

$$\log 0.237 = 2.3747 - 3$$
$$\log 58.1 \ \ = 1.7642$$
$$\log Q \quad \ \ = 0.6105 - 3$$
$$Q = \text{antilog } 0.6105 - 3 = 4.08 \times 10^{-3}$$
$$Q = 0.00408$$

Powers and Roots

To calculate a given power of a number, we apply directly the property that the logarithm of a power of a number is equal to the exponent times the logarithm of the number.

Since an indicated root of a number is expressible as a fractional power, this rule is the basis for computing roots as well as powers. When the exponent is fractional, it may be necessary to change the form of the logarithm to maintain an integral characteristic.

EXAMPLE 3.   Compute the cube root of 0.0534.

SOLUTION: Let $R = \sqrt[3]{0.0534} = (0.0534)^{1/3}$

Then $\log R = \dfrac{1}{3} \log 0.0534$ (by Theorem 10.3)

$$= \frac{1}{3}(0.7275 - 2)$$

Before dividing the logarithm by 3, it should be rewritten in an equivalent form so that the negative characteristic is a multiple of 3. Therefore we write

$$\log R = \frac{1}{3}(1.7275 - 3)$$

$$= 0.5758 - 1$$

$$R = \text{antilog } (0.5758 - 1) = 3.77 \times 10^{-1}$$

$$R = 0.377$$

General Computations

It is possible to calculate the value of a great variety of numerical expressions by means of logarithms. If a computation involves sums or differences, the operations of addition and subtraction must be performed arithmetically after the value of each term is obtained.

EXAMPLE 4.   Evaluate $\sqrt{\dfrac{x^3 + 1}{x^3 - 1}}$ where $x = 1.47$.

SOLUTION: $\log x = \log 1.47 = 0.1673$

$\log x^3 = 3 \log x = 0.5019$ (by Theorem 10.3)

$x^3 = \text{antilog } 0.5019 = 3.18$

Then $x^3 + 1 = 4.18$ and $x^3 - 1 = 2.18$

$$\text{Let } N = \sqrt{\frac{x^3 + 1}{x^3 - 1}} = \sqrt{\frac{4.18}{2.18}}$$

$$\log N = \tfrac{1}{2}(\log 4.18 - \log 2.18) \qquad \text{(by Theorems 10.1, 10.2)}$$

$$= \tfrac{1}{2}(0.6212 - 0.3385)$$

$$= 0.1414$$

$$N = \text{antilog } 0.1414 = 1.38$$

EXAMPLE 5. Find the value of the expression $\dfrac{(\sqrt{0.0139})(0.481)}{2.86}$

SOLUTION: Let N be the result. Then

$$\log N = \tfrac{1}{2} \log 0.0139 + \log 0.481 - \log 2.86$$

$$\log 0.0139 = 0.1430 - 2$$

$$\tfrac{1}{2} \log 0.0139 = 0.0715 - 1$$

$$\log 0.481 = \underline{0.6821 - 1}$$

$$\tfrac{1}{2} \log 0.0139 + \log 0.481 = 0.7536 - 2$$

$$\log 2.86 = \underline{0.4564}$$

$$\log N = 0.2972 - 2$$

$$N = 0.0198$$

EXERCISE 10.5

Logarithmic Computations

Evaluate each of the following by use of a table of logarithms. Express results to three significant figures.

1. 43.5×9.08 2. $\dfrac{6.09}{0.27}$ 3. $\sqrt{75.1}$

4. $\sqrt[3]{0.315}$ 5. $(0.0583)^4$ 6. $(0.0203)(0.00513)$

7. $\dfrac{0.0340}{357}$ 8. $\sqrt[3]{9.89}$ 9. $\sqrt[4]{0.0311}$

10. $(1.07)^9$ 11. $(3570)(0.463)$ 12. $\sqrt[5]{415}$

13. $\dfrac{2.97}{57.3}$ 14. 32.8^3 15. $(0.415)^{1/4}$

16. $(0.773)(0.0192)^2$. 17. $\dfrac{11.7^3}{45,300}$ 18. $72.5\sqrt{6.09}$

19. $\dfrac{\sqrt{0.000818}}{0.0133}$ 20. $(27.4 \times 1.09)^3$ 21. $\sqrt{\dfrac{47.1}{0.893}}$

22. $\sqrt[3]{\dfrac{7.38}{(5.87)(0.639)}}$ 23. $\sqrt[5]{0.344}$ 24. $(1.54)^{0.6}$

25. $(3.27 \times 10^{-4})^5$ 26. $\left(\dfrac{3.76}{71.2}\right)^7$ 27. $\dfrac{\sqrt[4]{548} \times 0.781}{(17.3)^2}$

28. $\dfrac{26.4(3.93)^3}{(72.4)^{1/2}}$ 29. $0.0612\sqrt[5]{\dfrac{0.613}{2.38}}$ 30. $\sqrt{(7.17 \times 10^{-4})^3}$

Given $r = 2.44$, $h = 7.13$, and $\pi = 3.14$, find the value of each of the following expressions:

31. $\dfrac{4}{3}\pi r^3$ 32. $4\pi r^2$ 33. $\dfrac{1}{3}\pi r^2 h$

34. $2\pi r h$ 35. $\dfrac{2}{3}\pi r^3 + r^r$ 36. $\pi r\sqrt{h^2 + r^2}$

37. $\dfrac{1}{3}\pi h(3r^2 + h^2)$ 38. $2\pi r(h + r)$ 39. $\dfrac{\pi h^2}{3}(3r - h)$

If a principal of P dollars is invested at a compound interest rate of r percent per period, the amount at the end of n periods will be

$$A = P(1 + r)^n$$

Using this formula, find approximately how much \$100 will amount to if:

40. $n = 10$, $r = 5\%$ 41. $n = 20$, $r = 4\%$
42. $n = 10$, $r = 7\%$ 43. $n = 20$, $r = 2\%$
44. $n = 30$, $r = 6\%$ 45. $n = 100$, $r = 3\%$

46. The approximate number of seconds, t, required for an object to strike the ground when dropped from an initial height of h feet can be calculated from the formula $t = \sqrt{\dfrac{h}{16.1}}$. Determine the time required for a stone to strike the ground if it is released from a height of 500 ft.

47. If an amount, a, is doubled n times, its final value is $a \cdot 2^n$. If a sheet of tissue paper $\dfrac{1}{1000}$ inch thick could be folded 50 times in such a way as to double its thickness each time, what would be its final thickness expressed in (a) inches, (b) feet, and (c) miles?

10.6 INTERPOLATION IN LOGARITHMIC COMPUTATIONS

It should be apparent, upon reflection, that a table of common logarithms is a schematic listing of ordered pairs of the function $y = \log x$. Table II is such a listing with values of x expressed to three significant figures and values of y expressed to four significant figures. It is obviously impossible to list in a table all ordered pairs of a relation which may be of subsequent concern. Therefore, a technique for estimating values between those listed in a table is very useful. A process for determining such intermediate values is known as *interpolation*. In the case of Table II, the process enables us to approximate logarithms for numbers of four significant figures.

To understand the concepts on which interpolation is based, let us first consider the graphic implications of determining $y = \log x$ for $x = 3.142$. A portion of the graph of $y = \log x$, exaggerated for clarity, is shown in Figure 10.3. The ordered pairs (3.140, 0.4969) and (3.150, 0.4983) are obtained from Table II.

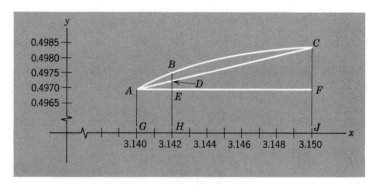

Figure 10.3

The value we are seeking (the value of y corresponding to $x = 3.142$) is the length BH in Figure 10.3. If a sufficiently large and accurate graph were available, this value could be read directly from the graph. Since this is generally not the case, the length DH is accepted as a useful approximation to the ordinate BH. Using the simple property of proportionality of sides in similar triangles, we have

$$\frac{DE}{CF} = \frac{AE}{AF}$$

But of these four quantities, three are available in the table of logarithms.

Therefore, the fourth, the distance DE, can be determined by solving the proportion, as follows:

$$\frac{DE}{0.0014} = \frac{2}{10}$$

$$DE = \frac{0.0028}{10} = 0.00028 = 0.0003 \text{ (approximately)}$$

Adding $DE = 0.0003$ to $EH = 0.4969$ we obtain $DH = 0.4972$, a reasonably good approximation to the required logarithm. The procedure, with all differences expressed as units, can be arranged for convenience of computation as follows:

x	$\log x$

$$
10 \left\{ 2 \begin{bmatrix} 3.140 \\ 3.142 \end{bmatrix} \right. \qquad 3.150
$$

$$
\begin{bmatrix} 0.4969 \\ ? \end{bmatrix} n \qquad 14 \\ 0.4983
$$

This leads directly to the proportion $\frac{2}{10} = \frac{n}{14}$, for which $n = 3$. Adding these 3 units (the units, of course, are ten-thousandths) to 0.4969 results in the final value $\log 3.142 = 0.4972$. With practice, it is possible to make the interpolation mentally in most cases.

EXAMPLE 1.   Using Table II, determine the logarithm of 14.57.

SOLUTION:

x	$\log x$

$$
10 \left\{ 7 \begin{bmatrix} 14.50 \\ 14.57 \end{bmatrix} \right. \qquad 14.60
$$

$$
\begin{bmatrix} 1.1614 \\ ? \end{bmatrix} n \qquad 30 \\ 1.1644
$$

$$\frac{7}{10} = \frac{n}{30}$$

$$n = 21$$

Therefore $\log 14.57 = 1.1635$.

In view of the element of approximation involved, Table II cannot be used to determine the logarithm of a number having more than four significant figures.

Such numbers should first be rounded off to four figures. Thus to find the logarithm of 83,268 by use of Table II, it is recommended that we merely evaluate the logarithm of 83,270.

Interpolation is also essential in determining an antilogarithm to four significant figures when the exact mantissa is not listed in the table. The procedure is shown in the following example.

EXAMPLE 2.   Determine the number whose logarithm is $0.8045 - 2$.

SOLUTION: Using Table II, we find the following correspondence of values:

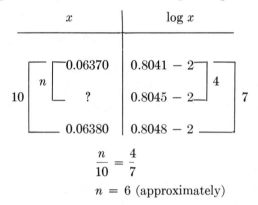

$$\frac{n}{10} = \frac{4}{7}$$

$$n = 6 \text{ (approximately)}$$

Therefore, antilog $0.8045 - 2 = 0.06376$.

EXERCISE 10.6

Interpolation in Logarithmic Computations

Using Table II, find the logarithm of each of the following numbers:

1. 3758
2. 0.4631
3. 64,790
4. 0.02074
5. 367.2
6. 100,700
7. 5,683
8. 0.001785
9. 70.66

In each of the following, find the number N to four significant figures.

10. $\log N = 3.3516$
11. $\log N = 0.5849 - 4$
12. $\log N = 1.9411$
13. $\log N = 5.8277$
14. $\log N = 2.7557$
15. $\log N = 0.2841 - 3$
16. $\log N = 0.9970 - 1$
17. $\log N = 4.1159$

Evaluate each of the following expressions to four significant figures.

18. $(0.04781)^4$

19. $\dfrac{31.68}{1.225}$

20. $(385.8)(0.001107)$

21. $\sqrt[5]{5.046}$

22. $\dfrac{56913 \sqrt{307.4}}{39.22}$

23. $\dfrac{(0.1688)(4.579)}{\sqrt[4]{50.41}}$

24. $\dfrac{(4.115)(3.774)(0.9793)}{(43.77)(0.2436)}$

25. $\sqrt{\dfrac{(0.1707)(6.533)}{811.4}}$

26. $\sqrt[3]{\dfrac{7.212}{(5.557)(1.229)}}$

27. $\dfrac{(15.44)^2(8.016)}{(0.01571)^2}$

28. $\dfrac{1000}{(1.065)^{10}}$

29. $7895(1.047)^{12}$

30. The diagonal of a cube is $e\sqrt{3}$ where e is the length of an edge. Find the diagonal of a cube whose edge is 7.118 in. long.

31. The weight w in tons that will crush a given kind of structural column is given by the formula

$$ w = 149.8 \, \frac{d^{3.55}}{l^2} $$

where d is the diameter of the column in inches and l is its length in feet. What force will crush a column 8 ft long and 5 inches in diameter?

32. For each 1000 bacteria in a culture, the number, n, to which they multiply after t hours is

$$ n = 1000(10)^{1.637t} $$

Determine the value of n when t is 7.

33. A formula used to approximate the distance from which an object of given height is visible above the surface of the earth is

$$ D = 1.320 \, \sqrt{h} $$

where D is the distance in miles and h is the height in feet. If the light of a lighthouse is 160.0 feet above sea level, for how many miles at sea is it visible?

34. According to Kepler's third law, a planet will make one complete revolution about the sun in T years, where

$$ T = a^{3/2} $$

and a is the average distance of the planet from the sun in astronomical units (1 A.U. = 93,000,000 miles approximately). How long does the planet Pluto require for one complete revolution if it is 39.52 A.U. from the sun?

35. The electrical resistance of a copper wire at 20° C is given by the formula

$$R = \frac{10.37l}{d^2}$$

where R is the resistance in ohms, l is the length in feet, and d is the diameter in mils (1 mil $= \dfrac{1}{1000}$ inch). Find the resistance of 1 mile of copper wire whose diameter is 0.2335 inch.

10.7 EXPONENTIAL AND LOGARITHMIC EQUATIONS

In certain equations variables appear as parts of exponential or logarithmic expressions. If a variable appears in an exponent, as in $5^x = 9$ or $2^{x+1} = 3^{x-1}$, the equation is called an *exponential equation*. If an equation involves the logarithm of a function of the variable, as in $\log x + \log (x + 2) = 4$, it is called a *logarithmic equation*.

In general, exponential and logarithmic equations cannot be solved by the methods we have considered previously, but many can be solved by applying various properties of logarithms. In effecting such solutions, we shall find it useful to make use of the following two assumptions.

For positive, real values of M, N, and b:

1. If $M = N$, then $\log_b M = \log_b N$.
2. And conversely, if $\log_b M = \log_b N$, then $M = N$.

These assumptions reflect the property that exponential and logarithmic functions are one-to-one functions. Although we are interested primarily in their application to common logarithms, it should be noted that they apply to logarithms expressed to any base.

EXAMPLE 1. Solve the equation $3^x = 10$.

SOLUTION: Taking the common logarithm of each member of the equation, we obtain

$$x \log 3 = \log 10$$

Therefore

$$x = \frac{\log 10}{\log 3} = \frac{1.0000}{0.4771} = 2.096$$

(A common error in evaluating the quotient $\dfrac{\log 10}{\log 3}$ is to subtract $\log 3$ from $\log$ 10. This is incorrect, since x equals the quotient of two logarithms, not the logarithm of a quotient.)

EXAMPLE 2. Solve $2^{x+1} = 7^{x+2}$.

SOLUTION: $(x + 1) \log 2 = (x + 2) \log 7$ (Taking logarithm of each member)

$$x \log 2 + \log 2 = x \log 7 + 2 \log 7 \qquad \text{(Distributive law)}$$

$$x \log 2 - x \log 7 = 2 \log 7 - \log 2$$

$$x(\log 2 - \log 7) = 2 \log 7 - \log 2 \qquad \text{(Factoring left member)}$$

$$x = \frac{2 \log 7 - \log 2}{\log 2 - \log 7} = \frac{\log 49 - \log 2}{\log 2 - \log 7} = \frac{\log 49/2}{\log 2/7}$$

Solutions may be left in logarithmic form, as above. If a decimal approximation is desired, the final expression can be evaluated by means of a table of logarithms.

EXAMPLE 3. Express the logarithm of 7 to the base 3 in terms of common logarithms.

SOLUTION: If $\log_3 7 = x$

then

$$3^x = 7 \text{ (Exponential form of a logarithmic relation)}$$

$$x \log 3 = \log 7 \text{ (Taking common logarithm of each member)}$$

$$x = \frac{\log 7}{\log 3}$$

EXAMPLE 4. Solve $\log (40x - 1) - \log (x + 1) = 3$

SOLUTION: The given equation can be rewritten, using Theorem 10.2, as

$$\log \frac{40x - 1}{x - 1} = 3$$

The definition of a logarithm results in

$$10^3 = \frac{40x - 1}{x - 1}$$

Therefore, $1000x - 1000 = 40x - 1$

$$960x = 999$$

$$x = \frac{999}{960} = \frac{333}{320}$$

EXAMPLE 5.   Solve the equation $\log 2 + 2 \log x = \log (5x + 3)$.

SOLUTION: Using properties of logarithms, we write the following chain of equivalent equations:

$$\log 2 + \log x^2 = \log (5x + 3)$$
$$\log 2x^2 = \log (5x + 3)$$
$$2x^2 = 5x + 3$$
$$2x^2 - 5x - 3 = 0$$
$$(2x + 1)(x - 3) = 0$$
$$x = 3 \text{ or } x = -\tfrac{1}{2}$$

Since the domain of the logarithmic function is the set of *positive* real numbers, it is important to check all proposed solutions of a logarithmic equation. In this example, the given equation is satisfied for $x = 3$, but $x = -\tfrac{1}{2}$ is not a solution since $\log (-\tfrac{1}{2})$ is not defined in the relation $\log 2 + 2 \log (-\tfrac{1}{2}) = \log \tfrac{1}{2}$.

EXERCISE 10.7

Exponential and Logarithmic Equations

Solve each of the following equations. Express each solution to four significant figures.

1. $3^x = 5$
2. $2^x = 14$
3. $2^{x+1} = 9$
4. $5^{x-2} = 19$
5. $7^{x-1} = 25.3$
6. $3.14^{x+3} = 8$

Solve each of the following. Express the solutions in terms of common logarithms.

7. $2^{5x} = 13$
8. $1.03^x = 2$
9. $75(1.05)^{4x} = 200$
10. $3^{x-1} = 4^{x+1}$
11. $2^{2x-1} = 5^{x+1}$
12. $7^{2x-1} = 2^x$
13. $15^{x+1} = 4^{2x}$
14. $6^{2x+1} = 7^{x+1}$
15. $8^{2x-1} = 11^{x-1}$
16. $75^x = 4$
17. $9^{x+2} = 1$
18. $3(5^{2x}) = 28$

Express each of the following in terms of common logarithms and evaluate the result to three significant figures.

19. $\log_2 3$
20. $\log_3 2$
21. $\log_5 10$
22. $\log_5 100$
23. $\log_4 9$
24. $\log_3 5$

Solve the following logarithmic equations. Check all solutions. (Problems 25–32).

25. $\log x + \log 3 = 1$
26. $\log t - \log 5 = 2$
27. $\tfrac{1}{2} \log y + \log 2 = \log 8$
28. $2 \log 3 - 3 \log 2 = \log x$

29. $\log (n + 3) + \log n = \log 10$ 30. $\log (2 - k) = \log 1 - \log k$

31. $\log z + \log (21 - 2z) = 1$ 32. $2 \log x + \log 2 = \log (3x + 2)$

33. If interest is compounded k times per year, the amount A of a principal P at the end of n years at an annual interest rate r is given by

$$A = P\left(1 + \frac{r}{k}\right)^{kn}$$

If \$100 is invested at 6%, find the number of years, n, it would require for the principal to double itself if the interest is compounded (a) once per year, (b) semiannually, (c) quarterly, and (d) monthly.

34. Using the compound interest formula, find the number of years it would require for a principal to double itself if the interest is compounded annually at a rate of (a) 4%, (b) 5%, (c) 6%, and (d) 7 %. (See Problem 33.)

35. Radioactive substances, such as radium, disintegrate as their atoms break up by emitting particles. Physicists found that the amount A of the substance which remains after t years is given by

$$A = A_0 e^{-kt}$$

where A_0 is the initial amount of the substance, e is the base of the system of natural logarithms ($e = 2.718$ approximately), and k is a constant which can be determined for a given substance.

(a) The half-life of a radioactive substance is the time it takes for one-half of the substance to disintegrate. If the half-life of radium 226 is 1622 years, show that the value of $k = 0.0004274$. (*Hint*: Let $A_0 = 1$, $A = \frac{1}{2}$).

(b) Using the value $k = 0.0004274$, find the fraction of a given sample which remains after 811 years.

chapter 11

the functional nature of variation

TWO FUNCTIONS THAT ARE WIDELY USED IN APPLIED mathematics are

$$y = kx^n \tag{1}$$

and

$$y = \frac{k}{x^n} \qquad x \neq 0 \tag{2}$$

The constant k, called the *constant of variation*, may be any nonzero number, but in this discussion we shall consider only values of k such that $k > 0$. The domain of x is the set of real numbers, with zero excluded in Equation 2, and n is any positive real number.

11.1 DIRECT VARIATION

Functions of the type $y = kx^n$ express *direct variation*; when k is a positive constant an increase in x causes an increase in y. We shall illustrate direct variation by examples from mathematics and physics.

EXAMPLE 1. The formula for the circumference of a circle

$$C = \pi d$$

may be read, "C varies directly as d." In this example, the constant of variation, k, is equal to π.

EXAMPLE 2. Kepler's third law of planetary motion,

$$T = kd^{3/2}$$

may be read, "T varies directly as the three-halves power of d." T is the time for a planet to complete its orbit around the sun, and d is the distance from the sun. The units are usually chosen so that $k = 1$.

EXAMPLE 3. The formula for the distance that a body falls from rest in a given time,

$$s = \frac{1}{2}gt^2$$

may be read, "s varies directly as the square of t." The constant k, equal to $\frac{1}{2}g$, is approximately equal to 16.1, when the units are feet and seconds.

Solving Problems Involving Direct Variation

It will be assumed, in the following examples, that the functional relationship of the variables has been determined, experimentally or otherwise, to be direct variation.

EXAMPLE 4. The pressure P on the bottom of a water tank varies directly as the height h of the water. If the pressure caused by 5 feet of water in a certain tank is 312 pounds per square foot, what is the pressure caused by 12 feet of water?

SOLUTION: The general equation for this variation is

$$P = kh \tag{1}$$

Since $P = 312$ when $h = 5$, we have

$$312 = 5k \tag{2}$$

Solving for k

$$k = 62.4 \tag{3}$$

Replacing $k = 62.4$ in Equation 1, we have the *specific equation*

$$P = 62.4h \tag{4}$$

When $h = 12$

$$P = 62.4 \times 12 = 748.8$$

Therefore the pressure is 748.8 pounds per square foot when the water is 12 feet deep.

Observe that the constant of variation k, equal to 62.4, represents the weight of a cubic foot of water.

EXAMPLE 5. A falling body strikes the ground with a velocity v which varies directly as the square root of the distance s it falls. If a body that falls 100 feet strikes the ground with a velocity of 80 feet per second, with what veolocity will a ball dropped from the Washington monument (approximately 550 feet high) strike the ground?

SOLUTION: The general equation for this variation is

$$v = k\sqrt{s} \tag{1}$$

Since $v = 80$ when $s = 100$, we have

$$80 = \sqrt{100}k \tag{2}$$

Solving for k

$$k = 8 \tag{3}$$

Replacing $k = 8$ in Equation 1

$$v = 8\sqrt{s} \tag{4}$$

When $s = 550$

$$v = 8\sqrt{550} = 188 \tag{5}$$

Therefore the velocity is approximately 188 feet per second.

It is shown in physics that the velocity of a falling body, derived from the equation $s = \frac{1}{2}gt^2$ (Example 3 of this section) is

$$v = \sqrt{2g}\,\sqrt{s} \tag{6}$$

Since g is approximately equal to 32, $\sqrt{2g} = \sqrt{64} = 8$ is the constant of variation for this problem.

EXAMPLE 6. The weight w of an iron ball varies directly as the cube of the radius. If the radius of a ball weighing 148 pounds is 5 inches, find the weight of a ball with a 10-inch radius.

SOLUTION: The general equation for this variation is

$$w = kr^3 \tag{1}$$

Since $w = 148$ when $r = 5$,

$$148 = 125k \tag{2}$$

Solving for k

$$k = 1.18 \tag{3}$$

Replacing $k = 1.18$ in Equation 1, we have the specific equation

$$w = 1.18r^3$$

When $r = 10$,

$$w = 1.18(1000) = 1180.$$

Therefore the weight of the ball is approximately equal to 1180 pounds.

The constant of variation, equal to 1.18, depends upon the density of iron. For an aluminum ball, k would be less than one-third of 1.18, since aluminum is much lighter than iron.

We may summarize the procedure for solving the direct variation $y = kx^n$ as follows:

1. Express the general equation of the particular variation given.
2. Replace the variables with the given values and solve for k.
3. Replace k in the general equation written in step 1, to get the specific function for the given problem.
4. The specific function may now be used to determine the value of one variable when a value is assigned to the other variable.

Direct Variation as Proportion

Suppose that the direct variation $y = kx^n$ is satisfied by two pairs of values, (x_1, y_1) and (x_2, y_2). Then we have

$$y_1 = kx_1^n \tag{1}$$
$$y_2 = kx_2^n \tag{2}$$

Dividing Equation 1 by Equation 2, we may eliminate the constant k, and the resulting equation is the proportion

$$\frac{y_1}{y_2} = \frac{x_1^n}{x_2^n} \tag{3}$$

It is clear, therefore, that the two expressions

$$y = kx^n \tag{4}$$
$$\frac{y_1}{y_2} = \frac{x_1^n}{x_2^n} \tag{5}$$

express the same functional relationship between x and y. This relationship may then be expressed as "y varies directly as the nth power of x" or "y is directly proportional to the nth power of x." As the following examples show, Equation 4 is useful when it is desirable to find the specific relation between x and y, and Equation 5 is useful when we wish to find just one particular pair of values of the variables.

EXAMPLE 7. The resistance R of a given size of wire at constant temperature varies directly as the length l. It is found that the resistance of 100 feet of number 14 copper is 0.253 ohm. Construct a table of values for the given lengths of number 14 copper wire, assuming the temperature is constant.

l	25	75	125	175	225
R					

SOLUTION: Since several values of R are to be found, we use the general equation for this variation

$$R = kl \tag{1}$$

Since $R = 0.253$ when $l = 100$

$$0.253 = 100k \tag{2}$$

Solving for k

$$k = 0.00253 \tag{3}$$

The specific equation is therefore

$$R = 0.00253l \tag{4}$$

The values of R corresponding to the given values of l may then be found directly from Equation 4, as follows.

l	25	75	125	175	225
R	0.0632	0.190	0.316	0.443	0.569

Notice that if values of l were to be determined from given values R, it would be convenient to solve Equation 4 for l in terms of R. Thus

$$l = \frac{R}{0.00253} \tag{5}$$

or

$$l = 395.26R$$

EXAMPLE 8. The pressure P of wind against a billboard varies directly as the square of the velocity v of the wind. The pressure is 2 pounds per square foot when the velocity of the wind is 30 miles per hour. A storm is predicted with wind velocity of 90 miles per hour. What pressure will the billboard be subjected to?

SOLUTION: Since but one value of P is required, we use the proportion

$$\frac{P_1}{P_2} = \frac{v_1^2}{v_2^2} \tag{1}$$

Substituting the given values in Equation 1

$$\frac{2}{P_2} = \frac{30^2}{90^2} \tag{2}$$

Solving Equation 2 for P_2

$$P_2 = 18 \text{ pounds per square foot}$$

EXERCISE 11.1

Direct Variation

Write each of the following examples of direct variation as an equation, using k for the constant of variation.

1. The circumference C of a circle varies directly as the radius r. What is the value of k?
2. The weight w of a given size of copper tubing varies directly as the length l. What is the meaning of k?
3. The area A of a square is directly proportional to the square of a side s.
4. The height h of mercury in a thermometer varies directly as the temperature t.
5. The area A of an equilateral triangle varies directly as the square of a side s.
6. The pitch p of a violin string of fixed length varies directly as the square root of the tension t.
7. The area A illuminated on a screen by a slide projector is directly proportional to the square of the distance d from the screen.
8. The safe load L for a circular pillar is directly proportional to the fourth power of its diameter d.

In Problems 9–12, find the specific equation and complete the table of values.

9. y varies directly as x, and $y = 8$ when $x = 2$.

x	1	4		6	
y			20		40

10. y varies directly as the square of x, and $y = 8$ when $x = 2$.

x	4	6		8	
y			98		200

11. y varies directly as the square root of x, and $y = 12$ when $x = 16$.

x	4	9		36		
y			15	18	21	

12. y varies directly as the $3/2$ power of x, and $y = 32$ when $x = 16$.

x	4	9		36	
y			62.5		171.5

In Problems 13–16, use the proportion form of direct variation.

13. y varies directly as x, and $y = 15$ when $x = 45$. Find y when $x = 90$.

14. y varies directly as the square of x, and $y = 16$ when $x = 2$. Find x when $y = 4$.

15. y varies directly as the square root of x, and $y = 42$ when $x = 16$. Find y when $x = 36$.

16. y varies directly as the $2/3$ power of x, and $y = 8$ when $x = 8$. Find y when $x = 64$.

In Problems 17–24, determine the specific equation if more than one value of the variable is to be found; otherwise use the proportion form of direct variation.

17. Hooke's law states that the extension s of a spring varies directly as the applied force, F. If a 10-pound weight stretches a spring 3 inches, what weights are required to stretch the spring (a) 5 inches, (b) 8 inches, and (c) 10 inches?

18. The indicated horse-power P of a ship varies directly as the cube of the velocity v in knots. If the indicated horsepower is 587 when the speed of the ship is 14 knots, what horsepower is required for a speed of 16.5 knots?

19. The time t required for a pendulum to make one oscillation varies directly as the square root of its length l. If a pendulum 36 inches long makes one oscillation in 1.92 seconds, find the length of a pendulum which makes one oscillation in 0.96 seconds.

20. The maximum range R of a projectile varies as the square of the initial velocity v. If a velocity of 400 feet per second is required for a range of 5000 feet, find the velocity required for ranges of (a) 1 mile (5280 feet), (b) 1000 feet, (c) 440 yards, and (d) 2 miles.

21. The distance s a person can see to the horizon from a point h feet above the surface of the earth varies directly as the square root of the height. If the horizon is 18 miles distant when the person is 144 feet above the ground, how far will the horizon be when the distance is 100 feet above the ground?

22. The distance d required to stop an automobile varies directly as the square of the speed s when the brakes are first applied. A car can stop in 70 feet from a speed of 40 miles per hour. Can the driver avoid hitting a stalled car 200 feet ahead if he is going at a speed of 60 miles per hour, and his reaction time is $3/4$ of a second?

23. The cost C of carpeting a room with a particular grade of carpeting varies directly as the area A of the room. If the cost of carpeting a room 20 feet

by 15 feet during a special sale was $240, what would be the cost of carpeting a room 9 feet by 12 feet?

24. A company makes a certain statue in various heights. The weight W of a statue varies as the cube of the height h, and a 20-inch statue weighs 15 pounds. Find the weight of a statue (a) 18 inches, (b) 24 inches, (c) 30 inches, and (d) 36 inches, in height.

25. In the direct variation $y = kx$, let $x = 4$, and $k = 10$.
    (a) How is y changed when x is doubled?
    (b) How is y changed when x is tripled?
    (c) How is y changed when x is made half as large?
    (d) How is y changed when x is made one-fourth as large?

26. In the direct variation $y = kx^2$, let $x = 4$ and $k = 10$. How is y changed as in a, b, c, and d, of Problem 25?

27. In the direct variation $y = k\sqrt{x}$, let $x = 4$ and $k = 10$.
    (a) How is y changed when x is taken 4 times as large? Nine times as large?
    (b) How is y changed when x is taken one-fourth as large? One-ninth as large?

28. Do the answers to Problems 25–27, depend on the value of k? Do they depend on the initial value of x?

11.2 INVERSE VARIATION

The second function discussed in the opening of this chapter, $y = \dfrac{k}{x^n}$, expresses *inverse variation*; when k is a positive constant an increase in x causes a decrease in y. We shall illustrate inverse variation by two examples.

EXAMPLE 9. Boyle's law in chemistry,

$$V = \frac{k}{P}$$

may be read "V varies inversely as P." In this function, V is the volume of gas at given temperature and P is the applied pressure.

EXAMPLE 10. The formula relating the intensity of light on a screen to the distance of the light from the screen,

$$I = \frac{k}{d^2}$$

may be read, "I varies inversely as the square of the distance d." Note that as the distance increases, the intensity decreases, as one would expect.

Inverse Variation as Proportion

The two expressions

$$y = \frac{k}{x^n} \tag{1}$$

$$\frac{y_1}{y_2} = \frac{x_2^n}{x_1^n} \tag{2}$$

express the same functional relationship between x and y. Equation 2 may be derived from Equation 1 in a manner similar to that for direct variation. The student should carefully note the difference between the proportion forms for direct variation and for inverse variation. As in direct variation, Equation 1 is useful in finding the specific relation between x and y when several pairs of values are to be found, and Equation 2 is useful when just one pair of values is required.

EXAMPLE 11. The current I in an electrical circuit varies inversely as the resistance R of the circuit. The current is 3 amperes when the resistance is 5 ohms. Construct a table of values of the resistance R, and the corresponding current I.

R	1.5	2.5	3.5	4.5	5.5
I					

SOLUTION: Since several values of I are to be found, we use the general equation for this variation

$$I = \frac{k}{R} \tag{1}$$

Substituting $I = 3$ and $R = 5$ in Equation 1, it is found that $k = 15$, hence the specific equation is

$$I = \frac{15}{R} \tag{2}$$

The values of I corresponding to the given values of R may then be found directly from Equation 2, as follows.

R	1.5	2.5	3.5	4.5	5.5
I	10	6	4.29	3.33	2.73

EXAMPLE 12. The weight W of an object above the earth varies inversely as the square of the distance d from the center of the earth. If a man weighs 180 pounds on the surface of the earth, what would his weight be at an altitude of 1000 miles? Assume the radius of the earth to be 4000 miles.

SOLUTION: Since but one value of W is to be found, we use the proportion

$$\frac{W_1}{W_2} = \frac{d_2{}^2}{d_1{}^2} \tag{1}$$

Substituting the given values in Equation 1

$$\frac{180}{W_2} = \frac{5000^2}{4000^2} \tag{2}$$

Solving Equation 2,

$$W_2 = 115.2 \text{ pounds}$$

EXERCISE 11.2

Inverse Variation

Write each of the following examples of inverse variation as an equation, using k for the constant of variation. Write the equivalent proportion for each example.

1. The acceleration of gravity g of a body varies inversely as the square of its distance s from the center of the earth.
2. The force F of attraction between two electrically charged particles varies inversely as the square of the distance s between them.
3. The time T to travel a given distance varies inversely as the average speed r.
4. The base b of a triangle of given area varies inversely as the altitude h.
5. The height h of a cylinder of given volume varies inversely as the square of the radius r.
6. The centripetal force F of a body moving at constant speed in a circular path varies inversely as the radius r of the path.
7. The mechanical advantage A of an inclined plane of given length varies inversely as the height h of the raised end.
8. On a balanced lever, the weight W is inversely proportional to the distance d from the fulcrum.

In Problems 9–12, find the specific equation and complete the table of values.

9. y varies inversely as x, and $y = 6$ when $x = 15$.

x	3	5	10	20
y				

10. y varies inversely as the square of x, and $y = 8$ when $x = 10$.

x	5	15	20	25
y				

11. y varies inversely as the square root of x, and $y = 25$ when $x = 100$.

x	16	25	64	81
y				

12. y varies inversely as the $\frac{3}{2}$ power of x, and $y = 10$ when $x = 16$.

x	9	25	36	64
y				

In Problems 13–16, use the proportion form of variation.

13. y varies inversely as x, and $y = 8$ when $x = 2$. Find y when $x = 4$.

14. y varies inversely as x, and $y = \frac{1}{3}$ when $x = 8$. Find y when $x = 4$.

15. y varies inversely as the square of x, and $y = 6$ when $x = 3$. Find y when $x = 2$.

16. y varies inversely as the square root of x, and $y = 5$ when $x = 9$. Find y when $x = 36$.

In Problems 17–20, use the appropriate form of inverse variation.

17. The repulsion F between electrical charges varies inversely as the square of the distance d between the charges. If $F = 40$ dynes when $d = \frac{1}{2}$ centimeter, find F when $d =$ (a) 1 centimeter, (b) 2.5 centimeters, and (c) 3.75 centimeters.

18. The acceleration g of gravity varies inversely as the square of the distance r from the center of the earth. If $g = 32$ when $r = 4000$, find r when $g = 16$.

19. The intensity I, in foot-candles, of light varies inversely as the square of the distance D, in feet, from the source. If $D = 10$ when $I = 120$, find I when $D = 20$.

20. If a weight tied to a string is given a circular motion in a horizontal plane, the height from the point of suspension is inversely proportional to the square of the number of revolutions per second. The height is 9.78 inches when the weight is revolving at one revolution per second, What is the height when the number of revolutions per second is (a) $1\frac{2}{3}$, (b) 3, (c) 2.5, and (d) 4?

21. In the inverse variation $y = \dfrac{k}{x}$, let $k = 10$ and $x = 2$.

   (a) How is y changed when x is doubled?
   (b) How is y changed when x is tripled?
   (c) How is y changed when x is taken one-half as large?
   (d) How is y changed when x is taken one-fourth as large?

22. Do the answers to Problem 21 depend on the value of k? Do they depend on the initial value of x?

23. For the inverse variation $y = \dfrac{k}{x^2}$, with $k = 10$ and $x = 2$, answer questions (a), (b), (c), and (d), of Problem 21.

24. For the inverse variation $y = \dfrac{k}{\sqrt{x}}$, with $k = 10$ and $x = 4$, answer questions (a), (b), (c), and (d), of Problem 21.

25. Do the answers to Problems 23 and 24 depend on the value of k? Do they depend on the initial value of x?

11.3 VARIATION INVOLVING MORE THAN TWO VARIABLES

In our study of variation thus far, we have considered only functional relationships between two variables. There are many relationships in applied mathematics which involve more than two variables as in the following examples.

EXAMPLE 13. The distance traveled depends on both the average rate of speed and the time.

EXAMPLE 14. The interest earned on money in a savings account depends on the principal, the rate of interest, and the time.

EXAMPLE 15. The safe load on a beam of given material depends on its width and thickness, and the distance between its supports.

Joint Variation

If the quantity z varies directly as the product of x^n and y^m, then we say that z varies jointly as the nth power of x and the mth power of y. Symbolically,

$$z = kx^n y^m \tag{1}$$

The proportion form of Equation 1 is

$$\frac{z_1}{z_2} = \frac{x_1{}^n y_1{}^m}{x_2{}^n y_2{}^m} \tag{2}$$

EXAMPLE 16. The lateral area L of a right circular cylinder varies jointly as the radius r and the height h. Symbolically,

$$L = krh$$

From geometry, we know that $k = 2\pi$, so that $L = 2\pi rh$.

EXAMPLE 17. The volume V of a right circular cylinder varies jointly as the square of the radius r and the height h. Symbolically,

$$V = kr^2 h$$

From geometry we know that $k = \pi$, so that $V = \pi r^2 h$.

Combined Variation

In Example 15 it seems reasonable that increasing either the width or the thickness of a beam will increase the safe load, while increasing the distance between the supports will decrease the safe load. This functional relationship involving both direct and inverse variation may be described as *combined variation* and may be stated, "The safe load of a beam varies jointly as the width and the square of the thickness, and inversely as the distance between supports." Symbolically,

$$L = \frac{kwh^2}{d}$$

The proportion form for this variation is

$$\frac{L_1}{L_2} = \frac{w_1 h_1{}^2 d_2}{w_2 h_2{}^2 d_1}$$

Note that the subscripts of letters involving inverse variation are in the reverse order.

As in direct and inverse variation, the specific equation for problems involving joint or combined variation may be found by evaluating the constant k, or the proportion form of variation may be used if only one set of values is to be found.

EXERCISE 11.3

Variation Involving More than Two Variables

Write each of the following examples of variation as an equation, using k for the constant of variation.

1. The pressure p of gas in a container varies jointly as the density d and the absolute temperature t.
2. The total force F of the wind on a wall varies jointly as the area A of the wall and the square of the velocity v of the wind.
3. The resistance R of a copper wire varies directly as the length l and inversely as the square of the diameter d.
4. The lift L of an airplane wing varies jointly as the area A of the wing and the square of the velocity v of the wind.
5. The number of vibrations v of a violin string varies directly as the square root of the tension t and inversely as the product of the length l and the diameter d.

6. The illumination E in foot-candles of a screen varies directly as the intensity I of the source in candle power and inversely as the square of the distance d in feet from the source.

7. The force F of friction between the tires and the road necessary to prevent a car from skidding when rounding a curve varies inversely as the radius r of the curve and directly as the square of the velocity v.

8. The volume V of a right circular cone varies jointly as the altitude h and the square of the radius r of the base.

In Problems 9–12, find the specific equation first.

9. z varies jointly as x and y, and $z = 14$ when $x = 4$ and $y = 28$. (a) Find z when $x = 8$ and $y = 15$ and (b) find x when $z = 2$ and $y = 4$.

10. z varies directly as x and inversely as y, and $z = 75$ when $x = 30$ and $y = 2$. (a) Find z when $x = 20$ and $y = 10$ and (b) find y when $x = 10$ and $z = 2$.

11. z varies directly as x and inversely as the square of y, and $z = 10$ when $x = 5$ and $y = 3$. (a) Find z when $x = 32$ and $y = 4$ and (b) find y when $z = 2$ and $x = 4$.

12. z varies jointly as x and y and inversely as the square of w, and $z = 40$ when $x = 2.5$, $y = 40$, and $w = 5$. (a) Find z when $x = 4.5$, $y = 60$, and $w = 10$ and (b) find z when $x = 5$, $y = 20$, and $w = 10$.

In Problems 13–16, use the proportion form of variation.

13. z varies jointly as x and y, and $z = 24$ when $x = 2$ and $y = 3$. Find z when $x = 3$ and $y = 5$.

14. z varies jointly as x and the square of y, and $z = 25$ when $x = 3$ and $y = 5$. Find z when $x = 6$ and $y = 4$.

15. z varies directly as x and inversely as the square root of y and $z = 10$ when $x = 5$ and $y = 81$. Find z when $x = 15$ and $y = 9$.

16. z varies jointly as x and y and inversely as the square root of w, and $z = 600$ when $x = 2$, $y = 3$, and $w = 4$. Find z when $x = 6$, $y = 6$, and $w = 25$.

Solve each of the following problems.

17. The weight of a cast iron cylinder varies jointly as the height and the square of the radius. A cylinder 2 inches high with a radius of 1 inch weighs 1.64 pounds. What is the weight of a cylinder 8 inches high with a radius of 4 inches?

18. The general gas law states that the volume of a gas varies directly as the absolute temperature and inversely as the pressure. If 20 cubic feet of gas at 300 degrees absolute temperature has a pressure of 760 millimeters, what

volume will the gas occupy at 310 degrees absolute temperature and 800 millimeters pressure?

19. As previously stated, the safe load of a beam varies jointly as the width and the square of the thickness and inversely as the distance between the supports. A beam 16 feet long, 3 inches wide and 6 inches thick can safely support a load of 1500 pounds. What is the safe load of a beam of the same material 12 feet long, 2 inches wide, and 4 inches thick?

20. If the 16-foot beam of Problem 19 is to carry a 3000-pound load, what should the thickness be if the width remains 3 inches?

11.4 THE POWER FUNCTION $y = kx^n$

It is apparent that the single function

$$y = kx^n$$

will represent direct variation for $n > 0$ and inverse variation for $n < 0$. We have noted that for $k > 0$, y tends to increase as x increases when n is positive, and y tends to decrease as x increases when n is negative. The function $y = kx^n$, where n is any real number except zero, is called the *power function*. An examination of the graph of this function will clearly reveal the roles of k and n in both direct and inverse variation.

Graph of $y = kx^n$, $n > 0$

In Figure 11.1 the graph of $y = kx^n$, $n > 0$, is shown for a fixed value of k ($k = 1$) and several values of n. The following properties of the graph may be observed.

1. As x increases, y increases.
2. All of the curves pass through the points $(0, 0)$ and $(1, 1)$.
3. For values of x near zero, the steepness of the curves decrease as n increases.
4. For values of x greater than 1, the steepness of the curves increase sharply as n increases. This means that as n increases, a change in x produces a much greater change in y.

In Figure 11.2 the graph of $y = kx^n$, $n > 0$, is shown for a fixed value of n ($n = 2$) and several values of k. The following properties of the graph may be observed.

1. All of the curves no longer pass through the point $(1, 1)$, but each curve passes through the point $(1, k)$.
2. For all values of x, the steepness of the curves increase as k increases.

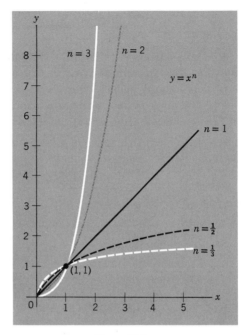

Figure 11.1

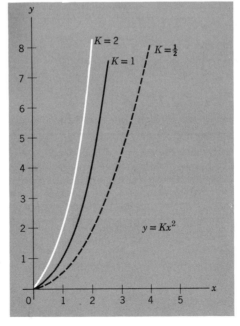

Figure 11.2

Graph of $y = kx^n$, $n < 0$

In Figure 11.3, the graph of $y = kx^n$, $n < 0$, is shown for $k = 1$ and several values of n. The following properties of the graph may be observed.

1. As x increases, y decreases and approaches zero.
2. There is neither an x nor a y intercept.
3. All of the curves pass through the point (1, 1).
4. For values of x less than 1, the steepness of the curves increase as n increases in absolute value.
5. For values of x greater than 1, the steepness of the curves decrease as n increases in absolute value.

In Exercise 11.4, the student will be asked to discuss the effect of varying k for fixed values of n in the graph of $y = kx^n$, $n < 0$.

We have previously referred to the "steepness" of the curves for the power function. The following examples indicate how we may show the increase or decrease in the steepness (or slope) of a curve, although we must leave to more advanced courses the definition of "slope" as related to curves, and the methods of assigning a numerical value to the slope of a curve.

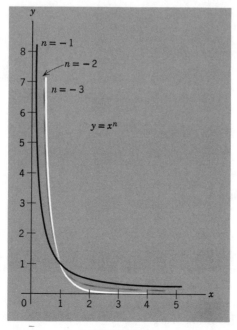

Figure 11.3

EXAMPLE 1. Referring to the graph of $y = x^{1/2}$ in Figure 11.1, find the slope of the line joining $(1, 1)$ and $(4, 2)$.

SOLUTION: By Definition 7.3, the slope is given by

$$\frac{y_2 - y_1}{x_2 - x_1} = \frac{2 - 1}{4 - 1} = \frac{1}{3}$$

Therefore, in this interval, y is increasing $\frac{1}{3}$ unit per unit increase in x.

EXAMPLE 2. For the curve $y = x^{1/2}$, how does the slope of the line joining the points $(4, 2)$ and $(9, 3)$ compare with the slope found in Example 1?

SOLUTION: The slope in this interval is $\dfrac{3 - 2}{9 - 4} = \dfrac{1}{5}$. This slope is less than the slope found in the interval $x = 1$ to $x = 4$. It appears that as x increases beyond 1, the steepness of the curve decreases. The slope is shown in Figure 11.4.

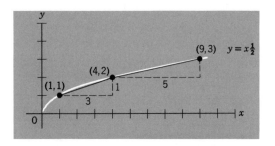

Figure 11.4

EXERCISE 11.4

The Power Function $y = kx^n$

1. (a) Draw the graph of $y = kx^{-1}$ for $k = 1, 2$, and 3, on the same axis. What is the effect of increasing k?

   (b) Draw the graph of $y = kx^{-2}$ for $k = 1, 2$, and 3, on the same axis. What is the effect of increasing k?

   (c) Does the effect of increasing k in the power function $y = kx^n$, $n < 0$, depend on the value of n?

2. (a) Draw the graph of $y = x^2$ and find the slope of the line joining $(0, 0)$ and $\left(\dfrac{1}{2}, \dfrac{1}{4}\right)$.

   (b) Draw the graph of $y = x^3$ and find the slope of the line joining $(0, 0)$ and $\left(\dfrac{1}{2}, \dfrac{1}{8}\right)$.

   (c) How does the slope found in part b compare with the slope found in part a?

   (d) Draw the graph of $y = x^2$ and find the slope of the line joining $(1, 1)$ and $(2, 4)$.

   (e) Draw the graph of $y = x^3$ and find the slope of the line joining $(1, 1)$ and $(2, 8)$.

   (f) How does the slope found in part e compare with the slope found in part d?

3. (a) Draw the graph of $y = x^{-1}$ and find the slope of the line joining $\left(\dfrac{1}{4}, 4\right)$ and $\left(\dfrac{1}{2}, 2\right)$.

   (b) Draw the graph of $y = x^{-2}$ and find the slope of the line joining $\left(\dfrac{1}{4}, 16\right)$ and $\left(\dfrac{1}{2}, 4\right)$.

   (c) How does the slope found in part b compare with the slope found in part a?

   (d) Draw the graph of $y = x^{-1}$ and find the slope of the line joining $(1, 1)$ and $\left(2, \dfrac{1}{2}\right)$.

   (e) Draw the graph of $y = x^{-2}$ and find the slope of the line joining $(1, 1)$ and $\left(2, \dfrac{1}{4}\right)$.

   (f) How does the slope found in part e compare with the slope found in part d?

chapter 12

permutations, combinations, and probability

THE THREE TOPICS INTRODUCED IN THIS CHAPTER ARE becoming of great significance in our modern technological world because they are the foundations of the discipline known as statistics.

Statistics is concerned with the collection, analysis, and interpretation of data. The data may be of annual family income, life expectancy of individuals, the frequency and cost of automobile accidents, unemployment studies, opinion polls, population trends, or trends in the changes in our environment (to mention only a few).

Most people are aware of the studies listed above through one form or another of news media. However, a branch of statistics known as sampling theory is not as well known. Some understanding of the work of sampling theory can be obtained from the following illustration. A manufacturer uses thousands of machine screws per day. It is not practical to test each machine screw of each keg he purchases. Instead he tests a small sample (say 100) from each keg or lot he purchases. The study of this sample would then determine whether the lot should be accepted or rejected or whether a further study is necessary with a larger sample.

Sampling theory is based on principles of mathematical probability. Statistics and probability are so interrelated that some knowledge of probability is essential to the understanding of statistics. Combinations and permutations deal with the grouping and arrangements of objects, and therefore are useful in calculating probabilities.

12.1 PERMUTATIONS

It is frequently desirable to determine the number of ways a given act can be performed. The fundamental principle that is used to determine this number may be stated as follows.

Fundamental Principle

If an act "A" can be done in m ways and a second act "B" can be done in n ways, then the number of ways in which the two acts can be done in the order "A" followed by "B" is mn. This principle is illustrated by the following example.

EXAMPLE 1. How many ways can co-chairmen (one man and one woman) be chosen from a group of 14 men and 12 women?

SOLUTION: There are 14 men so there are 14 ways to pick the man and there are 12 ways of selecting the woman. The number of ways of determining the co-chairmen equals (14)(12) equals 168 ways.

EXAMPLE 2. If the group of example 1 is to elect two officers, president and secretary, who could be of the same sex, in how many ways could the officers be elected?

SOLUTION: The group consists of 26 members, anyone of the 26 can serve as president. After the president has been elected, there are still 25 other members that could be elected as the secretary. Therefore the number of ways the two officers can be chosen is (26)(25) or 650 ways.

The fundamental principle can be extended to more than two events. The total number of ways the successive events could be performed is the product of the numbers of ways each of the events could be performed.

EXAMPLE 3. How many license plates can be made of two letters followed by four digits? Assume all letters can be used, all digits can be used, and the letters and digits can be repeated. For example, this would permit a license of AA-0000 or even *OO*-0000.

SOLUTION: There are 26 ways of choosing each of the two letters and ten ways of choosing each of the four numbers.

$$\text{Number of licenses} = (26)(26)(10)(10)(10)(10)$$
$$= 6,760,000$$

EXAMPLE 4. If in a series of license plates the letters I and O are not used and if four successive zeroes can not be used as the four digits, how many different license plates can be made?

SOLUTION: There are now 24 choices for each of the two letters. The digits would form the numbers from 0001 to 9999; so there are 9999 choices for the four digits.

$$\text{Number of license plates} = (24)(24)(9999)$$
$$= 5,759,424$$

Permutations (Distinct Objects): The different ways a set of different objects can be ordered is called the permutations of the set. The list of permutations of the letters a, b, and c using all three letters is

$$abc, \ acb, \ bac, \ bca, \ cab, \text{ and } cba$$

The number of permutations of the three letters taken three at a time is 6. The notation for the number of permutations of 5 things taken 4 at a time is $P(5, 4)$ or $_5P_4$. We shall use the notation of the form $P(5, 4)$.

We have seen from the illustration above that $P(3, 3) = 6$.

EXAMPLE 5. A baseball manager after determining his starting players now must determine his batting order. If the pitcher is to bat last, how many different ways can the manager turn in his batting order?

SOLUTION: Since the pitcher is to bat last only the order of the other eight players must be determined. Using the fundamental principle, he has 8 choices for the lead-off man. Once this choice is made, he has 7 choices for the second batter, and so on.

$$\text{Number of batting orders} = P(8, 8)$$
$$= 8(7)(6)(5)(4)(3)(2)(1)$$
$$= 8!$$
$$= 40,320$$

We can use the fundamental principle to determine the number of permutations of n different objects taken r at a time. Let us list the number of choices for each selection.

$$\text{No. of choices for 1st object} = n$$
$$\text{No. of choices for 2nd object} = (n - 1)$$
$$\text{No. of choices for 3rd object} = (n - 2)$$

$$\text{No. of choices for 4th object} = (n - 3)$$

$$.$$
$$.$$
$$.$$

$$\text{No. of choices for } r\text{th object} = (n - r + 1)$$

Therefore, $P(n, r)$ is the product of the right-hand members of the above equations.

THEOREM 12.1. $P(n,r) = n(n - 1)(n - 2) \ldots (n - r + 1)$.

If in the above formula for the number of permutations we replace r by n, we obtain the number of permutations of n objects taken n at a time, That is,

$$P(n, n) = n(n - 1)(n - 2) \ldots (2)(1)$$
$$= n!$$

EXAMPLE 6.   In how many ways can six books be arranged on a shelf?

SOLUTION: We are to determine the number of permutations of six objects taken six at a time. The solution is obtained by substituting $n = 6$ in the formula.

$$P(n, \ n) = n!$$
$$P(6, 6) = 6! = 720 \text{ ways}$$

EXAMPLE 7.   If ten books are to be arranged on a shelf and three of the books form a set and two other books form a second set, how many arrangements are possible if the numbered volumes of the two sets are to appear together and in proper order?

SOLUTION: Since the three volumes in the set are to be in a particular order and are to remain together for the purpose of determining the number of permutations, these three volumes must be treated as a single book, that is, as though the three volumes of the set were in a slip case. This is also true of the two volumes of the set of two books. We are then concerned with the number of permutations of the five remaining books which do not belong to a set and the two sets or with the equivalent of seven objects. Substituting $n = 7$ in our permutation formula we determine the number of permutations possible under the specified conditions.

$$P(7, 7) = 7!$$
$$= 5040 \text{ arrangements}$$

Permutations When Some Elements Are the Same

The preceding discussion was concerned with sets of objects in which no two members of the set were the same. We shall consider an example to show that a modification is necessary in the formula for the number of permutations when some objects are identical. Consider the number of permutations of the letters of the word *even*. A listing of the permutations is given below.

e v e n	v e e n	n v e e
e v n e	v e n e	n e v e
e e v n	v n e e	n e e v
e e n v		
e n v e		
e n e v		

Only twelve permutations are possible in this case; whereas, if all of the letters were different the number of permutations would be $P(4, 4) = 4! = 24$. Although the above example does not prove the following theorem, it does show that a different formula is necessary to determine the number of permutations when some objects of the set are the same.

THEOREM 12.2.   If in a set of *n* objects, *s* of them are the same, then the number of permutations of the *n* objects taken *n* at a time is given by the formula

$$P(n,n) = \frac{n!}{s!}$$

Theorem 12.2 can be extended to cover cases where there is also a second set of objects which are the same. If there are *t* objects in the second set of identical objects, then the formula becomes

$$P(n, n) = \frac{n!}{s!\,t!}$$

EXAMPLE 8.   Determine the number of permutations of the letters in the word BANANA.

SOLUTION: There are six letters so $n = 6$, the letter "n" appears twice so $s = 2$, and "a" appears three times so $t = 3$. Substituting these values in the formula

$$P(n, n) = \frac{n!}{s!\,t!}$$

we obtain

$$P(6, 6) = \frac{6!}{3!\,2!}$$

$$= \frac{\cancel{6}(5)(4)(3)(\cancel{2})(1)}{\cancel{3}(\cancel{2})(2)(\cancel{2})}$$

$$= 30$$

EXERCISE 12.1

Permutations

In the problems of this set the objects are all different unless the problem states or implies that some of them are identical.

1. If a group of three boys and three girls are to occupy six seats arranged in a row, how many arrangements are possible?

2. A bridge club is composed of 12 players, 7 men and 5 women. In how many ways can a team consisting of 1 man and 1 woman be chosen?

3. If a baseball team has 5 outfielders, 6 infielders, 2 catchers, and 4 pitchers, in how many ways can the starting team (3 outfielders, 4 infielders, a catcher, and a pitcher) be selected. Assume that all outfielders can play any outfield position and all infielders can play any infield position, and that the coach is to assign players to specific positions.

4. If a freshman is required to take a course in English, Social Science, Mathematics, and Physical Science, and he has a choice of 3 English courses, 5 Social Science courses, 3 Mathematics courses, and 4 Physical Science courses, how many different programs are available to him?

5. From a committee of 8 men and 6 women a subcommittee is to be formed. If the subcommittee is to consist of 1 man and 1 woman, in how many ways can the subcommittee be chosen?

6. A paint manufacturer uses letters of the alphabet to code batches of paint manufactured. If he uses all letters of the alphabet, how many batches could be identified using three letters if all three letters may be the same?

7. If a salesman is to call on six customers on a certain day, in how many ways can the order of the calls be arranged?

8. Four paintings are to be hung in a row on the wall of a gallery. The four paintings are to be picked from a collection of 13. In how many different ways could the display be arranged?

9. How many permutations of the letters A, B, C, D, E, and F are possible if the letters are (a) taken two at a time, (b) taken three at a time, and (c) taken four at a time?

10. How many permutations are there for the letters of the word SERENE?

11. How many permutations are there for the letters in the word GOODNESS?

12. How many permutations are there for the letters in the word ABSCISSA?

13. How many permutations are there for the letters of the word BOOK-KEEPER?

14. The number 134431 is called a palindrome because the sequence of digits is the same whether they are read from left to right or right to left. How many permutations are possible for the digits of this number? How many of these permutations will be palindromes?

15. If 6 people are to be seated in a row of 6 chairs, the formula for $P(6, 6)$ is used to determine the number of seating arrangements. However, if the seating is at a round table, the problem is changed. How many seating arrangements are possible for 6 people at a round table?

12.2 COMBINATIONS

We have learned that permutations were concerned with the order of a set of objects. Combinations are concerned with the different collections or sets of objects that are possible. There are 24 permutations of the set of leters, a, b, c, and d taken 3 letters at a time. The 24 permutations are:

a b c	a b d	a c d	b c d
a c b	a d b	a d c	b d c
b a c	b a d	c a d	c b d
b c a	b d a	c d a	c d b
c a b	d a b	d a c	d b c
c b a	d b a	d c a	d c b

In this table all of the permutations listed in the first column arise from one combination; the same is true of each of the other three columns. Therefore, the number of combinations of four objects taken three at a time is 4.

From another point of view, consider a set of 4 objects from which we are to pick 3 or we are not to select one of them. How many ways can we omit one object if there are 4 objects? Obviously this can be done 4 ways. This agrees with our tabulation above.

The formula for the number of combinations "n" different objects taken "r" at a time is denoted by $C(n, r)$ or $_nC_r$. We shall use the first form.

THEOREM 12.2.   The number of combinations of n different objects taken r at a time

$$C(n,r) = \frac{P(n,r)}{P(r,r)}$$

By substituting the values of the numerator and denominator from Theorem 12.1 we obtain

$$C(n,r) = \frac{n(n-1)(n-2)\ldots(n-r+1)}{r!}$$

$$= \frac{n(n-1)(n-2)\ldots(n-r+1)[(n-r)(n-r-1)\ldots(2)(1)]}{(n-r)!\ r!}$$

$$= \frac{n!}{(n-r)!\ r!}$$

EXAMPLE 9.   Problem 3 of Exercise 12.1 can be solved by means of combinations and the fundamental theorem. To determine the number of ways the outfield can be picked we find $C(5, 3)$.

$$C(5, 3) = \frac{5!}{3!\ 2!} = \frac{5(4)}{2!} = 10$$

The number of ways the infield can be picked is

$$C(6, 4) = \frac{6!}{4!\ 2!} = \frac{6(5)}{2!} = 15$$

The number of choices for catcher and pitcher, respectively, are 2 and 4.

The number of possible ways the starting team can be determined is then the product of 10, 15, 2, 4, or 1200.

EXAMPLE 10.   A manufacturer produces 7 different items. He packages assortments of equal parts of 3 different items. How many different assortments can be packaged?

SOLUTION: The number of assortments is the number of combinations of 7 items taken 3 at a time.

$$C(7, 3) = \frac{7!}{4!\,3!}$$

$$= \frac{7(6)(5)(4)(3)(2)}{4(3)(2)(3)(2)} = 35$$

EXAMPLE 11. How many different bridge hands are possible?

SOLUTION: Since the order in which the cards are dealt is immaterial, we are interested in determining the number of combinations of the 52 cards taken 13 at a time.

$$C(52, 13) = \frac{(52)(51)(50)(49)(48)(47)(46)(45)(44)(43)(42)(41)(40)}{(13)(12)(11)(10)(9)(8)(7)(6)(5)(4)(3)(2)(1)}$$

$$= 635{,}013{,}559{,}600$$

EXAMPLE 12. Find the value of $C(n, 0)$.

SOLUTION: Starting with the formula of Theorem 12.2

$$C(n, r) = \frac{n!}{(n - r)!\, r!}$$

and substituting $r = 0$, we have

$$C(n, 0) = \frac{n!}{(n - 0)!\, 0!}$$

Recall that $0! = 1$ by definition. Then

$$C(n, 0) = \frac{n!}{n!}$$

$$= 1$$

EXAMPLE 13. Show that the values of $C(5, 0)$, $C(5, 1)$, $C(5, 2)$, $C(5, 3)$, $C(5, 4)$, and $C(5, 5)$ are the coefficients of the terms of the expansion of the binomial $(a + x)^5$.

$$C(5, 0) = 1$$

$$C(5, 1) = \frac{5!}{(4!)(1!)} = 5$$

$$C(5, 2) = \frac{5!}{(3!)(2!)} = \frac{5(4)(3!)}{(3!)(2!)} = 10$$

$$C(5, 3) = \frac{5!}{(2!)(3!)} = 10$$

$$C(5, 4) = \frac{5!}{(1!)(4!)} = 5$$

$$C(5, 5) = \frac{5!}{(0!)(5!)} = 1$$

These are the same coefficients listed on page 275 in the line $n = 5$ of the Pascal triangle.

EXERCISE 12.2

Combinations

1. Find the value of $C(7, 4)$.
2. Find the value of $C(10, 7)$.
3. Find the values of $C(6, 2)$ and $C(6, 4)$.
4. Find the values of $C(8, 3)$ and $C(8, 5)$.
5. Show that $C(n,r) = C(n, n - r)$.
6. A committee of 5 is to be selected from a group of 10 men and 10 women.
   (a) How many ways may the committee be formed if it is to have three members of one sex and two members of the other sex?
   (b) How many ways may the committee be formed if there is no restriction on the basis of the sex of committee members?
7. If an athletic conference has eight track teams, how many dual meets must be arranged if each team is to have a track meet with each of the other teams?
8. How many lines can be drawn which must contain two of eight given points if no three of the points are colinear?
9. How many triangles can be drawn having vertices selected from a set of eight points, if no three of the points are colinear?
10. If a decagon is inscribed in a circle, how many diagonals could be drawn?
11. In how many ways can a person be dealt a bridge hand consisting of only jacks, queens, kings, or aces?
12. A bus company is considering printing tickets with the names of two stops on them. A ticket could then be used for travel in either direction between the two stops printed on the ticket. How many different kinds of tickets would be printed if the bus company had 30 stops?
13. At a picnic a group of 6 girls and 10 boys are to be divided into two teams so that each team will have 3 girls and 5 boys. Find the number of ways in which the teams may be selected.
14. From a faculty of twenty in a mathematics department, how many committees can be formed consisting of 3, 4, or 5 members?
15. If flags of four different colors are raised on a pole in a vertical row, how many different signals could be indicated if 1, 2, 3, or 4 flags were used?
16. At a party, all of the guests shake hands with all of the others present. If 16 attended the party, how many handshakes are necessary?
17. Fraternities and sororities use Greek letters for their names. How many different three-letter Greek names can be formed? The Greek alphabet has 24 letters. How many three-letter combinations could be formed if the English alphabet were used?

18. Prove that a polygon with "n" sides can have $\frac{1}{2}n(n-1)$ diagonals.
19. Prove that $C(n, r) = C(n-1, r) + C(n-1, r-1)$. Can you relate this to the entries in Pascal triangles (the coefficients of the expansion of a binomial to a power)?
20. The binomial expansion can be written as

$$(x + y)^n = C(n, 0)x^n + C(n, 1)x^{n-1}y + C(n, 2)x^{n-2}y^2 + \ldots$$
$$+ C(n, r)x^{n-r}y^r + \ldots + C(n, n-1)xy^{n-1} + C(n, n)y^n.$$

If we use $x = 1$ and $y = 1$, we have

$$2^n = C(n, 0) + C(n, 1) + C(n, 2) + \ldots + C(n, n-1) + C(n, n)$$

The above formula can be used to determine the number of ways coded information can be punched on a card. $C(n, 2)$ would be the number of ways two of the n spaces would be punched.

(a) If a card has 10 spaces for punching holes, how many different coded cards are possible by punching any number of holes from 1 to 10?

(b) Some cards used for coding have 800 spaces for punching. How many different coded cards are possible?

12.3 PROBABILITY

In many cities meteorologists give daily forecasts of the percent chance of precipitation. This is a prediction based on the conditions in the surrounding areas and their experience as to what has happened in the past when similar conditions existed. This percent chance of precipitation is a measure of probability, although in some sections of the country it may not have the reliability we would like it to have.

Before we define probability, let us consider several examples.

EXAMPLE 14. A deck of playing cards is thoroughly shuffled and a card is drawn from the deck. What are the chances that the card drawn is the ace of diamonds?

SOLUTION: Since there is one ace of diamonds in a deck of playing cards (52 cards), there is 1 chance in 52 of drawing the ace of diamonds.

EXAMPLE 15. Two ordinary dice are rolled. In how many different ways can they fall? How many of these ways will give a sum of nine?

SOLUTION: The solution can be simplified if we consider the two dice to be of different colors, a green die and a red die. The green die can land in any one of six positions and for each of these positions the red die can also land in six positions so there are 36 ways the dice can land.

If we indicate the point value of the green die and the red die as an ordered pair, in which the green die value is given first, then the values that will give a sum of nine are (6, 3), (5, 4), (4, 5), and (3, 6). There are four ways of obtaining a sum of nine of the 36 ways the dice may fall.

Obviously when a card is drawn from the deck it is either the ace of diamonds or it is not the ace of diamonds. However, we say the probability of drawing the ace of diamonds (or any other single predetermined card) from a deck of cards is $\frac{1}{52}$. By probability we mean that if this experiment, the drawing of a card, were performed thousands and thousands of times the ratio of the number of aces of diamonds drawn to the total number of trials conducted would approach $\frac{1}{52}$.

We would also say that the probability of casting two dice and obtaining a sum of nine is $\frac{4}{36}$ or $\frac{1}{9}$.

DEFINITION   If an event can succeed in s ways and fail in f ways then the probability of success P is given by the formula:

$$P = \frac{s}{s + f}$$

and the probability of failure Q is

$$Q = \frac{f}{s + f}$$

It can be seen from these definitions that $0 \leq P \leq 1$. A probability of zero means that it is not possible for the event to happen; while a probability of one means that the event must happen. For example, if a bag contains 5 red beads and 4 yellow beads, the probability of drawing a white bead from the bag is zero. If the bag contained only 5 red beads, the probability of drawing a red bead would be one.

EXAMPLE 16.   A bag contains 10 red, 15 green, and 5 yellow beads. If a single bead is drawn from the bag what is the probability (a) that the bead is red, and (b) that the bead is not red?

SOLUTION: (a) There are 30 beads in the bag, any one of which could be drawn from the bag. Ten beads are red, therefore $s = 10$. The total of nonred beads is 20, $f = 20$.

$$P = \frac{s}{s + f}$$

$$= \frac{10}{10 + 20}$$

$$= \frac{1}{3}$$

(b) We can determine the probability of drawing a nonred bead by using the relation $P + Q = 1$ using $P = \frac{1}{3}$ as determined in (a).

$$\frac{1}{3} + Q = 1$$

$$Q = \frac{2}{3}.$$

DEFINITION   Two or more events are said to be mutually exclusive if not more than one of them can occur in a single trial. If a card is drawn from a deck it cannot be a king and a queen. The two events of drawing a king and a queen are mutually exclusive. The drawing of a king and a club are not mutually exclusive because the card drawn might be the king of clubs.

THEOREM 12.4.   If n mutually exclusive events have probabilities $p_1, p_2, p_3, \ldots, p_n$, the probability that some one of the events will occur in a single trial is

$$P = p_1 + p_2 + p_3 + \ldots + p_n$$

EXAMPLE 17.   If a card is drawn from a deck of playing cards, what is the probability that it will be a jack or a ten?

SOLUTION: The probability of drawing a jack is $p_1 = \frac{4}{52}$ and the probability of drawing a ten is $p_2 = \frac{4}{52}$. The probability P of drawing a jack or a ten is $p_1 + p_2$.

$$P = p_1 + p_2$$

$$= \frac{1}{13} + \frac{1}{13} = \frac{2}{13}$$

In the notation of order pairs of Example 2 we can indicate in tabular form the 36 ways two dice may fall as follows.

(1, 1)	(1, 2)	(1, 3)	(1, 4)	(1, 5)	(1, 6)
(2, 1)	(2, 2)	(2, 3)	(2, 4)	(2, 5)	(2, 6)
(3, 1)	(3, 2)	(3, 3)	(3, 4)	(3, 5)	(3, 6)
(4, 1)	(4, 2)	(4, 3)	(4, 4)	(4, 5)	(4, 6)
(5, 1)	(5, 2)	(5, 3)	(5, 4)	(5, 5)	(5, 6)
(6, 1)	(6, 2)	(6, 3)	(6, 4)	(6, 5)	(6, 6)

By counting the number of ordered pairs on the diagonal lines shown in the table we can determine the number of ways any given sum can be attained from two dice. The diagonal through the ordered pairs (3, 1), (2, 2) and (1, 3) contains three ordered pairs so there are 3 ways the dice may fall (of 36 possible ways) and have a total of 4.

The probability of obtaining a sum of 2 $= \dfrac{1}{36}$.

The probability of obtaining a sum of 3 $= \dfrac{2}{36} = \dfrac{1}{18}$.

The probability of obtaining a sum of 4 $= \dfrac{3}{36} = \dfrac{1}{12}$.

EXAMPLE 18. If two dice are cast, what is the probability the sum will be less than 5?

SOLUTION: Since the obtaining of sums of 2, 3, and 4 are mutually exclusive events, the probability of obtaining a sum less than 5 is the sum of the probabilities of obtaining a sum of 2, 3, and 4.

Using the values of the preceding paragraph we have $p_1 = \dfrac{1}{36}$, $p_2 = \dfrac{1}{18}$, and $p_3 = \dfrac{1}{12}$.

$$P = p_1 + p_2 + p_3$$

$$= \frac{1}{36} + \frac{1}{18} + \frac{1}{12}$$

$$= \frac{1}{36} + \frac{2}{36} + \frac{3}{36} = \frac{6}{36} = \frac{1}{6}$$

DEFINITION   Two or more events are said to be independent events if the occurrence of one does not prejudice the probability of the occurrence of any of the other events.

If from a bag containing colored balls, a ball is withdrawn, the color noted, and then the ball is replaced, the color of the first ball would not affect the probabilities regarding the color of a second ball withdrawn. *Note:* If the ball is not replaced then the events would not be independent. Consider a bag which contains 5 black balls and 4 white balls. The probability of drawing a black ball is $\frac{5}{9}$. If a ball (either black or white) is withdrawn and then replaced, the probability of drawing a black ball on the second drawing is still $\frac{5}{9}$.

However, if the first ball drawn is not replaced, then the probability of drawing a black ball on the second try is not $\frac{5}{9}$. If the first ball drawn was black, the probability that the second will be black is $\frac{4}{8} = \frac{1}{2}$. The probability of the second ball being black if a white ball is drawn first and not replaced is $\frac{5}{8}$.

THEOREM 12.5. If the probability of an event "A" occurring is p_1, and if after this event has happened the probability of a second event happening is p_2, then the probability of both events occurring in the stated order is $p_1 p_2$.

Note this theorem is true if event B is dependent on or independent of event A.

EXAMPLE 19. If three cards are drawn from a deck of playing cards, what is the probability that the first card will be an ace, the second card will be a king, and the third card will be a queen?

SOLUTION: The respective probabilities on the successive draws are $\frac{4}{52}, \frac{4}{51}$, and $\frac{4}{50}$. The probability of all three events occurring in the prescribed order is the product of these probabilities by Theorem 12.5.

$$
\begin{aligned}
p &= \frac{4}{52} \cdot \frac{4}{51} \cdot \frac{4}{50} \\
&= \frac{1}{13} \cdot \frac{4}{51} \cdot \frac{2}{25} \\
&= \frac{8}{16,575}
\end{aligned}
$$

EXAMPLE 20. If three cards are drawn from a deck of playing cards, what is the probability that the cards will be an ace, a king, and a queen, although not necessarily in that order?

SOLUTION: One method of solution would be to multiply the probability of Example 19 by the number of permutations of three objects taken three at a time. $P(3, 3) = 3! = 6$. Therefore

$$p = 6\left(\frac{8}{16,575}\right) = \frac{48}{16,575} = \frac{16}{5,525}$$

A second method of solution would be to take p_1 as the probability of drawing either an ace, a king, or a queen. $p_1 = \dfrac{12}{52}$. Once this draw has been made there remain 51 cards in the deck and of these only 8 would be successful draws, so $p_2 = \dfrac{8}{51}$. Finally, of the 50 cards remaining for the third draw only 4 cards would remain which would be considered successful so $p_3 = \dfrac{4}{50}$. Again

$$p = p_1 p_2 p_3$$
$$= \frac{\overset{3}{\cancel{12}}}{\underset{13}{\cancel{52}}} \cdot \frac{8}{51} \cdot \frac{\overset{2}{\cancel{4}}}{\underset{25}{\cancel{50}}}$$
$$= \frac{48}{16,575} = \frac{16}{5,525}$$

EXAMPLE 21. A city council consists of 12 Republicans and 10 Democrats from which a 5-member ad hoc committee is to be appointed by drawing names. (a) What is the probability that the first three names drawn will be the names of Republicans and that the last two names drawn will be that of Democrats? (b) What is the probability that the committee will consist of 3 Republicans and 2 Democrats when we ignore the order in which the names are drawn?

SOLUTION, PART A: Since there are 22 members of the council the respective probabilities are:

$$p_1 = \frac{12}{22}, \; p_2 = \frac{11}{21}, \; p_3 = \frac{10}{20}, \; p_4 = \frac{10}{19}, \; p_5 = \frac{9}{18}$$
$$p = \frac{12}{22} \cdot \frac{11}{21} \cdot \frac{10}{20} \cdot \frac{10}{19} \cdot \frac{9}{18}$$
$$= \frac{5}{133}$$

SOLUTION, PART B: The probability can be determined by finding the number of ways we can pick 3 Republicans from a group of 12 Republicans. This is determined from $C(12, 3)$, determining the number of ways 2 Democrats can be selected from a group of 10 Democrats, $C(10, 2)$, and dividing the product of these combinations by the number of ways a committee of 5 can be selected from a group of 22, $C(22, 5)$.

$$C(12,\ 3) = \frac{\overset{2}{\cancel{12}}(11)(10)}{\cancel{3}(\cancel{2})(1)} = 2(11)(10): \quad C(10,\ 2) = \frac{\overset{5}{\cancel{10}}(9)}{\cancel{2}} = 5(9)$$

$$C(22,\ 5) = \frac{22(21)(\cancel{20})(19)(\overset{3}{\cancel{18}})}{\cancel{5}(\cancel{4})(\cancel{3})(\cancel{2})} = 22(21)(19)(3).$$

$$p = \frac{\cancel{2}(\cancel{11})(10)5(\cancel{9})}{\underset{7}{\cancel{22}}(\cancel{21})(19)(\cancel{3})} = \frac{50}{133}$$

The answer to Part B could also be determined by multiplying the answer of Part A by the number of permutations of 5 things taken 5 at a time where three of the items are identical and the other two items are identical. This is possible because we can consider the numbers of one political party to be equal since we are concerned, in this example, only with their party affiliation. The number of permutations in this case is

$$P = \frac{5!}{3!\ 2!} = \frac{5(\cancel{4})(\cancel{3})(2)(1)}{\cancel{3}(\cancel{2})(1)(\cancel{2})(1)} = 10$$

and the probability is

$$p = 10\left(\frac{5}{133}\right)$$

$$= \frac{50}{133}$$

EXERCISE 12.3

Probability

1. If a card is drawn from a shuffled deck, what is the probability that the card will be a king or a queen?
2. A card is drawn from a deck of playing cards. What is the probability of the card being a heart or the queen of spades?
3. What is the probability that a six will turn up if a single die is cast? What is the probability it will not be a six?
4. If a card is drawn from a deck of playing cards, what is the probability that it will be a face card (king, queen, or jack)?

5. If a card is drawn from a deck of playing cards, what is the probability that the card will be spade or a face card?

6. If a card is drawn from a deck of playing cards, what is the probability that it will be a red face card?

7. When a single die is cast, what is the probability that it will be less than a four?

8. Two dice are tossed. What is the probability for the sum to be six?

9. Two dice are tossed. What is the probability the sum will be seven?

10. When two dice are cast, what is the probability that their sum will be 6, 7, or 8?

11. From a set of 24 cards numbered 2–25 a card is drawn at random.
    (a) What is the probability that the number drawn will be a perfect square?
    (b) What is the probability that the number drawn will be a prime number?
    (c) What is the probability that the number drawn is divisible by 4?

12. From a box containing 8 red, 10 yellow, and 9 green balls, a ball is withdrawn. Find the following probabilities.
    (a) The ball is red.
    (b) The ball is green.
    (c) The ball is red or green.

13. Two coins are tossed in the air. What is the probability they will both land heads up? What is the probability of a head and a tail?

14. Four coins are tossed in the air. Find the following probabilities.
    (a) At least one coin will land heads up.
    (b) Not more than two coins will land heads up.
    (c) Either one or two coins will land tails up.

15. From a set of discs numbered from 1 to 100, a single disc is withdrawn. Find the following probabilities.
    (a) The number on the disc is divisible by 4.
    (b) The number ends in a 7.
    (c) The number is divisible by either 4 or 7.
    (d) The number will be a two digit number and the digits will be different.

16. Two boxes each contain two balls. One box contains a red ball and a green ball; the second box contains two red balls. If a red ball is drawn from a box, what is the probability that it was drawn from the second box?

17. Each of three boxes contains three balls. One box contains a red ball and two black balls, the second box contains two red balls and one black ball, and the third box contains three red balls. A single ball is drawn from a box. It is a red ball. What is the probability that the ball drawn is from the third box?

18. The letters of the word "star" are written on cards, one letter on each card. The cards are mixed and placed face down in a row. What is the probability that the cards will spell "rats" when they are turned over?

19. As a promotional scheme a manufacturer agrees to bring nine pairs of gloves to a women's club meeting. There are three pairs of white, brown and black gloves, and one short pair, one pair of medium length, and one pair of long gloves in each color. Each glove is placed in a separate envelope. A woman is allowed to draw two envelopes from a box. If the gloves she draws are a pair, she wins a pair of gloves in the color and size of her choice. What is the probability of a woman winning a pair of gloves?

20. The letters of the word "level" are written on cards, one letter on each card. The cards are mixed and then withdrawn one at a time. What is the probability that the letters will be withdrawn in the order to again spell the word "level"?

21. The executive board of a club consists of seven men and six women. A committee of seven is to be formed by drawing lots.
    (a) What is the probability the committee will consist of four women and three men?
    (b) What is the probability it will consist of two women and five men?

22. If each of the seven letters of the word "algebra" is written on a card and the cards are shuffled and then arranged in a row on a table, what is the probability that the cards with this random arrangement will spell the word "algebra"?

23. Mary and John are each asked to write a number from 1 to 9 on a card.
    (a) What is the probability that the number Mary wrote is even?
    (b) What is the probability that both of the numbers are even?
    (c) What is the probability that the sum of the two numbers is even?
    (d) What is the probability that the product of the two numbers is even?
    (e) What is the probability that the product is the square of an integer?

24. From twenty light bulbs, two of which are burned out, bulbs are put into eight light sockets. If the sockets are connected in series (that is, none will light unless all of the bulbs are good), what is the probability that the string of lights will light when it is plugged into an outlet?

25. $(x + x^2 + x^3 + x^4 + x^5 + x^6)^2$
    $= x^2 + 2x^3 + 3x^4 + 4x^5 + 5x^6 + 6x^7 + 5x^8 + 4x^9 + 3x^{10} + 2x^{11} + x^{12}$.

    The sum of the coefficients is 36. The coefficient of x^5 is 4 and this coefficient divided by the sum of the coefficients is the probability of having a sum of 5 when two dice are cast. Check the coefficients of the above expression against the listing of all of the ordered pairs listed in this section to show that this relation holds for all sums.

    Try to determine why this expansion is related to the casting of two dice and finding the sum.

26. Expand $(x + x^2 + x^3 + x^4 + x^5 + x^6)^3$. Then use the method of Problem 25 to determine the probabilities of getting a sum of 9, 10, 11, and 12 by casting 3 dice.

mathematical tables

TABLE I. POWERS AND ROOTS

SQUARES AND CUBES   SQUARE ROOTS AND CUBE ROOTS

No.	Square	Cube	Square Root	Cube Root	No.	Square	Cube	Square Root	Cube Root
1	1	1	1.000	1.000	51	2,601	132,651	7.141	3.708
2	4	8	1.414	1.260	52	2,704	140,608	7.211	3.733
3	9	27	1.732	1.442	53	2,809	148,877	7.280	3.756
4	16	64	2.000	1.587	54	2.916	157,464	7.348	3.780
5	25	125	2.236	1.710	55	3,025	166,375	7.416	3.803
6	36	216	2.449	1.817	56	3,136	175,616	7.483	3.826
7	49	343	2.646	1.913	57	3,249	185,193	7.550	3.849
8	64	512	2.828	2.000	58	3,364	195,112	7.616	3.871
9	81	729	3.000	2.080	59	3,481	205,379	7.681	3.893
10	100	1,000	3.162	2.154	60	3,600	216,000	7.746	3.915
11	121	1,331	3.317	2.224	61	3,721	226,981	7.810	3.936
12	144	1,728	3.464	2.289	62	3,844	238,328	7.874	3.958
13	169	2,197	3.606	2.351	63	3,969	250,047	7.937	3.979
14	196	2,744	3.742	2.410	64	4,096	262,144	8.000	4.000
15	225	3,375	3.873	2.466	65	4,225	274,625	8.062	4.021
16	256	4,096	4.000	2.520	66	4,356	287,496	8.124	4.041
17	289	4,913	4.123	2.571	67	4,489	300,763	8.185	4.062
18	324	5,832	4.243	2.621	68	4,624	314,432	8.246	4.082
19	361	6,859	4.359	2.668	69	4,761	328,509	8.307	4.102
20	400	8,000	4.472	2.714	70	4,900	343,000	8.367	4.121
21	441	9,261	4.583	2.759	71	5,041	357,911	8.426	4.141
22	484	10,648	4.690	2.802	72	5,184	373,248	8.485	4.160
23	529	12,167	4.796	2.844	73	5,329	389,017	8.544	4.179
24	576	13,824	4.899	2.884	74	5,476	405,224	8.602	4.198
25	625	15,625	5.000	2.924	75	5,625	421,875	8.660	4.217
26	676	17,576	5.099	2.962	76	5,776	438,976	8.718	4.236
27	729	19,683	5.196	3.000	77	5,929	456,533	8.775	4.254
28	784	21,952	5.292	3.037	78	6,084	474,552	8.832	4.273
29	841	24,389	5.385	3.072	79	6,241	493,039	8.888	4.291
30	900	27,000	5.477	3.107	80	6,400	512,000	8.944	4.309
31	961	29,791	5.568	3.141	81	6,561	531,441	9.000	4.327
32	1,024	32,768	5.657	3.175	82	6,724	551,368	9.055	4.344
33	1,089	35,937	5.745	3.208	83	6,889	571,787	9.110	4.362
34	1,156	39,304	5.831	3.240	84	7,056	592,704	9.165	4.380
35	1,225	42,875	5.916	3.271	85	7,225	614,125	9.220	4.397
36	1,296	46,656	6.000	3.302	86	7,396	636,056	9.274	4.414
37	1,369	50,653	6.083	3.332	87	7,569	658,503	9.327	4.431
38	1,444	54,872	6.164	3.362	88	7,744	681,472	9.381	4.448
39	1,521	59,319	6.245	3.391	89	7,921	704,969	9.434	4.465
40	1,600	64,000	6.325	3.420	90	8,100	729,000	9.487	4.481
41	1,681	68,921	6.403	3.448	91	8,281	753,571	9.539	4.498
42	1,764	74,088	6.481	3.476	92	8,464	778,688	9.592	4.514
43	1,849	79,507	6.557	3.503	93	8,649	804,357	9.644	4.531
44	1,936	85,184	6.633	3.530	94	8,836	830,584	9.695	4.547
45	2,025	91,125	6.708	3.557	95	9,025	857,375	9.747	4.563
46	2,116	97,336	6.782	3.583	96	9,216	884,736	9.798	4.579
47	2,209	103,823	6.856	3.609	97	9,409	912,673	9.849	4.595
48	2,304	110,592	6.928	3.634	98	9,604	941,192	9.899	4.610
49	2,401	117,649	7.000	3.659	99	9,801	970,299	9.950	4.626
50	2,500	125,000	7.071	3.684	100	10,000	1,000,000	10.000	4.642

TABLE II. COMMON LOGARITHMS

	0	1	2	3	4	5	6	7	8	9
10	0000	0043	0086	0128	0170	0212	0253	0294	0334	0374
11	0414	0453	0492	0531	0569	0607	0645	0682	0719	0755
12	0792	0828	0864	0899	0934	0969	1004	1038	1072	1106
13	1139	1173	1206	1239	1271	1303	1335	1367	1399	1430
14	1461	1492	1523	1553	1584	1614	1644	1673	1703	1732
15	1761	1790	1818	1847	1875	1903	1931	1959	1987	2014
16	2041	2068	2095	2122	2148	2175	2201	2227	2253	2279
17	2304	2330	2355	2380	2405	2430	2455	2480	2504	2529
18	2553	2577	2601	2625	2648	2672	2695	2718	2742	2765
19	2788	2810	2833	2856	2878	2900	2923	2945	2967	2989
20	3010	3032	3054	3075	3096	3118	3139	3160	3181	3201
21	3222	3243	3263	3284	3304	3324	3345	3365	3385	3404
22	3424	3444	3464	3483	3502	3522	3541	3560	3579	3598
23	3617	3636	3655	3674	3692	3711	3729	3747	3766	3784
24	3802	3820	3838	3856	3874	3892	3909	3927	3945	3962
25	3979	3997	4014	4031	4048	4065	4082	4099	4116	4133
26	4150	4166	4183	4200	4216	4232	4249	4265	4281	4298
27	4314	4330	4346	4362	4378	4393	4409	4425	4440	4456
28	4472	4487	4502	4518	4533	4548	4564	4579	4594	4609
29	4624	4639	4654	4669	4683	4698	4713	4728	4742	4757
30	4771	4786	4800	4814	4829	4843	4857	4871	4886	4900
31	4914	4928	4942	4955	4969	4983	4997	5011	5024	5038
32	5051	5065	5079	5092	5105	5119	5132	5145	5159	5172
33	5185	5198	5211	5224	5237	5250	5263	5276	5289	5302
34	5315	5328	5340	5353	5366	5378	5391	5403	5416	5428
35	5441	5453	5465	5478	5490	5502	5514	5527	5539	5551
36	5563	5575	5587	5599	5611	5623	5635	5647	5658	5670
37	5682	5694	5705	5717	5729	5740	5752	5763	5775	5786
38	5798	5809	5821	5832	5843	5855	5866	5877	5888	5899
39	5911	5922	5933	5944	5955	5966	5977	5988	5999	6010
40	6021	6031	6042	6053	6064	6075	6085	6096	6107	6117
41	6128	6138	6149	6160	6170	6180	6191	6201	6212	6222
42	6232	6243	6253	6263	6274	6284	6294	6304	6314	6325
43	6335	6345	6355	6365	6375	6385	6395	6405	6415	6425
44	6435	6444	6454	6464	6474	6484	6493	6503	6513	6522
45	6532	6542	6551	6561	6571	6580	6590	6599	6609	6618
46	6628	6637	6646	6656	6665	6675	6684	6693	6702	6712
47	6721	6730	6739	6749	6758	6767	6776	6785	6794	6803
48	6812	6821	6830	6839	6848	6857	6866	6875	6884	6893
49	6902	6911	6920	6928	6937	6946	6955	6964	6972	6981
50	6990	6998	7007	7016	7024	7033	7042	7050	7059	7067
51	7076	7084	7093	7101	7110	7118	7126	7135	7143	7152
52	7160	7168	7177	7185	7193	7202	7210	7218	7226	7235
53	7243	7251	7259	7267	7275	7284	7292	7300	7308	7316
54	7324	7332	7340	7348	7356	7364	7372	7380	7388	7396

TABLE II. COMMON LOGARITHMS—(Continued)

	0	1	2	3	4	5	6	7	8	9
55	7404	7412	7419	7427	7435	7443	7451	7459	7466	7474
56	7482	7490	7497	7505	7513	7520	7528	7536	7543	7551
57	7559	7566	7574	7582	7589	7597	7604	7612	7619	7627
58	7634	7642	7649	7657	7664	7672	7679	7686	7694	7701
59	7709	7716	7723	7731	7738	7745	7752	7760	7767	7774
60	7782	7789	7796	7803	7810	7818	7825	7832	7839	7846
61	7853	7860	7868	7875	7882	7889	7896	7903	7910	7917
62	7924	7931	7938	7945	7952	7959	7966	7973	7980	7987
63	7993	8000	8007	8014	8021	8028	8035	8041	8048	8055
64	8062	8069	8075	8082	8089	8096	8102	8109	8116	8122
65	8129	8136	8142	8149	8156	8162	8169	8176	8182	8189
66	8195	8202	8209	8215	8222	8228	8235	8241	8248	8254
67	8261	8267	8274	8280	8287	8293	8299	8306	8312	8319
68	8325	8331	8338	8344	8351	8357	8363	8370	8376	8382
69	8388	8395	8401	8407	8414	8420	8426	8432	8439	8445
70	8451	8457	8463	8470	8476	8482	8488	8494	8500	8506
71	8513	8519	8525	8531	8537	8543	8549	8555	8561	8567
72	8573	8579	8585	8591	8597	8603	8609	8615	8621	8627
73	8633	8639	8645	8651	8657	8663	8669	8675	8681	8686
74	8692	8698	8704	8710	8716	8722	8727	8733	8739	8745
75	8751	8756	8762	8768	8774	8779	8785	8791	8797	8802
76	8808	8814	8820	8825	8831	8837	8842	8848	8854	8859
77	8865	8871	8876	8882	8887	8893	8899	8904	8910	8915
78	8921	8927	8932	8938	8943	8949	8954	8960	8965	8971
79	8976	8982	8987	8993	8998	9004	9009	9015	9020	9025
80	9031	9036	9042	9047	9053	9058	9063	9069	9074	9079
81	9085	9090	9096	9101	9106	9112	9117	9122	9128	9133
82	9138	9143	9149	9154	9159	9165	9170	9175	9180	9186
83	9191	9196	9201	9206	9212	9217	9222	9227	9232	9238
84	9243	9248	9253	9258	9263	9269	9274	9279	9284	9289
85	9294	9299	9304	9309	9315	9320	9325	9330	9335	9340
86	9345	9350	9355	9360	9365	9370	9375	9380	9385	9390
87	9395	9400	9405	9410	9415	9420	9425	9430	9435	9440
88	9445	9450	9455	9460	9465	9469	9474	9479	9484	9489
89	9494	9499	9504	9509	9513	9518	9523	9528	9533	9538
90	9542	9547	9552	9557	9562	9566	9571	9576	9581	9586
91	9590	9595	9600	9605	9609	9614	9619	9624	9628	9633
92	9638	9643	9647	9652	9657	9661	9666	9671	9675	9680
93	9685	9689	9694	9699	9703	9708	9713	9717	9722	9727
94	9731	9736	9741	9745	9750	9754	9759	9763	9768	9773
95	9777	9782	9786	9791	9795	9800	9805	9809	9814	9818
96	9823	9827	9832	9836	9841	9845	9850	9854	9859	9863
97	9868	9872	9877	9881	9886	9890	9894	9899	9903	9908
98	9912	9917	9921	9926	9930	9934	9939	9943	9948	9952
99	9956	9961	9965	9969	9974	9978	9983	9987	9991	9996

ANSWERS TO ODD-NUMBERED PROBLEMS

EXERCISE 1.1

1. 1, 3, 5, 7, 9. 3. 15, 30, 45, 60, 75, 90. 5. February, April, June, September, November. 7. None. 9. Depends on the individual. 11. Pairs of natural numbers whose product is 24. 13. Positions on a baseball team. 15. Quadrilaterals. 17. Numbers with unit digit equal to 4. 19. Always true. 21. Not always true. 23. Not always true. 25. Not always true. 27. 3, 6, 9. 29. 1, 2, 3, 4, 5, 6, 8, 9. 31. 10, 12, 14, 16, 18. 33. Finite set. 35. Infinite set. 37. Finite set. 39. Has one-to-one correspondence. 41. Has one-to-one correspondence. 43. Does not have one-to-one correspondence. 45. $A = B$. 47. $A \neq B$. 49. True. 51. Not true. 53. Not true. 55. True. 57. True.

EXERCISE 1.2

1. $\{a, b, c, d, e\}$. 3. $\{a, e\}$. 5. $\{a, b, c, d, e, i, o, u\}$. 7. No, since there are elements in both sets. 9. $\{0, 2, 4, 6\}, \{2, 4\}$. 11. $\{2, 3, 5, 7\}, \{\ \}$. 13. $A \cap B = B, A \cup B = A$. 15. U, the universal set. 17. b, c, d. 19. a, b, c, d, e, f, g, h. 21. a, e, f, g, h. 23. e, g, h.

25.

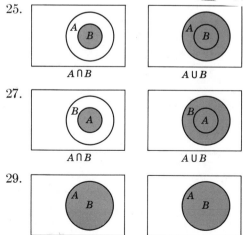

$A \cap B$ $A \cup B$

27.

$A \cap B$ $A \cup B$

29.

$A \cap B$ $A \cup B$

31.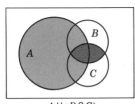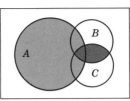

$A \cup (B \cap C)$ $(A \cup B) \cap (A \cup C)$

33. { }. 35. A.

EXERCISE 1.3

1. 90. 3. 29. 5. Closed. 7. Not closed. 9. Closed.
11. Closed. 13. Commutative. 15. Not commutative. 17. Not commutative. 19. Not associative. 21. Associative. 23. Not associative.
25. $2 + (3 \times 4) = 2 + 12 = 14, (2 + 3) \times (2 + 4) = 5 \times 6 = 30$.
27. $4 + 2 = 2, 4 \times 2 = 4$, etc. 29. $1 + (2 + 3) = 2, (1 + 2) + 3 = 2.$, etc.
31. $1 + 4 = 1, 1 \times 4 = 4.$, etc. 33. There is no element m such that
$3 \times m = 1$.

EXERCISE 1.4

1. $7 < 13$. 3. $-7 > -13$. 5. $0 > -4$. 7. $-3 < +3$. 9. 0.
11. 0. 13. No meaning. 15. No meaning.
17. $(a + 0) + b = (a) + b = a + b, a + (0 + b) = a + (b) = a + b$.
19. $a \cdot (0 + b) = a \cdot b, a \cdot 0 + a \cdot b = 0 + a \cdot b = a \cdot b$. 21. 15.
23. -4. 25. -9. 27. -10. 29. -42. 31. $+1$. 33. 18, 14, 32, 8.
35. 3, 5, -4, -4. 37. $-15, -25, -100, -4$. 39. $-6, -4, 5, 5$.
41. 0, 14, $-49, -1$. 43. 18, 0, 81, 1. 45. $-4, 4, 0, 0$.
47. $-11, -33, -242, -2$.

49.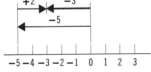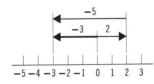

51. 5. 53. -6. 55. 4. 57. 6. 59. $(8, 9) = -1$.
61. $(10, 11) = -1$. 63. $(14, 10) = 4$. 65. $(26, 14) = 12$.
67. $(35, 55) = -20$. 69. $(15, 21) = -6$. 71. Commutative law of addition. 73. Associative law of addition. 75. Associative law of addition.
77. Definition of additive inverse. 79. Definition of additive inverse.

EXERCISE 1.5

1. $-2/3, 3/2$. 3. $-8, 1/8$. 5. $-3/8, 8/3$. 7. $5/2, -2/5$.
9. $6/8, 12/16, 15/20$. 11. $-4/10, -6/15, -8/20$. 13. Equal.
15. Not equal. 17. Z, R, I, W, N. 19. Z, R. 21. Z, R'.
23. Z, R, I, W. 25. 0.3125. 27. $0.777\cdots$. 29. 2.26.
31. 22.6. 33. 2.67. 35. $3.711, 3.712, 3.713$.

EXERCISE 2.1

1. x^3. 3. $-8x^3$. 5. $-x^3y^2$. 9. C represents the circumference of a circle, r represents the length of the radius. 11. A represents the area of a circle, r represents the length of the radius. 13. i represents interest, p represents principal, r represents the rate of interest, t represents time. 15. V represents the volume of a rectangular solid, l represents the length, w represents the width, h represents the height. 17. V represents the volume of a circular cylinder, r represents the length of the radius of the base, h represents the height. 19. c represents the length of the hypotenuse of a right triangle, a and b represent the length of the legs. 21. E represents electromotive force in a circuit, I represents current, R represents resistance.
23. $2^2 \cdot 2^3 = 2^5 \qquad 3^2 \cdot 3^3 = 3^5$
$4 \cdot 8 = 32 \qquad 9 \cdot 27 = 243$
$32 = 32 \qquad 243 = 243$
25. $2 + 2 + 2 = 3(2) \qquad 3 + 3 + 3 = 3(3)$
$6 = 6 \qquad 9 = 9$
27. $\sqrt{2^2 \cdot 3^2} = |2 \cdot 3| \qquad \sqrt{3^2 \cdot 4^2} = |3 \cdot 4|$
$\sqrt{36} = 6 \qquad \sqrt{144} = 12$
$6 = 6 \qquad 12 = 12$
29. Monomial, second degree. 31. Trinomial, first degree. 33. Binomial, first degree. 35. Binomial, first degree. 37. Binomial, fourth degree.
39. Binomial, second degree. 41. Second, first, third. 43. First, third, fourth. 45. $-v^3 - 3v^2 + 7v + 5$, third degree. 47. $x^n - 4x^{n-2} + x^{n-3} - 2$, nth degree. 49. $-xy, 3xy, -3yx$. 51. Not a polynomial. 53. A polynomial. 55. Not a polynomial.

EXERCISE 2.2

1. -32. 3. -24. 5. 9. 7. -2. 9. -11. 11. 39. 13. 13.
15. -41. 17. -120. 19. 13. 21. Equal. 23. Not equal. 25. Equal.

27. Not equal. 29. If $x = 3$, $\dfrac{9 + 3 - 6}{1} = 3 + 3$.

$$6 = 6.$$

31. If $c = 5$, $4(5 - 1) + 1 = 5 - 3(1 - 5)$

$$17 = 17$$

33. Decreasing. 35. Decreasing. 37. Increasing and decreasing.
39. Increasing and decreasing. 41. 130. 43. 158. 45. 33.49.
47. $c(2a + 3b)$. 49. $(m + n)(5m - 4n)$.

EXERCISE 2.3

1. $-11a$. 3. $-5k$. 5. $13ab^2c$. 7. 0. 9. $7(x + y)$. 11. $-5(a^2 - b^2)$.
13. k. 15. $-10mn$. 17. $-4pq$. 19. $11ab$. 21. $15(a^2 + a)$. 23. $16(x + 2y)$.
25. $-6x^3$. 27. $-30p^3q^2$. 29. xy. 31. $-6st$. 33. b^5. 35. $-12t^3$.
37. 7^5. 39. $-x^3$. 41. $9b^6$. 43. $16u^4v^8$. 45. -1. 47. -3. 49. $-2a$
51. $2p$. 53. $6p^2q$. 55. $11ax^2y$. 57. b^2 59. $-4m^2$. 61. ac^3.
63. $-xy$.

EXERCISE 2.4

1. $7x - 7$. 3. $x^2 - 5xy + 2y^2$. 5. $8x^2 + 2y^2$. 7. $18b^3 - 6b^2 - b + 13$.
9. $x^2 + 7x - 5$. 11. $-2m^3 - 4mn - 3n^2$. 13. $y^2 + 5y + 10$.
15. $-2u - 3v$. 17. $6a^2 + 3ac - 2ab - bc$. 19. $2y^2 + 11y - 21$.
21. $9u^2 - 64v^2$. 23. $4a^2 - 6ab + 3bc - c^2$.
25. $4p^2 + q^2 + r^2 - 4pq + 4pr - 2qr$. 27. $k^2 - 3k$. 29. $-x + y + z$.
31. $r + h$. 33. $-2ax + 3a - 1 - 7x + 4a^2$. 35. Not an exact divisor.
37. $3n + 2$ is an exact divisor. 39. $10x + 5h$. 41. $2x + h + 2$.

EXERCISE 3.1

1. Transitive. 3. Reflexive, symmetric, transitive. 5. Reflexive, transitive
7. Reflexive, symmetric, transitive. 9. Transitive. 11. Axiom 3.4.
13. Axiom 3.2. 15. Axiom 3.5. 17. Axiom 3.5. 19. Axiom 3.4.

EXERCISE 3.2

1. -4. 3. 10. 5. 5. 7. 12. 9. -3. 11. 4. 13. 9. 15. 2.
17. 4. 19. -5. 21. -13. 23. 7. 25. 29. 27. 12. 29. -2.

31. $m = F/a$. 33. $c = p - a - b$. 35. $I = E/R$. 37. $r = C/2\pi$.
39. $B = 3V/h$. 41. $h = V/lw$. 43. $h = V/\pi r^2$. 45. $r = (A - p)/pt$.
47. $h = (S - 2\pi r^2)/2\pi r$. 49. $d = (l - a)/(n - 1)$.

EXERCISE 3.3

1. Theorem 3.1. 3. Theorem 3.3. 5. Theorem 3.1. 7. Theorem 3.2.
9. Theorem 3.1. 11. Theorem 3.3. 13. Theorem 3.1 15. $>$. 17. $<$.
19. $<$. 21. $<$. 23. $<$.

EXERCISE 3.4

1. $x < -3$. 3. $x > 8$. 5. $x < -2$. 7. $x > 2$. 9. $x < -6$.
11. $x > -1/12$. 13. $x > 4$. 15. $x > -2$. 17. $x < 3/4$. 19. $x > 9/4$.
21. $x > 3$ or $x < 1$. 23. $-1/2 < x < 3/2$. 25. $x > 7/2$ or $x < -1/2$.
27. $-1 < x < 1/3$. 29. $x < 0$ or $x > 24$. 31. Equal.

EXERCISE 3.5

1. $3x$. 3. $2x + y$. 5. $\$20,000 - x$. 7. $10d + 5n$. 9. $540n$.
11. $6/11$. 13. $139/333$. 15. $667/495$. 17. 10 hr. 19. 48.
21. 2 gal. 23. 23 in. 25. $\$6000$. 27. 21 in. by 93 in.
29. 570 mph, 610 mph. 31. 17, 31, 34 yr. 33. $48°$.
35. $\$50,000,000$. 37. 39.

EXERCISE 4.1

1. x^5. 3. x^4. 5. $1/x$. 7. $a^2b^4c^6$. 9. $-x^6$. 11. $3c^6$. 13. x^9.
15. 1. 17. $-3/4x$. 19. -81. 21. -243. 23. 1. 27. x^{mn}.
29. x^{2n}. 31. 1. 33. $x^{2n+2m-2}$.

EXERCISE 4.2

1. 1. 3. 1. 5. $2a + 1$. 7. 1. 9. 0. 11. 2. 13. $x - y \neq 1$.
15. $\sqrt[3]{27} = 3$. 17. $\sqrt{49} = 7$. 19. $\sqrt[3]{(-125)^2} = 25$. 21. $\sqrt{4a^2} = 2a$.
23. $\sqrt[4]{81} = 3$. 25. $-\sqrt[5]{32^2} = -4$. 27. $\sqrt[5]{(-32)^2} = 4$.
29. $\sqrt[3]{81} \cdot \sqrt{9} = 9\sqrt[3]{3}$. 31. 2. 33. $\sqrt[3]{8} + \sqrt{9} = 5$.

35. $\sqrt[3]{\sqrt[3]{64} + \sqrt{16}} = 2$.   37. $\sqrt[3]{\sqrt[3]{64^2}} = 2\sqrt[3]{2}$.   39. $1/9$.   41.   9.
43. $1/2$.   45. $1/9$.   47. $27/8$.   49. $1/x$.   51. $1/x^2$.   55. $2 \cdot 5^{-1}x^{-1}$.
57. $3xy^{-1}4^{-1} + (2y)^{-1}$.   59. a^{-1}.   61. b^2.   63. $y^{-1}x^{2n}$.   65. $x < 16/3$.
67. $x < 7$.   69. $x > -1$.   71. $x < 30$.

EXERCISE 4.3   (In problems 1 to 21, the proper units should be given.)

1. 1.47×10^7.   3. 4.4×10^8.   5. 4.2×10^{-5}.   7. 1.29×10^{-3}.
9. 2×10^{-11}.   11. 4.3×10^9.   13. 2×10^{-12}.   15. $3,600,000$.
17. $0.000\,03531$.   19. $0.000\,000\,01$.   21. $1,196,000$.   23. 8.5.
25. 0.2.   27. $18,000$.   29. 0.3.

EXERCISE 4.4

1. $8\sqrt{2}$.   3. $10\sqrt{5}$.   5. $6\sqrt{7}$.   7. $12\sqrt{5}$.   9. $6x\sqrt{3x}$.   11. $4\sqrt[3]{3}$.
13. $\sqrt[3]{3}$.   15. $x\sqrt[3]{7y^2}$.   17. $6xy\sqrt[3]{2y}$.   19. $10\sqrt{10}$.   21. $xy\sqrt[3]{2x^2}$.
23. $3xy\sqrt[4]{3xy^2}$.   25. $xy\sqrt[5]{xy^2}$.   27. $2y^2\sqrt[4]{4xy}$.   29.   5.   31. $\sqrt{3xy}$.
33. $\sqrt{2x}$.   35. $y\sqrt{x}$.   37. $\sqrt[n]{5ab^2c^3}$.   39. $\sqrt{6}/3$.   41. $\sqrt{5}/5$.
43. $\sqrt[3]{2}/2$.   45. $\sqrt[3]{4}/2$.   47. $\sqrt[3]{10}/5$.   49. $\sqrt[3]{3}/3$.   51. $\sqrt[3]{2x^2}/x$.
53. $\sqrt{xy}/y$.   55. $\sqrt[4]{2xy}/y$.   57. $\sqrt[3]{20xy^2}/2y$.   59. $\sqrt[3]{50x}/5y$.   61. $\sqrt{2}$.
63. $27\sqrt{2} - 2\sqrt{3}$.   65. $19x\sqrt{3x} - 9x\sqrt{2x}$.
67. $3\sqrt[3]{2} + 8x\sqrt[3]{2} = (8x + 3)\sqrt[3]{2}$.   69. $(2 - 5x^2)\sqrt{3x} + x\sqrt{6x}$.
71. $3x$.   73.   20.   75. $18x\sqrt{10}$.   77.   6.   79. $\sqrt{6} - 2\sqrt{3} + 3$.
81. $\sqrt[6]{1125}$.   83. $\sqrt[6]{243}$.   85. $\sqrt[12]{432}$.   87. $x\sqrt[12]{x^5}$.   89.   2.
91. $2x\sqrt[12]{2x}$.   93. $\sqrt[6]{7^3 11^2}$.   95. $9x^2$.   97. -1.   99. $9 - 4\sqrt{5}$.
101. $18 - 6\sqrt{5}$.   103.   1.   105.   2.   107. $\sqrt{6}/3$.   109. $\sqrt{3x}/x$.
111. $5\sqrt{5}/8$.   113. $\sqrt{2}$.   115.   2.   117. $\sqrt[3]{3x^2}/x$ 119. $4(\sqrt{3} + \sqrt{2})$.
121. $6 + 2\sqrt{6}$.   123. $(\sqrt{5} - 1)/2$.   125. $(3 + \sqrt{3})/2$.
127. $6\sqrt{3} - 11$.   129. $(x + 2\sqrt{x} + 1)/(x - 1)$.

EXERCISE 4.5

1. $6\sqrt{3}i$.   3. $11\sqrt{2}i$.   5. $17i$.   7. $-6\sqrt{6}$.   9. $-4\sqrt{6}$.   11. $5i$.
13. $2i$.   15. $-2i$.   17.   4.   19. $x = 1, y = 0$.   21. $x = 5, y = -1$.
23. $x = 4, y = 2$.   25. $x = -1/2, y = -1/4$.   27. $x = \pm 1, y = \pm 2$.
29. $2 + 2i$.   31. $3 + i$.   33. $3 - 3i$.   35. $2x$.   37.   10.   39. $4 - 8i$.
41. $3 - 4i$.   43.   7.   45. $3i + 3$.   47. $-2i$.   49. $-2\sqrt{3}i/3$.
51. $3/5 + (\tfrac{1}{5})i$.   53. $2/3 + (\sqrt{2}/3)i$ 55. $12/13 - (5/13)i$.
57. $(-1 + i)^2 + 2(-1 + i) + 2 = i^2 - 2i + 1 - 2 + 2i + 2$
$= -1 - 2i + 1 - 2 + 2i + 2 = 0$.   59. $-(a + bi)$.

EXERCISE 5.1

1. $a^3b + ab^3 - ab$. 3. $2\pi R - 2\pi r$. 5. $2x^3y + 4x^2y^2 + 4xy^3$.
7. $-2x^2 - 2xy + 2xz$. 9. $x^n + 1$. 11. $2x^2 + 9xy + 9y^2$.
13. $4t^2 + 4t - 15$. 15. $2x^2 + 21x + 49$. 17. $3x^2 + xy - 2y^2$.
19. $x^2 - 10x + 21$. 21. $3x^2 + 8ax + 4a^2$. 23. $4x^2 + 12xy + 9y^2$.
25. $4x^2 - 12xy + 9y^2$. 27. $16 + 24x + 9x^2$. 29. $4\pi^2r^2 + 4\pi rh + h^2$.
31. $b_1^2 + 2b_1b_2 + b_2^2$. 33. $r^2 - 2rr' + r'^2$. 35. $9x^2 - 16$. 37. $\pi^2r^2 - h^2$.
39. $x^4 - 36$. 41. $4x^4 - 9y^2$. 43. $b^2, 8a^3 - b^3$. 45. $2y, x^3 + 8y^3$.
47. $2a + 3b, 8a^3 + 27b^3$. 49. $x^2 + 2xy + y^2 + 10x + 10y + 21$.
51. $x^2 + 2xy + y^2 + 5x + 5y + 6$. 53. $4s^2 - t^2 - 6t - 9$.
55. $9x^2 - y^2 + 2y - 1$. 57. $x^2 + y^2 + z^2 + 2xy + 2xz + 2yz$.
59. $x^2 + y^2 + z^2 - 2xy + 2xz - 2yz$. 61. $4x^2 + y^2 + 1 + 4xy + 4x + 2y$.
65. $x^4 - 8x^2 + 16$. 67. $x^4 - 16$. 71. 841. 73. 3249. 75. 8281.
77. 159,201. 79. 399. 81. 3596. 83. 39,900.
85. $x^{2/3} - x^{1/3}y^{1/3} + y^{2/3}$. 87. $x^{2/3} - 2x^{1/3} + 4$.

EXERCISE 5.2

1. $2(x + 2y + 3z)$. 3. $7a(a - 7b)$. 5. $9ax(9a - 1 + 3x)$.
7. $5x(3x^2 + 2a^2x - 3)$. 9. $P(1 + rt)$. 11. $3x^{2n}(2 - x)$.
13. $2\pi h(R + r)$. 15. $2\pi(R - r)$. 17. $(x - 1)(x - 3)$.
19. $(2a + 3)(a + 3)$. 21. $(a + 4)(a - 3)$. 23. $(2x + y)(x + 3y)$.
25. $(2x + 5)(3x - 1)$. 27. $(x - 1)(x + 43)$. 29. $(t - 6)(t + 5)$.
31. $(3x + 1)(2x - 5)$. 33. $(2x - 3y)(x - y)$. 35. $(3x - a)(x - 2a)$.
37. $(a + 11)(a - 10)$. 39. $(x - 19)(x + 8)$. 43. $(x + 11)^2$.
45. $(x + 5y)^2$. 47. $(2x - 3y)^2$. 49. $(3x + 5)^2$. 51. $(3 - a)^2$.
53. $(2x + 1)^2$. 55. $(3x - 5y)^2$. 59. Perfect square.
61. Not a perfect square. 63. Perfect square. 65. Not a perfect square.
67. Not a perfect square. 69. Perfect square. 71. $(a + 1)(a - 1)$.
73. $(12a - 7b)(12a + 7b)$. 75. $(x - 1/3)(x + 1/3)$.
77. $(0.9x - 1.4y)(0.9x + 1.4y)$. 79. Not factorable.
81. $(2x + 3)(x - 2)$. 83. Not factorable. 85. $2(x^2 - 3xy + 18y)$.
87. Not factorable. 89. $4(x^2 - 7xy - 12y^2)$. 91. $3(2x^2 - 4xy + 3y^2)$.
93. $(7 - 4x)(7 + 4x)$. 95. $(3x - 5y)^2$. 97. Not factorable.
99. Not factorable. 101. $3(x - 2)^2$. 103. $6(a + 3b)(a - 3b)$.
105. $2(3x + 2)(x + 5)$. 107. $(4n^2 + 3)(n^2 - 3)$. 109. $5x^4(a - 4x)$.
111. $2(2x + 3)(2x - 3)(x - 1)(x + 1)$. 113. $bx^4(1 - x)(1 + x)(1 + x^2)$.
115. $(x^2 + 9y^2)(x - 3y)(x + 3y)$. 117. $a(2 + 3y)(1 - y)$.

EXERCISE 5.3

1. $(a - 2)(a^2 + 2a + 4)$.   3. $(x + 3)(x^2 - 3x + 9)$.
5. $(xy - 1)(x^2y^2 + xy + 1)$.   7. $(y + 2x)(y^2 - 2xy + 4x^2)$.
9. $(2x - 5b)(4x^2 + 10bx + 25b^2)$.   11. $(4x + 5y)(16x^2 - 20xy + 25y^2)$.
13. $(x + 1)(x^2 + 5x + 7)$.   15. $(2x + 3)(4x^2 + 3)$.
17. $(x - 1)(x^2 + 7x + 19)$.   19. $(a + b)(a + c)$.   21. $(a - b)(x - y)$.
23. $2(x + y)(3x - b)$.   25. $(2x + 5)(3y - 4x)$.   27. $(3x - 2y)(3a + 2b)$.
29. $(5b - 1)(a - c)$.   31. $(a - 1)(a + 2b)$.   33. $(ab - 1)(a + 6)$.
35. $(a + b)(2m + n)$.   37. $(a + b + 2)(a + b - 2)$.
39. $(x + y + 1)(x - y + 1)$.   41. $(x + a + 1)(x - a - 1)$.
43. $(x + y)(x - y - 1)$.   45. $(x + y - z)(x + y + z)$.
47. $(a + b + m - n)(a + b - m + n)$.   49. $(x + y)(x^2 - xy + y^2 + 2)$.
51. $(x + y)(2m + 3n)$.   53. $(m + n)(m - n - 1)$.
55. $(a + 2b + m + n)(a + 2b - m - n)$.   57. $(1 - x - y)(1 + x + y)$.
59. $(a + d)(c - b)$.   61. $(x + y - 2)(x^2 + 2xy + y^2 + 2x + 2y + 4)$.
63. $(a^2 + 1)(a - 1)$.   65. $(a + 1)(3a - 5)$.
67. $(x - 2)(x + 2)(x^2 + 2x + 4)(x^2 - 2x + 4)$.

EXERCISE 5.4

1. Quadratic.   3.   Not Quadratic.   5.   Quadratic.   7.   Quadratic.
9. Quadratic.   11.   Not Quadratic.   13.   Not Quadratic.   15.   Quadratic.
17. $2x^2 - 3x - 4 = 0$.   19. $x^2 - 3x - 5 = 0$.   21. $x^2 + 2x - 15 = 0$.
23. $6x^2 + 2x - 13 = 0$.   25. $5x^2 - 6 = 0$.   27. $2x^2 - 9x + 3 = 0$.
29. $2x^2 - x - 50 = 0$.   31. $a = 2, b = -7, c = -6$.
33. $a = 4, b = 3, c = -7$.   35. $a = 3, b = -2, c = 4$.
37. $a = 2, b = 0, c = 81$.   39. $a = 3, b = -4, c = 0$.
41. $a = 1, b = -6, c = 0$.   43. $a = 1, b = -7, c = 7$.
45. $a = 3, b = -4, c = 2$.   47. $7, -7$.   49. $7, 0$.   51. $3, -5$.
53. $4, 4$.   55. $15, -2$.   57. $5/2, -3$.   59. $-1/3, 5/2$.   61. 0.
63. $0, 4, -4$.   65. $2, -2, 3$.

EXERCISE 5.5

1. $1, 3/2$.   3. $-5/2, 2$.   5. $4, -2/5$.   7. $1/2, 4$.   9. $-2, 3$.
11. $0, 7$.   13. $(-1 \pm \sqrt{7})/2$, $-1.823, 0.823$.
15. $(-1 \pm \sqrt{33})/4$, $-1.686, 1.186$.   17. $-2 \pm \sqrt{2}$, $-3.414, -0.586$.
19. $(-5 \pm \sqrt{65})/10$, $-1.306, 0.306$.
21. $(-1 \pm \sqrt{13})/2$, $-2.303, 1.303$.   23. $(7 \pm \sqrt{33})/2$, $6.372, 0.628$.
25. Real, unequal, rational.   27.   Real, equal, rational.

29. Nonreal conjugate complex. 31. Real, unequal, rational.
33. Nonreal conjugate complex. 35. Nonreal conjugate complex.
37. $b = 0$. 39. $6, -6$. 41. $6x^2 - 7x + 2 = 0$.
43. $x^2 + 3x - 10 = 0$. 45. $5x^2 - 179x + 140 = 0$.
47. $x^2 - 4x - 1 = 0$. 49. $x^2 - x - 1.19 = 0$.

EXERCISE 5.6

1. $x = 1, x = 3$. 3. $x = 2$. 5. $x = 2, x = 4$. 7. $x = 5/2$.
9. None. 11. $x = -5, x = 4$. 13. $x = 2, x = 4$. 15. $x = 5$.
17. $x = 0, x = 4$. 19. $x = 4$. 21. None. 23. $x = 13/4$.
25. $x = 2, x = 10$. 27. $x = 9$. 29. $x = 4$. 31. $x = 3$.

EXERCISE 5.7

1. $27, 28$. 3. 324. 5. 62. 7. 48 in. 9. 27 ft by 20 ft.
11. 10 in sq. 13. 6-1/3 in by 19 in. 15. 3,4,5.
17. 7, 24, 25. 19. 3.09 in. 21. 13.09. 23. 0.586.

EXERCISE 6.1

1. $2/5$. 3. $2/3$. 5. $4/(x + 4)$. 7. $3/(x - 2)$. 9. $(x + 3)/(x - 4)$.
11. $(x - 2)/(x + 4)$. 13. $(x + 2)/(x + 3)$. 15. $(x - 3)/(x - 5)$.
17. $(x - 1)/(x - 3)$. 19. $(x^2 + 1)/[(x - 1)(x - 2)]$.
21. $(4x + 1)/(5x + 3)$. 23. $(2x - 3)/(x + 3)$ 25. $2(x + 6)/(x + 3)$.
27. $(x - 1)/x$. 29. $3(x - 3)/2$. 31. $2/b, b = 0$. 33. $a/(a - 2), a = 2$.
35. $(x - 3)/(x + 5), x = -5$. 37. $(x - 7)/(x + 3), x = -3$.
39. $(x + 3)/(x - 1), x = 1$. 41. $3x^2z/xyz$. 43. $xy(x + 2)/xy^2$.
45. $3x(x - 1)/(x^2 - 1)$. 47. $3n(n - m)/(n^2 - m^2)$.
49. $-5x(y + x)/(y^2 - x^2)$.

EXERCISE 6.2

1. 30. 3. 66. 5. 210. 7. 540. 9. 1008. 11. $4x^3$. 13. $12x^2y^4$.
15. $24x^3y^2$. 17. $6(x + 1)$. 19. $15(x - 2)$. 21. $(x + 2)(x - 1)$.
23. $(x + 1)^2(x - 1)$. 25. $(x^2 + 4)(x + 2)^2(x + 3)$. 27. $6x(x - 3)(x + 3)$.
29. $x^3(x + 1)(x - 1)(x^2 - x + 1)$. 31. $3(x + 2)(x - 2)(x + 3)$.
33. $3(x + 1)(x + 2)(x - 3)$. 35. $3(x + 2)(x - 2)(x + 7)(3x - 2)$.
37. $(x + 1)(3x - 2)(2x - 3)$. 39. $(x - 1)^2(x + 1)^2(x^2 + x + 1)$.

EXERCISE 6.3

1. $7/12$. 3. $6/x$. 5. $2/x$. 7. $-11/12y$. 9. $(18x + 1)/6x$.
11. $(5x - 1)/[(x + 1)(x - 2)]$. 13. $(3x - 4)/[(x - 2)(x - 3)]$.
15. $(3x^2 - 2x - 1)/x^3$. 17. $(36x^2 + 9x - 10)/6x^3$.
19. $(x^3 - x + 3)/x^3$. 21. $47/6(x + 1)$. 23. $-2/(2x - 3)$.
25. $(10x + 11)/[(2x + 1)(x + 2)]$. 27. $(15x - 12)/[(x - 2)(2x - 1)]$.
29. $(-8x + 40)/[(2x - 3)(x + 2)]$. 31. $(3x - 2)/(x^2 - 1)$.
33. $(3x + 2)/(x^2 + x - 6)$. 35. $(9x^2 + 7x + 10)/[2(x - 2)(x + 1)]$.
37. $(15x + 29y)/[2(x - y)(x + 3y)]$. 39. $(5x^2 - 3x - 5)/[x(x - 2)(x + 1)]$.
41. $2/11$. 43. $2/7$. 45. 15. 47. $10/3x^4y^2$. 49. $5y$.
51. $[x(4x - 7)]/[4y(2x - 7)]$. 53. $3/(x^2 + 1)$. 55. $(x - 1)/(x + 1)$.
57. 1. 59. $(y - 3)/(y + 3)$. 61. $(x^2 + 2xy + 4y^2)/3$.
63. $(x^2 - 3xy + 9y^2)/(x + 9y)$. 65. $12acd^2/b$. 67. $(x + 2)/(x - 2)$.
69. $[16(x - 2)(x + 2)]/[3(x^2 + 1)(x + 1)]$. 71. $(y + 3)/(2y + 3)$.
73. $y + 1$. 75. $[2(y^2 - y + 1)]/[3(y^2 + 1)]$.

EXERCISE 6.4

1. $2/3$. 3. 1. 5. $(3b - 6a)/(4b + 6a)$. 7. $2xy/(y - x)$.
9. $[(2x + 1)(x + 2)]/[x(2x + 3)]$. 11. $xy/(y - x)$. 13. $(2 - x)/(2x^2 - 3x)$.
15. $(x + 1)/(x - 1)$. 17. $x/(4x + 1)$. 19. $x^2 - 1$.

EXERCISE 6.5

1. 2. 3. 7. 5. 2. 7. -6. 9. $5, -2$. 11. $2, -1$. 13. $3, -5$.
15. -1. 17. 1. 19. No solution. 21. 5. 23. $0, 13/3$. 25. 3.
27. $5/2$. 29. -7.

EXERCISE 6.6

7. 88 ft. 9. 4-$5/8$ in. 11. $100/11$ Ω. 13. 100 Ω.
15. 2 mph. 17. $5/8, 8/5$. 19. 1-$29/31$ in.

EXERCISE 7.1

1. Is a function. 3. Is not a function. 5. Is a function.
7. Is not a function. 9. Many to one. 11. Not a function.
13. One-to-one. 15. One to one. 17. c. 19. b. 21. 26. 23. 3.

25. -1. 27. -4. 29. 3. 31. -15. 33. -2. 35. 7.

37. All real numbers, all real numbers. 39. All real numbers, all positive real numbers and zero. 41. All real numbers equal to or greater than 1, or equal to or less than -1, all positive real numbers and zero.

43. $f(x) = x^4 - 5x^2 + 2, f(-x) = (-x)^4 - 5(-x)^2 + 2 = x^4 - 5x^2 + 2 = f(x)$.

45. 22, -2, -2, 22, even. 47. 61, 9, 5, -47, neither. 49. -21, 1, -1, 21, odd. 51. (a) $s = 16t^2$, (b) $f(3) = 144$ ft, the distance traveled in 3 sec, (c) $f(3) - f(2) = 80$ ft, the distance traveled during the third second.

EXERCISE 7.2

1. II, IV. 3. I, III. 5. II, III. 7. IV. 9. Isosceles right triangle.

11. Rectangle. 13. Square. 15. $(4, 2)$. 17. $(3, -3)$. 19. $(3, -2)$.

21. $(12, -5)$. 23. (c) $(8, 4)$, $(-6, -3)$, $(12, 6)$ etc., (d) the ordinate equals one-half the abscissa, (e) $y = x/2$, (f) no, since $-49 \neq -96/2$.

25. (a) $(15, 12)$, (b) 12, (c) 5, (d) 13. 27. 10. 29. $\sqrt{13}$.

EXERCISE 7.3

1. $(-7, 2)$, $(-7, -2)$. 3. $(-2, -9)$, $(-2, 9)$. 5. $(-4, 0)$, $(-4, 0)$.

7. $(-13, -1)$, $(-13, 1)$. 9. $(-a, b)$, $(-a, -b)$. 11. (a, b), $(a, -b)$.

13. Origin. 15. y-axis. 17. Origin. 19. Origin. 21. Origin.

23. $(6, 0)$, $(0, 4)$. 25. $(0, -25)$, $(5, 0)$, $(-5, 0)$. 27. $(0, 0)$.

29. $(0, 2)$, $(1, 0)$, $(2, 0)$.

31. 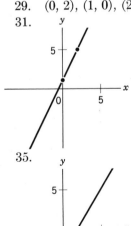 Intercepts, $(0, 1), (-1/2, 0)$. No symmetry. Domain, all real numbers. Range, all real numbers.

33. 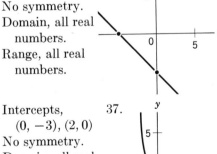 Intercepts, $(0, -5), (-5, 0)$. No symmetry. Domain, all real numbers. Range, all real numbers.

35. Intercepts, $(0, -3), (2, 0)$. No symmetry. Domain, all real numbers. Range, all real numbers.

37. Intercepts, $(0, 0)$. Symmetry, Origin. Domain, all real numbers. Range, all real numbers.

39. 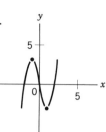 Intercepts, (0, 0)
Symmetry, y-axis.
Domain, all real numbers.
Range all positive real numbers and zero.

41. 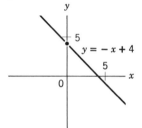 Intercepts, (0, 0), (2, 0), (−2, 0)
Symmetry, Origin.
Domain, all real numbers.
Range, all real numbers.

EXERCISE 7.4

1.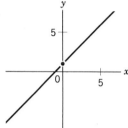

3.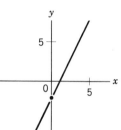

5.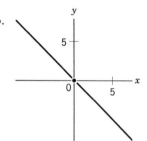

7. 3, −5.   9. 1, 9.   11. 7, 0.   13.

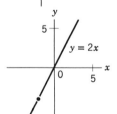
$y = -x + 4$

15.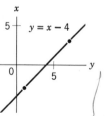
$y = x - 4$

17.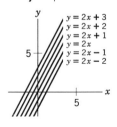
$y = 2x$

19.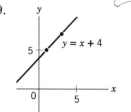
$y = x + 4$

21.
$y = 2x + 3$
$y = 2x + 2$
$y = 2x + 1$
$y = 2x$
$y = 2x - 1$
$y = 2x - 2$

23. $y = 3x + 6$. 25. $3y - 2x = 6$. 27. $y = -3x + 9$.

29. $y = (-1/2)x + 4$. 31. $y = (5/3)x - 5$.

33.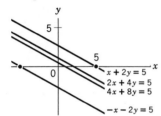

35.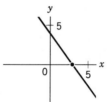

37.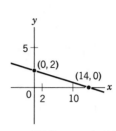

39. All lines are parallel.

41. All lines coincide.

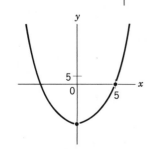

EXERCISE 7.5

1. (a)

x	-4	-3	-2	-1	0	1	2
y	27	7	-5	-9	-5	7	27

(c) $x = 1/2, x = -5/2$. The roots of the equation are the x-intercepts of the graph.

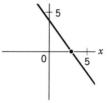

3. (a) $(3, -4)$, (b) minimum.

5. (a) $(-1, 2)$, (b) maximum.

7. (a) $(-1/2, 35/4)$, (b) minimum.

9. (a) $(-1/3, 7/3)$, (b) maximum.

11. $(7, -49/2)$ minimum.

13.

(a) $(0, -25)$.

(b) $(0, -25)$.

(c) The y-axis.

(d) $(0, -25)$.

(e) $(5, 0), (-5, 0)$.

15.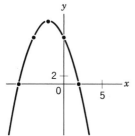

(a) $(-2, 16)$.
(b) $(0, 12)$.
(c) The line $x = -2$.
(d) $(-4, 12)$.
(e) $(2, 0)$, $(-6, 0)$.

17.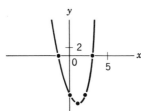

(a) $(3/4, -81/8)$.
(b) $(0, -9)$.
(c) The line $x = 3/4$.
(d) $(3/2, -9)$.
(e) $(3, 0)$, $(-3/2, 0)$.

19.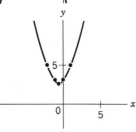

(a) $(-4, 0)$.
(b) $(0, -16)$.
(c) The line $x = -4$.
(d) $(-8, -16)$.
(e) $(-4, 0)$, $(-4, 0)$.

21.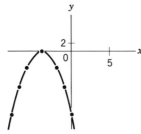

(a) $(-1/2, 11/4)$.
(b) $(0, 3)$.
(c) The line $x = -1/2$.
(d) $(-1, 3)$.
(e) No real zeros.

23.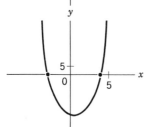

(a) $(1/2, -49/2)$.
(b) $(0, -24)$.
(c) The line $x = 1/2$.
(d) $(1, -24)$.
(e) $(4, 0)$, $(-3, 0)$.

25. (a) $x < 2$ or $x > 5$ (b) $2 < x < 5$ (c) $x = 2$, $x = 5$ (d) $x = 7/2$, minimum.
27. (a) $x < 1$ or $x > 5/2$ (b) $1 < x < 5/2$ (c) $x = 1$, $x = 5/2$
(d) $x = 7/4$, minimum.

29.   (a) $-7 < x < 3$ (b) $x < -7$ or $x > 3$ (c) $x = -7, x = 3$
      (d) $x = -2$, maximum.
31.   (a) No values (b) $x \neq 5/3$ (c) $x = 5/3$ (d) $x = 5/3, x = 5/3$, maximum.
33. $-9/4$.   35. $12, 12$.   37. $144\,\text{ft}$.   39.   \$9.75 (or \$10.00 to nearest dollar).

EXERCISE 7.6

1.   5.   3. $\sqrt{157}$.   5.   2.   7. $4x + 6y - 13 = 0$.

9.

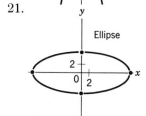

Circle

11.

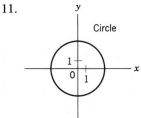

Circle

13.

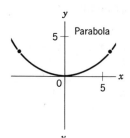

Parabola

15.

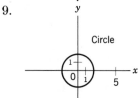

Parabola

17.

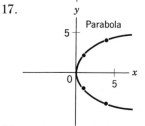

Parabola

19.

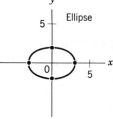

Ellipse

21.

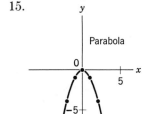

Ellipse

23.

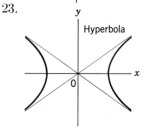

Hyperbola

25.

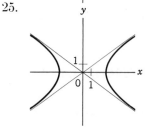

27. $y = \sqrt{9 - x^2}$, domain, $-3 \le x \le 3$, range, $0 \le y \le 3$.
      $y = -\sqrt{9 - x^2}$, domain, $-3 \le x \le 3$, range, $-3 \le y \le 0$.
29. $y = 4\sqrt{x}$, domain, $x \ge 0$, range, $y \ge 0$.
      $y = -4\sqrt{x}$, domain, $x \ge 0$, range, $y \le 0$.
31. $x^2 + y^2 = 64$.   33. $x^2 = 20y$.

EXERCISE 8.1

1.   Consistent and independent (intersecting lines). $x = 4, y = 1$.
3.   Consistent and dependent (coinciding lines). $x = 3, y = 2; x = 6, y = 6$, etc.

5. Inconsistent (parallel lines).
7. Consistent and independent (intersecting lines). $x = 4$, $y = 7$.
9. Consistent and independent (intersecting lines). $x = 5/2$, $y = 7/2$.
11. Inconsistent (parallel lines).
13. Consistent and independent (intersecting lines). $x = 6$, $y = 1$.
15. Consistent and independent (intersecting lines). $x = 10/3$, $y = 7/3$.

EXERCISE 8.2

1. $x = 8$, $y = 5$.   3. $x = -7$, $y = 4$.   5. $x = 7$, $y = 1$.
7. $x = -5/2$, $y = 3/2$.   9. $x = 8$, $y = -3$.   11. $x = 6$, $y = -9$.
13. $x = 3$, $y = -3$.   15 $x = 58/13$, $y = -4/13$.
17. $x = -4/3$, $y = 5/3$.   19. $x = 3$, $y = 6$.   21. $x = 8$, $y = 4$.
23. $x = 12$, $y = 3$.   25. $x = 3$, $y = 7$.   27. $x = 2$, $y = 3$.
29. $x = 5$, $y = 4$.

EXERCISE 8.3

1. $x = 2$, $y = -4$; $x = -3$, $y = 6$.   3. $x = 3$, $y = 3$ (double root).
5. $x = 1$, $y = 0$; $x = 3$, $y = 2$.   7. $x = 2$, $y = 5$; $x = -5$, $y = -2$.
9. $x = -2$, $y = -10$; $x = 4$, $y = -4$.   11. $y = 2x - 3$.
13. $y = 2x - 12$.   15. $y = 6x - 3$.

EXERCISE 8.4

1. $x = 2$, $y = 1$, $z = 4$.   3. $x = 4$, $y = 5$, $z = 4$.
5. $x = 7/2$, $y = 3/2$, $z = -7/2$.   7. $x = -1$, $y = 1$, $z = -1$.
9. $x = 1$, $y = 2$, $z = 3$.   11. $x = 3$, $y = -1$, $z = 4$.

EXERCISE 8.5

1. 7.   3. -29.   5. -6.   7.   0.   9. $a^2 - b^2$.   11.   21.   13.   0.
15. 0.   17.   —both rows or both columns are the same.
19. —a row or column are zero.
21. —of a row or column are changed in sign.

23. —the value of the determinant is multiplied by that number.
25. $x = 3, y = 2$.   27. $x = 1/14, y = -2/7$.   29. $x = a, y = 2a$.
31. $x = 3, y = 4$.

EXERCISE 8.6

1. $D = \begin{vmatrix} 1 & 2 \\ 2 & -1 \end{vmatrix}, \; D_x = \begin{vmatrix} 7 & 2 \\ 3 & -1 \end{vmatrix}, \; D_y = \begin{vmatrix} 1 & 7 \\ 2 & 3 \end{vmatrix}$.

3. $D = \begin{vmatrix} 1 & 1 \\ 2 & -1 \end{vmatrix}, \; D_x = \begin{vmatrix} 1 & 1 \\ -3 & -1 \end{vmatrix}, \; D_y = \begin{vmatrix} 1 & 1 \\ 2 & -3 \end{vmatrix}$.

5. $D = \begin{vmatrix} 1 & 2 \\ -1 & 2 \end{vmatrix}, \; D_x = \begin{vmatrix} 13 & 2 \\ 4 & 2 \end{vmatrix}, \; D_y = \begin{vmatrix} 1 & 13 \\ -1 & 4 \end{vmatrix}$.

7. $x = 2, y = 3$.   9. $x = 3, y = -3$.   11. $x = 3, y = -1$.
13. $x = 9, y = 6$.   15. $x = 1/2, y = 3/2$.

17. $D = \begin{vmatrix} 1 & 1 \\ 2 & 2 \end{vmatrix} = 0, D_x = 29, D_y = -29$. If $D = 0$, but D_x and D_y are not
equal to zero, the system is inconsistent.   19. $D = -11, D_x = -44, D_y = 0$.
If D is not equal to zero, then $x = 0$ if $D_x = 0$, and $y = 0$ if $D_y = 0$.
21.   If D, D_x, and D_y all equal zero, the system is consistent and dependent, that is, there is an unlimited number of solutions.
23.   The nature of a system of linear equations may be determined from the values of D, D_x, and D_y. If $D = 0$, $D_x \neq 0$, $D_y \neq 0$; parallel lines. If $D = 0$, $D_x = 0$, $D_y = 0$, coincident lines; If $D \neq 0$, intersecting lines.

EXERCISE 8.7

1.   12.   3. -151.   5. -20.   7.   4.   9.   30.   11. $x = 1, y = -3, z = 3$.
13. $x = -7, y = -1, z = -3$.   15. $x = 5, y = 2, z = 2$.

EXERCISE 8.8

1. $x - y + z = 4$.   3. $y = x^2 + x - 1$.   5.   12 mph; 2 mph.
7.   5 mph; 2.5 mph.   9. $x^2 + y^2 - 3x + y - 4 = 0$.   11. -20 lb.
The strings must be compressed with a force of 20 lb. Both springs will then be 11 in long.

EXERCISE 8.9

1.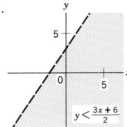

$y < \dfrac{3x + 6}{2}$

3.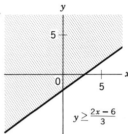

$y \geq \dfrac{2x - 6}{3}$

5.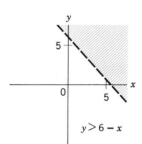

$y > 6 - x$

7.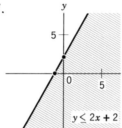

$y \leq 2x + 2$

9.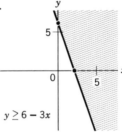

$y \geq 6 - 3x$

11.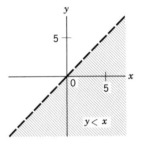

$y < x$

13. To the right of the line $x = y - 2$.

15.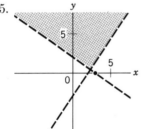

17.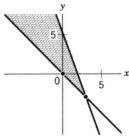

19.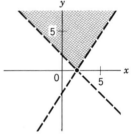

21. $(0, 0), (6, 0), (6, 2), (0, 8)$.   23. $(3, 0), (8, 0), (3, 5), (0, 5)$.

25. $(3, 4), (7, 8), (10, 2)$.

EXERCISE 8.10

1. $(8, 3)$.   3. $(0, 7)$.   5. 200 of A, 400 of B.

7. 5 units of formula 1, 2 units of formula 2.

9. 60 of Model A, 40 of Model B. The profit is \$2650.

EXERCISE 9.1

1.   22, 26.   3.   17, 23.   5. -4. -6.   7.   19, 24.   9.   486, 1458.
11.   4, 7, 10, 13.   13. $-1, 2, 7, 14$.   15. $-1/5, 1/5, 3/5, 1$.
17.   3, 5/4, 7/9, 9/16.   19.   4, 10, 28, 82.   21.   81/2, 81/8, 81/26, 81/80.
23.   3, 4, 17/3, 8.   25.   1, 4, 36, 512.   27.   210.   29.   24.   31.   1.
33.   5/24.   35. n.   37. $n^2 + n$.   39. $(n - 1)!$.

EXERCISE 9.2

1.   31, 64.   3.   Not an arithmetic progression.   5.   16, 38.   7.   56, 89.
9.   Not an arithmetic progression.   11.   46, 123.   13.   11, 77/3.   15.   49, 115
17. $-17, -139/3$.   19.   Not an arithmetic progression.   21. $-3, -1, 1, 3$;
arithmetic progression.   23.   7/3, 8/3, 3, 10/3; arithmetic progression.
25.   3, 4, 5, 6; arithmetic progression.   27.   3/2, 4, 15/2, 12; not an arithmetic
progression.   29.   2, 3, 4, 5; arithmetic progression.   31.   3280.
33. -1660.   35.   205/6.   37. -3580.   39. 860π.   41.   8, 12, 16.
43.   24/5, 33/5, 42/5, 51/5.   45.   Arithmetic mean $= (m + n)/2 =$ average
47.   2842.

EXERCISE 9.3

1.

x	-4	-3	-2	-1	0	1	2	3	4
y	1/81	1/27	1/9	1/3	1	3	9	27	81

3.

x	-4	-3	-2	-1	0	1	2	3	4
y	16	8	4	2	1	1/2	1/4	1/8	1/16

5.

x	-4	-3	-2	-1	0	1	2	3	4
y	2/81	2/27	2/9	2/3	2	6	18	54	162

7.

x	-4	-3	-2	-1	0	1	2	3	4
y	16/81	8/27	4/9	2/3	1	3/2	9/4	27/8	81/16

9.

x	-4	-3	-2	-1	0	1	2	3	4
y	48	24	12	6	3	3/2	3/4	3/8	3/16

11.

x	-4	-3	-2	-1	0	1	2	3	4
y	$-1/16$	$-1/8$	$-1/4$	$-1/2$	-1	-2	-4	-8	-16

EXERCISE 9.4

1. 4, 2, 1; $64(1/2)^{n-1}$.   3. $1/81, 1/243, 1/729; (1/3)^{n-1}$.
5. Not a geometric progression.   7. $81, 243/2, 729/4; 16(3/2)^{n-1}$.
9. $1/10, 1/100, 1/1000; 1000(1/10)^{n-1}$.   11. $1/3, -1/9, 1/27; 27(-1/3)^{n-1}$.
13. Not a geometric progression.   15. $2/3, -4/3, 8/3; (1/24)(-2)^{n-1}$.
17. 2, 4, 8, 16.   19.   2, -6, 18, -54.   21.   48, 24, 12, 6.
23. 32, -16, 8, -4.   25.   8, 4/5, 2/25, 1/125.   27.   2040.   29.   255/128.
31. 1640/243.   33.   6305/2.   35. $-85/32$.   37.   24.   39.   9/4.   41.   108.
43. 34/99.   45.   32/99.   47.   127/999.   49.   229/999.   51.   60   ft.
53. $128 + 64\sqrt{2} = 218.5$ in.

EXERCISE 9.5

1. $8b^3 + 12b^2x + 6bx^2 + x^3$.   3. $81y^4 - 108y^3z + 54y^2z^2 - 12yz^3 + z^4$.
5. $243b^5 - 810b^4y + 1080b^3y^2 - 720b^2y^3 + 240by^4 - 32y^5$.
7. $a^5 - 10a^4y + 40a^3y^2 - 80a^2y^3 + 80ay^4 - 32y^5$.
9. $a^6 + 18a^5y + 135a^4y^2 + 540a^3y^3 + 1215a^2y^4 + 1458ay^5 + 729y^6$.
11. $x^6 - 12x^5y + 60x^4y^2 - 160x^3y^3 + 240x^2y^4 - 192xy^5 + 64y^6$.
13. $a^8 + 8a^7x + 28a^6x^2 + 56a^5x^3 + 70a^4x^4 + 56a^3x^5 + 28a^2x^6 + 8ax^7 + x^8$.
15. $b^4/16 - b^3y/2 + 3b^2y^2/2 - 2by^3 + y^4$.
17. $y^4 + 4y^3\sqrt{y} + 6y^3 + 4y^2\sqrt{y} + y^2$.
19. $y^4 - 8y^3\sqrt{y} + 24y^3 - 32y^2\sqrt{y} + 16y^2$.   21. $20412x^2y^5$.
23. $210a^6x^4$.   25. $594a^{10}y^2$.   27. $-30ay^9$.   29. $40095a^4y^8$.

EXERCISE 10.1

1. $\log_{11}121 = 2$.   3. $\log_2 32 = 5$.   5. $\log_9 3 = 1/2$.   7. $\log_9 1 = 0$.
9. $\log_5 125 = 3$.   11. $\log_3(1/9) = -2$.   13. $6^2 = 36$.   15. $49^{1/2} = 7$.
17. $3^{-2} = 1/9$.   19. $3^0 = 1$.   21. $2^4 = 16$.   23.   5.   25.   0.   27.   1.
29. 5.   31.   5.   33.   3.   35.   1/2.   37.   3.   39.   4.
41. 4, 2, 6; $\log 81 \cdot 9 = \log 81 + \log 9$.
43. 2, -3, -1; $\log (100/1000) = \log 100 - \log 1000$.
45. 7, 3, 4; $\log (128/8) = \log 128 - \log 8$.
47. 2, -1, 3; $\log (100/0.1) = \log 100 - \log 0.1$.
49. 1, 1, 1.   51.   No, we cannot have $b^x = -N$, if $b > 0$.

EXERCISE 10.2

1. 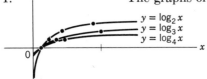 The graphs of $y = \log_b x$ all pass through the point $(1,0)$.

3. 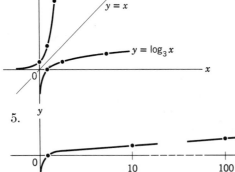 The graphs are symmetric with respect to the line $y = x$.

5.

For $1 \leq x \leq 10$, the range is 0 to 1.
For $10 \leq x \leq 100$, the range is 1 to 2.

EXERCISE 10.3

1. $2m$. 3. $n - m$. 5. $n/3$. 7. $(m - n)/2$. 9. $\frac{1}{2}m - 2n$. 11. $-m$.
13. 1.1761. 15. 0.9030. 17. 5.4467. 19. 1.0970. 21. 0.9375.
23. 0.2500. 25. 0.3525. 27. 0.7390. 29. 0.6880. 31. $\log_2 x^3$.
33. $\log_{10} p^5 q^3$. 35. $\log_3 \sqrt{R}/S^2$. 37. $\log a + \log b$. 39. $2 \log a + 3 \log b$.
41. $\log b - \log a$. 43. $\frac{1}{2} \log a - \log b$. 45. $\frac{1}{2} \log a - \frac{1}{3} \log b$.
47. $2 \log a + \frac{1}{2} \log b$. 51. $\log p + \log r + \log t$. 53. $\log p + n \log 1.07$.
55. $\log K + \log T - \log p$.

EXERCISE 10.4

1. 4. 3. 1. 5. 3. 7. 1. 9. 0. 11. -4. 13. -2. 15. -3.
17. 87,400. 19. 0.874. 21. 0.00874. 23. $0.7201 - 1$. 25. 1.3160.
27. $0.9542 - 3$. 29. 0.3075. 31. $0.8808 - 2$. 33. 4.4871.
35. 1.5740. 37. 5.0000. 39. $0.4886 - 7$. 41. 4.92. 43. 4770.

45. 0.155. 47. 1000. 49. 0.520. 51. 0.00002. 53. 0.00658.
55. 10,000. 57. 135,000. 59. 14. 61. 7.16. 63. 1,950,000.
65. 1,040,000.

EXERCISE 10.5

1. 395. 3. 8.67. 5. 0.0000116. 7. 0.0000952. 9. 0.420. 11. 1650.
13. 0.0518. 15. 0.803. 17. 0.0354. 19. 2.15. 21. 7.26. 23. 0.808.
25. 3.74×10^{-18}. 27. 0.0126. 29. 0.0467. 31. 60.8. 33. 44.4.
35. 39.2. 37. 513. 39. 10.1. 41. \$219. 43. \$149. 45. \$1910.
47. 1.12×10^{12}, 9.33×10^{10}, 1.77×10^{7}.

EXERCISE 10.6

1. 3.5750. 3. 4.8115. 5. 2.5649. 7. 3.7545. 9. 1.8492.
11. 0.0003845. 13. 672,500. 15. 0.001923. 17. 13,060. 19. 25.86.
21. 1.382. 23. 0.2901. 25. 0.03707. 27. 7,743,000. 29. 13,700.
31. 709 t. 33. 16.7 m. 35. 1.004 Ω.

EXERCISE 10.7

1. 1.465. 3. 2.170. 5. 2.659. 7. $x = \log 13/\log 32$.
9. $x = (\log 200 - \log 75)/4 \log 1.05$.
11. $x = (\log 5 + \log 2)/(\log 4 - \log 5) = \log 10/\log 0.8 = 1/\log 0.8$.
13. $x = \log 15/(\log 16 - \log 15)$.
15. $x = (\log 8 - \log 11)/(\log 64 - \log 11)$.
17. $x = -2$. 19. 1.58. 21. 1.43. 23. 1.58. 25. $x = 10/3$.
27. $y = 16$. 29. $n = 2$. 31. $z = 10, z = 1/2$.
33. 11.9 yr, 11.7 yr, 11.6 yr, 11.6 yr. 35. 0.707.

EXERCISE 11.1

1. $C = kr, k = \pi$. 3. $A = ks^2$. 5. $A = ks^2$. 7. $A = kd^2$.
9. $y = 4x$, (1, 4), (4, 16), (5, 20), (6, 24), (10, 40).
11. $y = 3\sqrt{x}$, (4, 6), (9, 9), (25, 15), (36, 18), (49, 21).
13. 30. 15. 63. 17. 50/3, 80/3, 100/3. 19. 9 in. 21. 15 m.
23. \$86.40. 25. (a) y is doubled, (b) y is tripled, (c) y is one-half as large,
(d) y is one-fourth as large. 27. (a) y is twice as large, y is three times as large,
(b) y is one-half as large, y is one-third as large.

EXERCISE 11.2

1. $g = k/s^2$, $g_1/g_2 = s_2^2/s_1^2$. 3. $T = k/r$, $T_1/T_2 = r_2/r_1$.
5. $h = k/r^2$, $h_1/h_2 = r_2^2/r_1^2$. 7. $A = k/h$, $A_1/A_2 = h_2/h_1$.
9. $y = 90/x$, (3, 30), (5, 18), (10, 9), (20, 9/2).
11. $y = 250/\sqrt{x}$, (16, 62.5), (25, 50), (64, 31.25), (81, 27-7/9). 13. 4.
15. 27/2. 17. 10, 1.6, 0.711. 19. 30. 21. (a) y is one-half as large, (b) y is one-third as large, (c) y is twice as large, (d) y is four times as large.
23. (a) y is one-fourth as large, (b) y is one-ninth as large, (c) y is four times as large, (d) y is 16 times as large. 25. no, no.

EXERCISE 11.3

1. $P = kdt$. 3. $R = kl/d^2$. 5. $V = k\sqrt{t}/ld$. 7. $F = kv^2/r$.
9. $z = xy/8$, (a) 15, (b) 4. 11. $z = 18x/yz$, (a) 36, (b) 6. 13. 60.
15. 90. 17. 104.96. 19. 592.6.

EXERCISE 11.4

1. (a) The ordinates are multiplied by k, (b) the ordinates are multiplied by k, (c) No. 3. (a) -8, (b) -48, (c) greater negative slope, (d) $-1/2$, (e) $-3/4$ (f) greater negative slope.

EXERCISE 12.1

1. 720. 3. 172,800. 5. 48. 7. 720. 9. (a) 30, (b) 120, (c) 360.
11. 10,080. 13. 151,200. 15. 120.

EXERCISE 12.2

1. 35. 3. 15, 15.
5. $C(n,r) = [n!/(n - r)!r!]$; $C[n, (n - r)]$
$$= \{n!/[n - (n - r)]!(n - r)!\} = n!/[r!(n - r)!] = C(n, r).$$
7. 28. 9. 56. 11. 560. 13. 5040. 15. 1, 12, 24, 24. 17. 24^3, 26^3.

EXERCISE 12.3

1. 2/13. 3. 1/6, 5/6. 5. 11/26. 7. 1/2. 9. 1/6.
11. (a) 1/6, (b) 3/8, (c) 1/4. 13. 1/4, 1/2.
15. (a) 1/4, (b) 1/10, (c) 9/25, (d) 81/100. 17. 1/2. 19. 1/17.
21. 175/572, 315/1716. 23. (a) 4/9, (b) 16/81, (c) 36/81, (d) 56/81, (e) 17/81.

Index